HEREDITY AND
YOUR LIFE

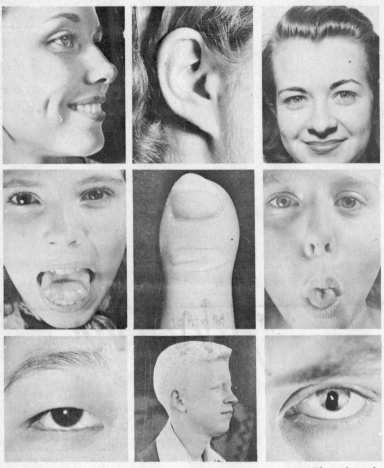

Some common inherited human traits. Dimples in cheeks (dominant). Attached ear lobes (recessive). Widow's peak, a point of the hair line extending down in the center of the forehead (dominant). Ability to fold the tongue (dominant). Clubbed thumb (dominant). Ability to roll tongue (dominant). Mongolian eye-fold, upper lid folded down (dominant). Albinism (recessive). Elongated pupil of the eye (dominant).

HEREDITY
AND
YOUR LIFE

by

A. M. WINCHESTER, Ph.D.

Head of Department of Biology
and
Professor of Genetics
Stetson University
DeLand, Florida

Second Edition

Dover Publications, Inc.
New York

*To past and present generations, and
those yet unborn, who each has its predestined
part to play in the great drama
which we call heredity*

OTHER BOOKS BY A.M. WINCHESTER

Genetics, A Survey of the Principles of Heredity,
HOUGHTON MIFFLIN.
Biology and Its Relation to Mankind, VAN NOSTRAND.
Zoology, The Science of Animal Life, VAN NOSTRAND.
Heredity, BARNES AND NOBLE.

Contents

List of Illustrations

xi

FIGURES IN TEXT

Preface

Almost everyone is interested in heredity, especially the heredity that is related directly to his or her life; yet it has been difficult for the average person to find information on this subject which is accurate, reliable and, at the same time, on the level of popular understanding. During recent years our understanding of human heredity has been greatly extended, but most of this new information is hidden away in technical treatises which are beyond the comprehension of a person untrained in the methods of advanced scientific research.

This volume was written for the purpose of bridging the broad chasm separating the technical presentation of heredity from common understanding. It has not been an easy task, because many of the details of human heredity have complex ramifications, but I feel that any person who can read intelligently will find it possible to learn much about hereditary processes through a careful perusal of this book.

It is a book which should appeal to all ages. To the bride and groom, about to embark on one of life's greatest adventures, I would especially recommend it. I believe that they will find many explanations here that will help them understand the marvelous powers of procreation which are entrusted to them. They should find information that will help them plan their families, and enable them to understand better the bewildering offspring which come following their union. To adolescent boys or girls, just becoming aware of life's great secrets, there is much in this volume which will help establish a firm factual foundation that will counteract the superstitions and misinformation to which they are certain to be exposed during their teens. To mature people, with immediate families completed, there is still much of interest and value in the pages of this book that may affect their descendants. Often it is not until this more leisurely period of life that we take time to consider the wonders of ancestry and develop desires to trace inherited characteristics through family genealogy. A good understanding of the fundamental principles of heredity is essential for the best results in establishing such a family background.

Since the mechanism of heredity is so intimately linked with the process of reproduction, it is not possible to get a clear picture of heredity without some understanding of this important bodily function. Accordingly, two chapters are written on this topic. Every effort has been made to handle this section of the book in a manner which will not offend even the most conservative. Some of the more mature readers may feel sufficiently informed about this subject already and may wish to skip over these chapters and get into the mechanism of heredity itself. This can be done without breaking the sequence.

The latter part of the book, especially, should be of value to ministers, social workers, and others who are called upon to give counsel on problems of heredity and environment. The tabulations on the method of inheritance of many human characteristics in the last four chapters can do much to answer perplexing questions which arise in the course of such counseling.

Finally, I want to take this opportunity to express my deepest gratitude to my many colleagues who encouraged me to proceed in the preparation of this volume, and who offered constructive criticisms during its progress. Appreciation is also due the editors and staff of Dover Publications, Inc., for their part in the preparation of the book.

A. M. WINCHESTER

Deland, Florida,
July, 1960.

CHAPTER 1

GENES—
THE MASTER SCULPTORS

When we visit art museums and see human images carved in stone by great sculptors, we may marvel that they can so accurately reproduce the physical features of the human body. Within the bodies of each of us, however, there are many tiny sculptors with the ability to reproduce human bodies, not in cold stone, but in warm flesh and blood. These master sculptors can transform a shapeless mass of chemical elements into living, breathing human beings with all the small details of features which make them recognizable as members of a particular race or family. We call these master sculptors "genes."

Of all the events that transpire on this planet of ours there is nothing more marvelous than the action of these tiny artists which mold our bodies and influence our lives from the time of conception until death. They do not necessarily die with us, however, for genes are potentially immortal. Those which we transmit to our children will continue living and can carry on their activities through countless future generations with undiminished vigor.

The influence of genes is so common in everyday life that we seldom realize the almost miraculous happenings which are associated with their activities. To be sure, probably no woman ever experiences the first movements of life within her body, after she crosses the threshold of motherhood, without feeling some great sense of awe about the marvelous construction process which is taken place. And a man, first gazing into the eyes of a newborn son—seeing his own features mirrored in this tiny bundle of life—can hardly help but marvel at the wonder of the actions of the genes. And yet, in spite of this, we still do not often contemplate the great depth and extent of the various phenomena which are connected with this highly complex process of constructing a human body.

To illustrate, think of yourself. When and where did you come from? "Why, I was born on such and such a date in so and so," you may answer. Yet your life did not start with birth. Let us go back further. You began life as an individual when your entire being consisted of only one small cell—a cell no larger than the period at the end of this sentence. Ten ordinary drinking glasses would be adequate to hold all of the cells which produced all of the people that are alive on the earth today (about two billion of them). Just think of it: all of the people living on the earth today from about two and one-half quarts of cells.

What marvelous cells these must be. Within the tiny pinpoint of a cell from which you came there were all of the genes which were necessary to produce your body as it is today. For about the first nine months of your life these genes did their work within your mother's body. Here you were warmed, protected, and supplied with food which served as the raw material from which the genes molded your body. Is it not remarkable that these genes can take food and reconstruct the elements in that food to build living protoplasm which eventually assumes human shape? Exactly the same food might be fed to a pregnant cat, yet the genes within an embryo in her body would convert it into protoplasm which would take the form of a kitten. Why is it that the protoplasm developing within a woman's body does not sometimes form a kitten instead of a human being? A ridiculous question, yes—but is the answer so simple after all? What manufacturing process conceived by man can take the same basic raw materials and come up with such a great variety of complex products as are exhibited by the various forms of life?

The marvels do not cease here—the cell not only always

produces a human being (when it comes from a human being), but it produces a human being with distinctive characteristics of the race of the parents. And it reproduces not only the racial characteristics, but the individual characteristics peculiar to the parents. Even such a small mannerism as the way you fold your hands is conditioned by genes. Yes, all of the countless physical traits, mannerisms, and abilities that stamp you as a son or daughter of your parents, as a member of the race to which you belong, and as a human being, come from your genes. All of these were contained in a single cell and that cell was filled mostly with food material, or yolk, which served your needs until you could begin absorbing food from your mother's body. This left only a small part of the cell for those marvelous entities, the genes. We do not, by any means, wish to minimize the influence of environment, for the scope of gene action is limited by the surroundings; yet environment can only bring out what is inherent in the genes—nothing more. There is an old saying, "You can't make a silk purse out of a sow's ear." Similarly, environment cannot turn out a fine product without the potentialities of a fine product in the genes.

Next, you may wish to ask, "Where did this marvelous cell come from, with all its genes which have produced the complex body which I now have?" It was formed by a union of two cells—we might even call them half-cells—a sperm from your father and an egg from your mother. In a sense, we can call the sperm and the egg half-cells because each contains only one-half as many of the precious genes as may be found in cells of the other body organs. Each is a half-cell because alone each is impotent, useless, unable even to sustain its own life for more than a brief period; yet when combined, these insufficient halves merge to form a whole—a powerful unit able to produce the many intricate parts of a human body.

But how did these two half-cells come to unite? Two separate persons originally housed them. How could the half-cells have been brought together? First of all, there must have been something to attract the two persons housing them to one another—sexual attraction, we can call it. But what is sexual attraction? Why does a particular woman appear attractive to a particular man and vice versa? Have you who are newly in love, especially, ever tried to analyze your feelings? Just why does your lady fair (or your Prince Charming) seem so appealing? Oceans of ink and tons of paper have been used by gallant swains in praise of a lady's eyebrow or some other such minor anatomical detail, yet none could truly tell you just why the object of his admiration held such a fatalistic appeal. Hormones, scientists will say. But what do the hormones do to us to bring out this all-prevailing emotion? To answer questions opens the way for more questions.

Even though we take simple sexual attraction for granted, just what is the more powerful force that goes beyond mere physical attraction into that even more complex state known as love—that state of blissful ecstasy in which all the world takes on a rosy hue and one so afflicted is willing to sacrifice his or her individuality to form a union in marriage? The ancient Greeks had an interesting myth to explain love. This myth held that at one time there were no separate sexes of people on the earth—all were the same. Then some great god, in punishment for the wrongdoing of the people, separated their bodies, one-half of each body becoming male and the other half female. Since that time there has been an eternal struggle for reunion. Neither sex is sufficient by itself and it is only through union that completeness is obtained. (This is strongly suggestive of the union of half-cells to form a whole which was discussed earlier in this chapter.) While we do not take such myths seriously, still it comes about as close as anything man has devised to explain love.

Even though we accept this mysterious power of love without further investigation, there are still many problems which must be overcome before there can be a union of sperm and egg. Normal married love reaches its culmination in intimate relationships which are climaxed by the transfer of sperms from the body of the man into the body of the woman.

But these sperms are deposited at quite some distance from the eggs with which they must unite if they are to fulfill their missions. The sperms are very small and they have a limited amount of food—they must achieve their goal within a few hours or they lose the power to penetrate the egg. Under normal conditions, furthermore, only one egg is released by a woman during a reproductive cycle, which averages about twenty-eight days, and this egg remains receptive to the sperm for only a few hours. Hence, most sperms are released only to find no egg awaiting them. If the egg is present the sperms still must negotiate a journey equivalent to one of about sixty-four miles by a man on foot in order to reach the egg. The journey has obstacles along the way which must be overcome, and even when the sperms reach the egg, they find a mass of tissue surrounding it which must be torn away before the ultimate union can be accomplished. When we learn of the many obstacles to be overcome we may sometimes wonder how fertilization is ever accomplished, but it is—and freqently—too frequently in some instances where there is a battle to balance the budget against the patter of little feet.

This accomplishment of impregnation, however, by no means ends the dangers. This tiny bundle of human life must implant itself within the womb of the woman where it will receive the life-giving nourishment that will enable it to realize its potentialities. Many women never bear children because they do not have a womb which allows for easy implantation. The rocky road to existence continues during pregnancy with the ever-present danger of predisposition in the mother to abortion, miscarriage, or premature birth which may terminate the life before it reaches the stage for normal birth. Then, birth, itself, has its hazards. Certain valves in the heart must close and change the course of circulation over the body at the time of birth or a blue baby results and death often follows. If the lungs fail to expand properly and take over the function of respiration within a few minutes after birth, death will result. Furthermore, injuries may be received during birth which may cause death and there may be stillbirths from a large variety of other causes. The fact that you are here is testimony to your success in weathering these storms of early life. Considering the many possible failures along the way, being born is, in itself, an accomplishment of which we may be proud.

With your curiosity now aroused you may wish to go further—to inquire into the origin of the sperm in your father and the egg in your mother and how a continuous stream of genes are passed down through generations by the reproductive cells. Then there are many questions about small details of heredity—how can a person show some characteristics which are present in one parent, some which are present in another, and some which are obvious in neither? How can some genes lie dormant for one or several generations and then manifest and express themselves? Perhaps you know of some characteristics in your own family which were present in past generations, but which have skipped a generation or two before reappearing. Surely you will want to know how the genes influence the determination of sex. Why were you a girl or boy—what mechanism operates to cause children of the same parents to show the many variations which distinguish the two sexes? Also, how does it happen that the sexes are produced in such even quantities that there are usually enough of each when the time for marriage and reproduction arrives? You may want to know what your children are likely to inherit from you, or, if you are older, you will be interested in knowing how some of your traits were transmitted to children you already have. As you read of the dangers of atomic radiation, perhaps you will want to know more about the possible effects of such radiation on future generations. Is it possible to so damage the genic material of a race through excessive radiation that the genes will no longer be able to carry on their intricate construction process and the race will become extinct?

These are typical questions which come to mind as one thinks about the mechanism of heredity. Many of them are not easy questions to answer and our answers are not always as complete as we would like them to be. Through many years of patient studying, experimenting, and testing, scientists, known as geneticists, have learned much about genes and their activities. In the pages which follow it is the purpose of the author to present some of the answers to the questions which we have developed in this introductory chapter.

CHAPTER 2

OUT OF THE PAST

Man has not always known as much about human reproduction and heredity as he knows today. As we delve into the musty records of the distant past we find many strange and curious assumptions which sought to explain the conception of new life, its development within a woman's body, and the resemblances between parents and offspring. Perhaps we can better appreciate the present rather advanced state of our understanding of these topics if we learn something about these beliefs which come to us from the past.

Is Sex Necessary?

Is sex necessary for reproduction? Man's first step towards an understanding of the procreation of life came about when he first realized that sexual relations were a necessary part of the cycle of events which leads to the birth of a child. This may appear to be so obvious a case of cause and effect that it is difficult to conceive of any human group that did not realize the relationship. Still, in a primitive group, struggling from day to day for bare existence, the time elapsing between the cause and the effect might be so long by their means of reckoning time that it could easily be overlooked. Even today there are isolated ethnic groups which make no connection between sex and reproduction. The Trobriand tribes, which inhabit some of the islands of the South Pacific, for instance, think of pregnancy as a condition resulting from some supernatural force which descends upon a woman. In the minds of these primitive people, the sexual relations which the woman has had are not related to the development of the new life within her body. In Queensland, certain natives believe that the thunder god fashions a baby out of mud and inserts it into the womb of a woman while she is sleeping. The mud baby is supposed to be very small and is inserted into the woman through her navel.

We do know, however, that a more accurate explanation was known to most ancient people as far back as human records can be traced. In fact, we find records which indicate that man once had rather advanced knowledge in this field, but that much of the knowledge disappeared with the passage of time. For instance, an ancient Egyptian papyrus has been found which dates back to about 3,000 B.C. On this, there are prescriptions for preventing conception and for inducing abortion, and a method of causing sterility. Knowledge can be lost as well as found.

Man's Curiosity

Man is a very inquisitive creature—the question "why?" is one of the first learned and most frequently used by a developing child, often to the dismay of his parents. Curiosity continues throughout life, especially about matters which appear mysterious and complicated. Having observed the connection between sex and reproduction, man was not content—he wanted to know more. Just how could the act of sexual intercourse induce the formation of human life? Many strange and curious explanations have been formulated—some of them persist even today—and have been passed down from generation to generation through the ages. Man's fertile mind tends to invent explanations where facts are not available. We hear so much about reproduction and heredity—yarns, superstitions, old wives' tales—that it is sometimes difficult to know what is true. In this chapter we shall review some of the old beliefs.

Early Speculations

To Aristotle, the great Greek philosopher who lived several hundred years before the time of Christ, is given the credit for one of the earliest recorded theories of reproduction and heredity, a theory which was based on observed facts. Aristotle dissected many female mammals and within the body of each he found a muscular sac which we now know as the womb or uterus. In some females he found embryos in various stages of development within the wombs. This was common knowledge later during Biblical times, as we find frequent reference to the womb in the Bible. But Aristotle wanted to know just how the act of sexual intercourse caused an embryo to begin developing in the womb. He knew that at a certain time each month a mature woman would have a certain amount of bleeding from this organ, provided she was not pregnant. With the beginning of pregnancy this bleeding would stop. From the standpoint of logical reasoning he concluded that the embryo was formed by a mingling of this fluid from a woman with the reproductive fluid (semen) from a man. The menstrual fluid was supposed to furnish the substance from which the embryo was formed, while the male semen added the form-giving power to the mixture of the two. In other words, the female furnished the building material for the embryo while the male contributed the properties of life and form.

Aristotle further proposed that the semen of man was produced from his blood—that it was, in fact, highly purified blood and this was why it had the power to give life and form to a new human being. The menstrual fluid of a woman was supposed to be semen also, but he thought that a woman did not have the power to achieve the high degree of purification which was characteristic of a man. This relatively unpurified "semen" of the woman could be used to build an embryo, but had no life in itself. This theory, of course, was pure speculation, but it did give some definite course to the thinking about reproduction which was to be somewhat generally accepted for about two thousand years.

A later Greek philosopher, Empedocles, who lived several hundred years after the time of Christ made some interesting amendments to Aristotle's theory in an effort to explain heredity more fully. He proposed that the "semen" of the parents was derived directly from the body parts which were to be produced in the embryo. In other words, the hands of a man would produce semen which would migrate to the reproductive organs where it would mingle with semen produced by the other body parts; when introduced into a woman's body it would stimulate the formation of hands in the embryo. The so-called "semen" of the woman was supposed to have a similar origin. Through this supposed blending of "semen" from different body parts of both the parents, the child developed characteristics of both. Some philosophers of this time believed that this "semen" originated as a moist vapor in all parts of the body during sexual intercourse and at the climax of this act it was drained to the sex organs where it condensed and became available to form a new human life.

Harvey's Deer

During the seventeenth century it was still generally believed, according to Aristotle's theory, that an embryo was slowly coagulated in the womb from a mixture of "semens" from the father and mother. In some of the contemporary medical books there were illustrations showing the stages of this supposed coagulation of the embryo. It was at this point that William Harvey, who is perhaps better known for his discoveries concerning the circulation of the blood, undertook some studies to test the theory of Aristotle.

He was given twelve mature female deer from the private reserves of Charles I, who supported Harvey in this work. All of these were mated with males. Six of these he killed and examined at various stages of pregnancy. At no time did he find anything which resembled coagulating fluids in the uterus. When he first observed an embryo, it was in a deer killed several weeks after mating and the embryo at this stage was very small. Also, upon closer examination he found that the embryo did not look like a deer at all. As he examined embryos at later stages of pregnancy he found that the embryo gradually took the shape of a deer as it increased in size. The six remaining deer had normal fawns about eight months after mating. Well, this made it quite obvious that Aristotle's theory, which had been generally accepted for 2,000 years, was no longer tenable. But what was to take its place? With the props knocked out from under a conception which had been accepted so long, what new explanation could be offered? It was not long before the development of the instruments of science made it possible to find the factual explanation.

Discovery of Sperms

When the microscope was developed during the latter part of the seventeenth century, natural curiosity led man to examine all sorts of substances to determine their microscopic appearance. A vast new world was opened to his vision—the world of substance and life which had existed unknown throughout centuries because it lay below the power of man's normal vision. It was inevitable that, sooner or later, sperms would be discovered.

This honor went to Anton van Leeuwenhoek, an early Dutch lensmaker who placed some human semen under the lens of his primitive microscope and turned it to the light for examination. He was amazed to find that this fluid was swarming with tiny living creatures. We can imagine his great excitement as he gazed on these squirming, wiggling organisms which had come from his own body. Surely, he pondered, these small bits of life must be related to the reproductive process of man. He suggested that each of these "animalcules," as he called them, was a potential human being; that any one of them needed only a place within the womb of a woman in which to develop and be nourished and it could grow into a human being. While this was a faulty theory in many respects, still it represented a tremendous stride toward scientific fact and away from the vague generalizations which had preceded it.

At first, many scientists of the time ridiculed the idea, saying that these small creatures which were seen in the semen were actually parasites and that they had nothing to do with reproduction. As continued studies showed them to be present in all semen, however, it became evident that they must play a part in reproduction.

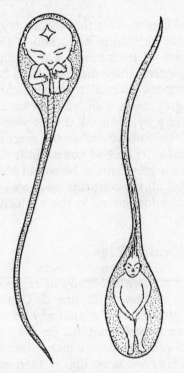

Fig. 1.   Preformed embryos in sperms.
(Drawing on left from Hartsoeker, 1694; right from Dalempatius, 1699)

Preformed Embryos

The imagination of the scientists was so stimulated by this conclusion that some of them even imagined that they could see miniature human beings within the heads of the sperms. There are some drawings made by men of those times to show the embryos within the sperms as they supposedly saw them under the microscope. They did not always agree, however, on the position of the embryo. Some of the drawings showed the head of the embryo pointing away from the tail of the sperm, while in others the head extended down toward the tail of the sperm with the hair streaming down into the tail itself.

The great difficulty with this theory lay in the fact that it left no clear-cut indication as to how a child could inherit any characteristics of its mother. The mother seemed to be left out of the picture altogether so far as heredity was concerned. Leeuwenhoek seemed to believe this, for he reports that he bred a grey male with a white female rabbit and all the offspring were grey. He took this as proof of his theory of preformation of the embryo within the sperm and total inheritance from the male. If he had gone a little further and mated a white male with a grey female, he would have been surprised to have found that all the offspring were also grey. This would have upset his conclusions as to the exclusive importance of the male in heredity.

Discovery of Human Eggs

The door for a scientific study of reproduction had been opened, however, and later, Regnier de Graaf, another Dutch scientist, in his studies of the anatomy of the human body, noticed that there were formations on the ovary of a woman that were quite similar to those which produced eggs from the ovaries of birds. He concluded that women must produce eggs similar to those of birds, but much smaller in size. He also reasoned correctly that the egg from a woman's ovary unites with a sperm to form an embryo which then develops within the womb of the woman. This gave a true picture of the process of reproduction, but it only intensified the false beliefs in the preformation of embryos. Some turned from the idea of a preformed embryo in the sperm to the idea that the embryo was actually in the egg and that the sperm was used only to stimulate the development of this embryo.

As the science of embryology developed during the latter

part of the eighteenth century it became evident that the idea of preformation of the embryo in either sperm or egg was erroneous. A German, Friedrich Wolf, studied the developing embryos of many different animals and he found that invariably all of the very early embryos consisted only of a mass of undifferentiated tissue. As these cells divided and the mass became larger the organs and systems were formed which were to make up the animal's body at birth. Thus, it became clear that, rather than a preformed embryo, the sperm and egg contained some definite substances which had the power to cause the cells of the developing embryo to form definite body parts. Here was another great milestone in arriving at a true understanding of the rather complicated process of human development.

Guesses, Good and Bad

Speculation next turned to the way in which the sperms and eggs acquired the ability to direct the embryonic cells to produce such an accurate prototype of the parents. A Frenchman, Jean Baptiste Lamarck, came forth with an intriguing theory which captured the imagination of the scientists of the time and which grew into the wide acceptance, not only of the scientists, but of the people in general. This theory proposed that reproductive cells were in some way influenced by the parents' bodies, so that the cells transmitted characteristics which had been acquired by the parent producing them. A giraffe was supposed to have a long neck because it continually stretched its neck in an effort to reach leaves on high trees, and each generation's stretching was passed on to the offspring so their necks became longer and longer. Lamarck even stated that if a number of children had their left eyes removed and these married, and their children also had their left eyes removed, and so on for several generations, then children would eventually be born that had no left eyes. The son of a blacksmith would have strong arms because his father developed powerful biceps in the practice of his trade. A fine singer would have a child with a good voice because of the concentration on voice development by their parent.

The famous English scientist, Charles Darwin, came onto the heredity scene during the middle of the nineteenth century. He suggested a way in which acquired characteristics could be transferred to offspring. This proposal was that if a blacksmith used his arms extensively and the muscles of his arms became highly developed, then little bodies—he called them *pangenes*—would migrate from these muscles to his reproductive glands and take part in the formation of the sperms. If this blacksmith then had a child, the sperms would transmit this trait and a child would be born predisposed to have strong muscular arms. This was supposed to hold true for all body parts. This was very much like some of the early Greek theories, the main difference being that Darwin assured that the bodies made their way to the sperms or eggs, while the

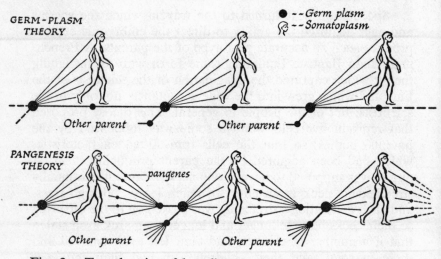

Fig. 2.   Two theories of heredity. At the top is shown the germ plasm theory where the germ plasm forms each generation, but is not influenced by it. At the bottom is shown inheritance of acquired characteristics through pangenes which come down to the reproductive cells from the body.

ancient Greeks assumed that the bodies became a part of the "semen" itself. Darwin even had a theory to account for the fact that sometimes a child is born with a characteristic which shows in a grandparent, but which does not show in either parent. In such cases he said that some of the pangenes from the grandparent were not used in the developing embryo and remained to take part in the formation of reproductive cells in one of the parents and these then found expression in the next generation.

This all sounded logical and was generally accepted until someone decided to test the theory. The first man to get credit for this was a German, August Weismann, who began experimenting by cutting the tails off a group of newborn mice. These were bred together and as soon as their offspring were born, the tails were again removed and so on for twenty generations. When the twenty-first generation was born they were allowed to mature without this mutilation and, lo and behold, they had tails just as long as mice that did not have an ancestry of tailless antecedents. If Darwin's theory was correct, then where did the pangenes come from to produce tails in this twenty-first generation of mice? As a result of this and many other experiments, Weismann proposed that the reproductive cells (germ cells) were merely carried by the body and were in no way influenced by what happened to the body during its lifetime. In other words, the hereditary factors which a person can transmit to his offspring are determined at the time his life begins as a single cell and there is nothing he can do to alter the traits which may be transmitted through his reproductive cells.

This theory does not appeal to the imagination as much as the idea of the inheritance of acquired characteristics, but it is essentially correct. Many people would prefer to believe that somehow their attainments in life can be transmitted to their children; it seems frustrating to think that each individual must build each achievement anew. Still, we have the satisfaction of knowing that, even though we cannot transmit the good traits which we have developed, neither will we transmit those many undesirable traits which we acquire during our lifetimes. Certainly we could not expect to transmit one without the other. Human nature being what it is, it is probably a good thing that acquired characteristics cannot be transmitted—in many of us our bad habits might outweigh the good. It is true that we can make the achievements easier for our offspring by providing maximum environmental conditions for the attainment of worth while objectives in life, but no matter whether we lead an exemplary life or a corrupt one, the hereditary qualities which we will transmit to our children will be the same.

There are still many people today, however, who believe—in part at least—in the inheritance of acquired characteristics. To them it would seem as if the incentive to lead a good life would be lessened if we knew that the good qualities we develop are to be interred with our bones. It may help to know, however, that many of our good qualities have a basis in heredity and we can transmit potentialities of these to our children. A great musician may have children who become great musicians, but this does not mean that he has transmitted his *acquired* abilities in music. If a person is a great musician, it is quite evident that he must have received genes from his parents which made it possible for him to develop this talent. Hence, it is quite natural that some of these genes would be passed on to his own children, thus making it possible for them, with the rich opportunities provided for them by their parents, to develop the latent talents which they have inherited. The musical attainments of the parents still have not influenced the basic hereditary factors.

As an illustration of how this works, let us suppose there are identical twin brothers each of whom has inherited the genes for great musical ability. Then let us suppose that one of the brothers has both hands cut off in an accident. The other brother goes on to become a world-renowned pianist who spends hours every day at the piano, but the injured brother is never able to develop his musical ability because of the loss of his hands. If both married and had children, those of the injured brother would receive just as much potential musical ability from their father as the children of the brother who developed his talents to their fullest extent.

Gene Change Through Mutation

This idea that genes are passed from generation to generation without being altered in any way is all right except for one very important feature. There is no provision for change. Unless the genes can change in some way there can never be any perceptible alteration in the different forms of life throughout all time. Our studies of prehistoric remains, however, show us that there have been extensive changes in the forms of different kinds of plants and animals that have existed on our globe. A Dutchman, Hugo De Vries, suggested a way in which this could occur without any inheritance of acquired characteristics. He noted that sometimes offspring were produced which were quite different from the parent stock. A black sheep would appear in a flock of white sheep; a bed of flowers would produce an occasional plant which was quite different from those from which it derived. These unusual types tended to breed true; that is, they would transmit the new characteristic to their descendants. De Vries called such changes "mutations" and he reasoned that they appeared as sudden alterations of the genes. His observations indicated that these changes occur at random and neither their occurrence nor the nature of the change is influenced by acquired traits of the parents.

We know today that his reasoning was correct. A man may carry a gene for blue eyes in one of the sperms within his body, then—presto—the gene becomes of such a nature as to produce brown eyes. If this particular sperm is effective in reproduction, a child will be born with brown eyes even though both parents may come from a race that has had blue eyes for many generations. It is, therefore, through such sudden jumps rather than through a gradual change that new traits make their appearance.

Mendel's Peas

While all the arguments and speculations about heredity took place during the latter half of the nineteenth century, an obscure monk in a monastery at Brün in Central Europe performed some experiments which revealed one of the most important principles of heredity—the principle of dominance and recessiveness. This man was Gregor Mendel who employed crosses between garden peas to determine the possibility of inheritance of individual characteristics. Of all things to reveal the secrets of heredity we might least suspect the garden pea, but we now know that the principles which he uncovered in the crossing of his peas apply accurately to human beings.

He secured seeds from all parts of Europe and began growing plants with many different characteristics. Some of his plants had purple flowers, others had white; some produced yellow seed, others, green; some had flowers only at the tips of the stems, others had them along the sides of the stems; some seeds were round, others were wrinkled; and some had long stems, others, short. By controlled crossing of these different kinds of plants with each other, Mendel discovered the way in which genes are passed down from one generation to the next. He reported his work before scientific gatherings, but the scientists were so engrossed with the work of Darwin, Weismann, and others that they failed to realize the full significance of Mendel's work. It was not until the beginning of the present century that Mendel's papers were found and he was accorded recognition for his great work.

The groundwork for an understanding of heredity was now laid. Scientists of our present century have gone on to greatly extend our knowledge of the principles of heredity; some of which we will describe in the chapters to follow.

CHAPTER 3

SUPERSTITIONS AND FACTS

We may smile at the naïveté of some of the ancient philosophers as they speculated about the process of reproduction and heredity, but before we feel too complacent about our modern knowledge we might examine some of the beliefs which are held in our own country today. Some of these may be just as erroneous as the concepts of the ancients. When a young bride assumes the duties of a household she is often besieged with advice and suggestions from older wives who seem to have the answers to all kinds of questions which arise in connection with the new type of life which the bride is undertaking. Some of this may be reliable and valuable information. On the other hand, there are times when facts are mixed with superstitions and false beliefs. The bewildered bride may have difficulty in deciding just what to accept. This book would not be complete without a survey of some of the superstitions about reproduction and heredity which prevail in our society, together with an evaluation of their accuracy.

Acquired Characteristics and Heredity

A short time ago a young married couple sought advice from the author about having children. This was not an ordinary young couple—both were totally blind. They were greatly concerned over the possibility that they might bear children who also would be afflicted. There are some types of hereditary blindness; therefore, children may inherit blindness. In this case, however, it turned out that both of these young people were blind because of environmental factors. Both had possessed normal vision at birth. At the age of three, the girl had a severe case of scarlet fever which resulted in eye infections that eventually destroyed her sight. Unfortunately, the boy had an accident with exploding kerosene which resulted in blindness. The young couple were very relieved to know that any children which they might have would have no more chance of being born blind than they would have if their parents had not lost their vision after birth.

This case illustrates the still prevalent concept that acquired characteristics can somehow make their imprint upon the reproductive cells and thence be transferred to offspring. The controversy over this idea which took place during the last century is discussed in Chapter 2, and although those who have mastered the principles of genetics have long since agreed that there is no such transmission of acquired characteristics, the question still continues to arise in the public mind. Once there is an understanding of genes and how they are carried as separate entities within our reproductive cells, one can readily see that the activities, the accidents, and the thoughts of parents do not change these units of heredity. Genes can be changed by exposure to X rays and other forms of radiation, but this cannot be interpreted as inheritance of acquired characteristics.

The acquired characteristics which a person develops during his lifetime are not transmitted to his children through heredity.

Love Babies

There is a rather widespread belief in the superstition that the emotional state of the parents at the time of conception has an important bearing on the nature of the resulting child, especially in regard to the nervous system of the child. A child conceived under conditions of intense emotion generated by great love and affection between the partners in intercourse is supposed to have a highly developed nervous system, to be very sensitive, perhaps a great genius. On the other hand, when conception takes place as a result of intercourse between couples who may actually despise each other—who tolerate the association purely for physical gratification—the child is likely to be dull and lethargic in disposition. This seems to be an attractive idea. We might like to believe that great love between parents could produce a superior child, but the prosaic fact remains that the conditions of conception cannot influence a child's inherited characteristics.

In an effort to remove the stigma which often brands an illegitimate child throughout life, the fact has been brought out that some of the world's most outstanding people have been born out of wedlock—Alexander Hamilton, Leonardo da Vinci, and Sir Francis Bacon, to name a few. Those who adhere to a belief in "love babies" point to men such as these to support their contention. It is assumed that illegitimate children are usually conceived under the stress of such an overpowering love that it blots out all restraints which morals, conventions, and consequences might ordinarily impose. Thus, children born as a result of such a stormy relationship should be radically different from those resulting from the less intense relationship of everyday married cohabitation. When we consider the many thousands of illegitimate children who become ordinary, everyday people, we cannot assign the outstanding achievements of a few to the conditions under which they were conceived. The factors of heredity have no knowledge of whether a wedding ceremony preceded the intercourse which resulted in conception nor could they respond to these conditions if they knew them. Any differences which might result would be due solely to environment. It is, however, true that a child growing up in a home where there is love and affection, will develop into a better-adjusted personality than one who is subjected to constant emotional clashes between its parents. Likewise, if an illegitimate child grows up knowing the conditions of his birth, in a region where he may be taunted by his playmates because of it, there is no doubt but that his personality will be influenced. He may even achieve greatness spurred by his handicap. In his effort to prove to the world and to himself that he is as good as anyone else, he may work harder and achieve a success denied those lacking such an incentive.

Artificial insemination seems to provide us with a clear-cut case which refutes any claim of hereditary modifications among so-called "love babies." There have been quite a few cases during the past twenty years in which childless couples have resorted to artificial insemination when it was found that the husband was sterile. To do this, a doctor using seminal fluid removed from a disinterested man, introduces it into the woman by means of a special instrument. Certainly one cannot imagine any method of conception more prosaic and devoid of emotion than such a coldly scientific procedure carried out in a medical laboratory. Yet, the many children who have been born as a result of artificial insemination show no hereditary differences from those resulting from normal intercourse.

The emotional state of a couple at the time of conception has nothing to do with the nature of the child produced, although the emotional state of the child as influenced by its parents and other childhood associations may have a very profound environmental influence.

Blood and Heredity

The idea that blood is the primary force of heredity dates back at least to the times of Aristotle when it was thought that the embryo was formed from highly purified blood coming from the two parents, particularly, from the male. Thus, there was thought to be a continuity of blood which determined hereditary traits through the generations. Just think of some of the terms we use today and you can see how prevalent this concept has been. We hear the terms, "blood will tell," "blue blood," "blood line," "blood relative," and "bad blood," used in connection with heredity. Of course, many of us use some of these terms today in a metaphorical sense which is all right as long as we understand the actual hereditary conditions. There are some, however, who still believe that there is a literal relationship between blood and heredity. It has long been proved that genes are responsible for heredity. Strange to say, blood is the one component of the body containing cells which do not have genes. These cells have genes, as do the other body cells, when they are developing within the marrow of the bones, but they lose the genes before they are released into the blood stream as red blood cells. Hence, blood would be the least likely of all the body tissues to influence heredity.

Testimony as to the prevalence of belief in the hereditary force of blood was found during the past war when many service men refused transfusions from members of another race for fear that they would thus acquire some of the characteristics of the donor. There is certainly no foundation for such a belief; in fact, there have been a number of cases in which a person's entire blood supply has been replaced by transfusion without influencing his characteristics.

Blood plays no part in the transmission of hereditary characteristics.

Influence of Age of Parents

Another popular misconception about heredity concerns the possible influence of the parents' age. There are some who believe that children born during the earliest period of the reproductive life of a couple will be consistently inferior in hereditary qualities to the children of more mature parents. This is a throwback to the concept of acquired characteristics, which assumes that a person cannot transmit qualities which he has not yet developed. It is true that a baby born of a very young mother may not be as robust and healthy as that of a woman in her twenties, but heredity has nothing to do with this. Cattle breeders will usually prevent the mating of young heifers, for they have learned from experience that inferior calves are likely to result. The small, young heifers mature sexually before they mature physically, and they must supply the needs of their own growing bodies as well as those of the embryos within their bodies. Both are likely to suffer as a result. The same principle holds in human beings. Many a

young girl of twelve begins ovulation and becomes a potential
mother, but she may have several years of body growth ahead
before she herself has developed physically to the point where
she can give an embryo the best conditions for development
within her body. Hence, she cannot bear a child that will have
as good a start in life as if she had waited for her own physical
maturity.

On the other hand, an adolescent boy who has just begun
to produce sperms in sufficient quantities to make him fertile
can father a child who will be just as strong and healthy as
would be possible after the boy had achieved greater physical
maturity. The father has nothing to do with the nourishment
of the embryo and the genes which his sperms carry are the
same regardless of age.

At the opposite end of the scale we have similar beliefs
about older parents. It is thought that when there is a decline
in physical vigor as a result of advancing age, there will be a
corresponding decline in vigor of the reproductive cells and
that a child produced from these cells will lack the vitality of
children born to younger parents. There are some cattle
breeders who will not use a fine bull for breeding after it
passes its prime, for fear of a loss of vitality among the calves.

Heredity in no way is affected by the elderly state of the
parents, but the question of environment before birth again
enters the picture. During the latter years of a woman's reproductive life there may be certain degenerative changes in her
organs which do not provide as favorable a place for the
development of the embryo and there will be a somewhat
lessened vitality in the embryo as a result. A man of eighty
may have a child through marriage with a thirty-year-old
woman (and there are such cases) yet the child will be just
as vigorous as if the father had been in his twenties. Several
horse breeders have come to realize this fact and on the blue-
grass farms of Kentucky many an old champion stallion is
used to sire colts which inherit the same fine qualities of a
good race horse as those which the stallion sired in his prime.
Man o' War, the greatest horse in racing history, sired some

of his finest offspring during his later years when he was old and rather feeble.

Heredity is not influenced by the age of either parent, but women at the beginning and end of their reproductive life may not provide an embryo with the best conditions for development.

Telegony and Infection

One of the favorite superstitions about reproduction holds that once a woman has had a child by one man, then all successive children will be influenced to some degree by the heredity of this first man. The idea originated from observations of horse breeders in England during the last century. A striped horse was mated with a solid-colored mare and a colt was produced which showed some striping, certainly nothing unusual. When this mare was later mated with a solid-colored horse, however, a colt was produced which showed very faint stripes on its neck and withers. Not understanding the principles of heredity which make the appearance of recessive characteristics possible, the idea originated that this was some carry-over from the first mating. This became known as telegony and soon was believed to affect all types of animals including human beings. Many a fine female dog has been destroyed because she accidentally bred with a mongrel and the owner thought it impossible for her to ever produce pure-bred puppies again. In cases of rape when a child has been produced, women have sometimes felt that they were contaminated by this pregnancy and that all future children whom they might bear would show some of the characteristics of the man or men with whom they had had the forced relationship.

Along this same line of reasoning it is sometimes believed that when a woman has a number of children by the same man, each successive child will be more like the father because of accretion of the man's characteristics in her body.

Although less commonly heard, there is a male counterpart of this superstition which holds that a man who mates

with one woman will somehow acquire some of her characteristics and will communicate these to any children he might
father through another woman. This is known as infection.

The heredity of a child is in no way influenced by previous children that have been borne by either its mother or
fathered by its male parent. Hereditary characteristics can
be transmitted only from the one father and the one mother
who are the direct parents of the child.

Influence of Drugs

It is believed by some that drugs may have an influence
on reproductive cells and the genes which they contain, which
may affect offspring. Alcohol, nicotine, and morphine are
some of the drugs most commonly mentioned in this connection. Occasionally one may hear a misinformed person tell
of a tragic case in which a deformed child was fathered by a
man who was a chronic alcoholic with the implication that
the alcohol was the cause of the deformity. Alcohol does not
alter the genes, however, and, therefore, could not alter the
heredity. It is true that habitual, excessive use of alcohol over
a long period of time may cause a man to be sterile through
destruction of his sperms, but if these sperms retain sufficient
vitality to fertilize an egg, the resulting child will be just the
same as if the man had been a model of sobriety during his
entire life. Thus a newborn child is not penalized in its heredity
by the indiscretions of its parents.

As an argument to the contrary, some may point to cases
in which a father who was a chronic alcoholic bore children
who, in the course of time, followed in their father's footsteps.
This by no means proves that the drinking by the father
influenced his sperms so that the children would be more likely
to imbibe too freely of alcoholic beverages. There may be two
factors which enter into such a correlation. Many persons can
drink socially and control their drinking so that it does not
become an obsession with them. Others seem to be of such
a disposition that extensive drinking leads to a compulsion for

further drinking which is so powerful that they cannot stop, even though it becomes evident that the habit is wrecking their lives. All the evidence indicates that this tendency to addiction may be inherited. Hence, if a father has the addiction, then he must have inherited genes which make such an addition possible. It is quite likely, therefore, that some of his children will receive the same gene complex which brings about such an uncontrollable compulsion to drink after the habit is formed. Couple this with the fact that the children of such a parent are more likely to have the opportunity to develop the habit through precept and opportunity and we can understand the correlation. Of course, if the children never develop a taste for alcoholic beverages through common use, then they may never express their inherited weakness, but it is there, nevertheless, and may show in some other compulsion. It is possible that one of the children will begin taking heroin simply for the "kick" which he gets out of it and he will soon find himself hopelessly addicted to this drug. Not all people can become dope addicts—addiction requires a particular type of personality which will develop a compulsion which makes it impossible for the victim to withstand administrations which actually may destroy his life. Heredity certainly influences the possession of such a personality, but the expression of an inherited weakness, in itself, will not enhance the chances of transmission of the trait through heredity.

It is true, however, that a drinking, expectant mother can harm the embryo she is carrying, for the alcohol can pass directly into the blood stream of her child and when it is born it may actually show symptoms of alcoholism. Also, a child may be born who is a heroin addict if its mother was accustomed to taking the drug regularly during her pregnancy. Neither alcohol, heroin, or other narcotic drugs can influence the determiners of heredity in either man or woman.

Drugs do not influence the transmission of hereditary characteristics, although a mother who uses drugs may harm the embryo she is carrying by direct transmission of these substances to the embryo.

CHAPTER 4

MARKED BABIES?

There is an old Norwegian law which prohibits butchers from displaying the carcasses of hares (rabbits) which they have prepared for sale to their customers. The reason—to prevent expectant mothers from viewing the hares and, thereby, running the risk of marking the children which they carry and causing them to be born with harelip. About one baby out of every thousand is born with harelip, a condition in which there is a vertical fissure in one of the lips. This split which usually appears in the upper lip, may extend up to the nose. The lip of such children bears a superficial resemblance to the upper lip of a rabbit, and the superstition is that such a condition would be induced in an embryo when the woman carrying it was strongly impressed by a view of a rabbit's mouth.

This is an excellent illustration of one of the oldest and most common of all superstitions about heredity—maternal impressions. There are few who read these lines who have not heard one or more instances of so-called marked babies, told seriously. A child is born with a red, strawberry-shaped birthmark, and the mother recalls that she craved strawberries during the latter part of her pregnancy. Another child is born with a skin which chaps easily and sloughs off like the scales of a fish, and the mother remembers cleaning some fish a short time before the child was born. The apparent relationship between the impression on the mother and the abnormality of the child is sometimes striking and may lead one to wonder if perhaps there might be something to it after all.

This is an extremely vicious superstition which can do

much harm, for it can cause a pregnant woman to worry unduly for fear that she may see something, or hear something, or do something, which could doom the little bundle of life within her to an existence handicapped by an abnormality. And when a child is born that is defective, the mother may spend a lifetime of regret believing that she caused the defect during the pregnancy. It is a superstition which is not easily contradicted, however, because so many who believe in it have apparently authentic cases to support their belief. In this chapter we shall examine the evidence critically and try to determine the facts.

Mind Over Matter

At a county health center in Florida, the author recently talked to a woman and her young son who was born without a left hand. There were little stumps of fingernails protruding from the end of the arm which appeared to be severed between the wrist and the elbow. This woman lived near one of the major Florida highways and one day, about two months before the expected delivery of the child, she heard a loud crash on the highway in front of her home. She went out to investigate and found to her horror that there had been a serious automobile accident, and she viewed the mangled bodies of several occupants of one of the cars. She became sickened at the sight and suffered from nausea. When her child was born two months later, the left hand was missing. In accord with the many tales of maternal impressions which she had heard from others, this woman assumed that the view of the accident had so strongly impressed her that the child within her body became deformed.

Such cases give strong support to the perpetuation of belief in maternal impressions. A few other striking illustrations might be mentioned before we begin inquiry into the validity of such consequences. Some years ago one of the most vicious criminals of the time was captured and brought to trial. He was a hardened murderer who seemed to kill for the love of killing—some of his innocent victims were slaughtered for no reason except his lust to destroy life. Throughout the trial the man's mother stood by him as though he were being victimized by an unsympathetic public. When questioned by reporters she maintained that his crimes were actually due to her actions before he was born. The woman's husband was a butcher in a small shop and she had the habit of taking him his lunch every day. She said that it was inevitable that her eyes should rest on the bloody carcasses hanging around the shop when she entered, and that it was certainly logical that the child which she was carrying in her body should be so impressed that he would have bloody thoughts and would want to kill when he matured. In this way she excused her son for all his crimes and accepted the blame herself.

In another instance, a mentally defective child was born to a rural couple. The mother felt that a maternal impression was the cause of this defect. She stated that her husband had killed a large snake on their farm about a month before the child was born. Her husband showed her the snake, which seemed thoroughly dead, and then threw it into a pile of burning leaves in the yard. The heat caused the snake to squirm and twitch violently as it was burning and this greatly horrified the expectant mother. It preyed on her mind for several days and she assumed that this influenced the mind of her child so that its mentality was subnormal. These are cases where it is assumed that the mind has an influence over matter.

Biblical Record of Belief

The belief in maternal impressions is probably the oldest of all the superstitions about reproduction and heredity. Even in the first book of the Bible, the thirtieth chapter of Genesis, we find an account of the general acceptance of this superstition. This relates how Jacob (who worked fourteen years to get the wife he wanted) made a bargain with his crafty father-in-law who had got the better of him in the wife deal. When the work for his wives was completed (he contracted for one and ended up with four) Jacob persuaded his father-in-law to pay him for his work in livestock. Jacob said, in effect, "Let me take all the cattle, sheep, and goats that are striped or spotted, and you keep those which are solid." His proposition was accepted. Thinking that he could increase the percentage of his take, Jacob took willow twigs and peeled the bark down in stripes and placed these at the watering troughs and other places. Later he guided the best-looking animals to these places so that, as they conceived with these stripes before them, their offspring would be so marked that they would be born with uneven coloration. The account indicates that he did very well with the project, although actually he would have done just as well if he had saved himself the trouble of working with the willow twigs.

Evidence Against Maternal Impressions

We could go on and on with examples of supposed cases of maternal impressions—almost everyone has heard a number of stories of this nature. All of the biological evidence, however, shows that such markings do not, and cannot, occur. First of all, there is no conceivable mechanism by means of which they could occur. Think of an embryo in its mother's body. It is surrounded by membranes which it has produced from its own cells and it is floating in a fluid which is a product of its own body. From its body there is an umbilical cord which extends out from its navel and connects with a broad mass of tissue (the placenta) which fits closely against the womb of the mother. The embryo has its own heart and its own blood supply which circulates into this placenta and absorbs food and oxygen from the blood which flows through the womb of the mother. There is no blood from the mother that flows into the embryo and there are no nerves from the mother that are connected with the embryo—actually, the embryo is no more than a parasite in the woman's body. Now, suppose the woman craves strawberries, but cannot satisfy that craving. How would it be possible for this craving to stamp an imprint on the embryo? There is no conceivable mechanism for such an effect.

Even though we assume that there is some connection between the mother and her child through which an impression might be sent, we would, almost always, have to concede the still more unlikely assumption that the mark altered embryonic development which had already been completed. For instance, take the case of the woman who had a son born without a hand. The accident which was supposed to have caused the impression took place only about two months before the birth of her child, yet the hands of an embryo are fully formed about six months previously. We would be forced to the rather ridiculous assumption, therefore, that her child had perfect hands before the accident, but the sight of the accident, through some mysterious means, caused one of these hands to be dissolved so that the child was born with the deformity. This is generally true of most cases of supposed markings—the impression comes during the latter part of the pregnancy, while the embryonic organs which are supposed to be affected are mainly formed during the early stages, when the woman may not even be sure that she is pregnant. Human reasoning can hardly accept the idea of a dissolution of perfectly formed organs due to the mental impulses of the prospective mother.

It may also be noted that the so-called markings are always accounted for after the birth of the child. Now any normal woman in the course of her pregnancy will certainly come in contact with literally thousands of stimulations which may be quite impressive. Should her child be perfectly normal she then gives no further thought to the things that she has contacted. On the other hand, should there be a deformity, a birthmark, or any other unusual condition, she can then look back on her pregnancy and recall some event which may seem to fit the particular case. In her zeal to relate the event it is quite natural that she might exaggerate the degree of the impression which she felt at the time. A very common household chore, such as cleaning fish, may loom as an event of outstanding importance in retrospect, as the story goes the rounds. Thus, it is easy to understand how there may be cases of rather close correlation between an impression and the supposed mark.

There was once a doctor who had seen this happen so many times that he determined to go about the matter scientifically and see what results he would obtain. Accordingly, he made it a practice to talk to all women who were about ready for the delivery of a child. He asked them to tell him of all the events which they had experienced during their pregnancy which made an unusually strong impression on them, and which might possibly mark their children. He carefully tabulated their answers, but when the babies were born there was not a single correlation between the impressions which the women had listed and the abnormalities among the children. He did find, however, that when an abnormality did appear, some of the mothers were quick to remember some impression which they had forgotten to list in order to account for it.

Proxy Mothers

The most convincing bit of evidence against any sort of maternal impression, in the sense in which the term is commonly used, comes from newly developed scientific techniques of embryo transplantation. Among the forms of animal life which lay eggs, the possibility of foster motherhood is taken for granted. Take the rather comical case of a hen hatching a nest of duck eggs and her great concern when her brood takes to the water in spite of her warning clucks. These ducklings are manifesting the genes from their true mother and do not take on any of the characteristics of a chicken simply because a chicken took over the duty of incubating the eggs. In recent years it has become possible to accomplish motherhood by proxy in mammals. Rabbits have been born of virgin mothers who received a transplantation of eggs which had been fertilized in a test tube. Let us see how this is done.

Ovary transplanted

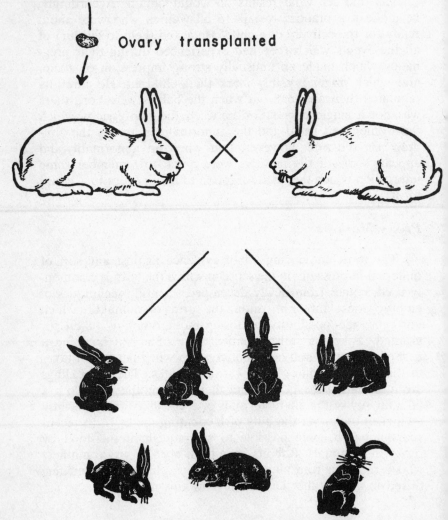

Fig. 3. Black bunnies from white rabbits.

First, rabbits are obtained which are in the estrous cycle (ready for mating). They can be induced to go into this cycle at any time by the injection of the proper hormones. Then the oviducts are removed and the eggs within are washed out into a test tube. Sperms are removed from a male rabbit and mixed with the eggs to allow fertilization to take place. When viewed under a microscope it can be seen that the cells then begin division and the early stages of an embryo are formed. These embryos may be introduced into the uterus (womb) of a virgin female rabbit which is also in the proper phase of the reproductive cycle. Some of these transplanted embryos will become implanted in the uterus and will develop and be delivered in due time.

The heredity of these rabbits, however, is that of their true parents who furnished the eggs and sperms, and their characteristics are not altered by their sojourn in the body of their proxy mother. For instance, embryos formed from eggs and sperms of pure white rabbits have been transplanted to a foster mother who was black, yet the fur of the offspring is pure white, just as if they had remained in the womb of their true mother.

Similar results have been accomplished in other mammals. Recently a very practical application of the technique has been worked out on a cattle ranch in Texas. By use of hormones it is possible to induce cows to release rather large numbers of eggs at one time instead of the usual one or two. These eggs can be collected by use of specially devised instruments without injuring the cows in any way. The eggs can then be fertilized with sperms from a bull and transplanted to proxy mothers. Ultimately, it is hoped that this method can be used to increase the number of offspring which can be obtained from prize cows. We now use artificial insemination which enables prize bulls to father many more calves than would be possible by natural mating, and the time may not be too far distant when we can increase the yield of offspring from desirable cows also. Since there is no danger of a maternal impression, any sort of "scrub" cow could be used to bear

the offspring. Thus, it is possible to obtain hundreds of offspring from one fine cow by using "scrub" females, that would
have little economic value otherwise, as proxy mothers.

Human Birth by Proxy

If such transplantation is possible in cattle, what about
using it in human beings? The process of ovulation, fertilization, and embryonic development is quite similar in the two.
Could a woman have a child through a proxy mother? We
have every reason to believe that it is possible. Such a plan
might seem quite attractive to some famous professional
women who want children, but who feel that they cannot spare
the time from their careers to bear a child in the normal way.
It would be easy to find women in the lower socio-economic
strata of our society who would be willing to serve as proxy
mothers to children of other women if there was an attractive
financial reward. It is frightening to think of the legal tangles
which might be involved, however, when questions of legiti-
macy and inheritance came up—our lawmakers did not
anticipate the advances of science when the laws on such
matters were framed.

While we may not sympathize with wealthy or busy
women who would wish to escape the burdens of bearing their
own children, there are cases which might justify foster
motherhood. The desire to reproduce children of one's own
flesh and blood is one of the strongest drives of mankind.
There are cases where the attainment of this desire is frustrated. A woman may marry late in life when her reproductive
organs are no longer fit for childbearing and it might be
dangerous to attempt it. An egg from this woman, fertilized
by a sperm from her husband, could safely develop in the body
of another woman with young, healthy reproductive organs
and the couple could have a child which was entirely their
own—just as much so from the standpoint of heredity as if
the older woman had borne it. Some might prefer this process

to the adoption of a child who had no heredity from either parent.

There probably are cases where younger women are sterile because of certain defects of the reproductive organs, but in whom ovulation is normal. In still others, the women might be fertile, but have diseases of vital body organs such as the heart or kidneys which make it unwise for them to carry and bear children.

Should the practice of proxy motherhood ever become common, the question of morality would surely be raised. Is there anything in the procedure which would be antagonistic to religious principles and concepts of morality? Some might feel that it is contrary to all religious concepts and is no more to be condoned than illegitimate births or abortion. Others might say that, for thousands of years, women have often depended on the so-called "wet nurse" to feed their babies after birth. Why not then carry the process a step further and have prenatal "wet nurses" to feed the babies before birth when circumstances warrant? Some might feel that a mother could not love her child as much if she did not experience the stages of pregnancy and birth herself. Others would say that the reactions of foster parents to adopted children indicate that their love is just as great as that of natural parents for their children. In fact, even greater in some cases where the parents are first faced with the prospect of a life without children and then appreciate them more when they do obtain them through adoption.

Ovary Transplantation

Using a somewhat different technique it has also been demonstrated that entire ovaries may be transplanted from one animal to another to achieve proxy motherhood. Such work has been carried out successfully on dogs. The ovaries have been removed from old female dogs of a pure breed and transplanted into the bodies of young mongrel females. When these mongrels were mated with males of the pure breed, puppies resulted which were just as true to the breed characteristics as if the original mother had borne them. (It will be interesting to see what the dog breeder's associations will do about the registration of such pups.) This technique can have a very practical importance—in fact, a rejuvenation of reproductive tissues has sometimes resulted from transplantation. When a grand champion female dog reaches the senile state where degenerative changes of the reproductive organs begin, it will be possible to transplant her ovaries to a young female and the precious germ plasm will not be lost. Thus, even after the death of the champion, pups will be born for which she will be the true genetic mother. There is no reason why a similar transplantation cannot be made when the mongrel female reaches old age and thus the reproduction can be carried on for an unlimited period of time. The body cells grow old and die, but the germ plasm is potentially immortal—it can continue as long as it is in a body which can support it. There is no reason to restrict this procedure to dogs—it has also been used with mice and other mammals. We would hardly expect it to be used in human beings, but it would be entirely possible. In this case the offspring of the mother would have no genetic connection with her, but she would experience the pregnancy and birth.

All of these assorted facts show that the only maternal impression which a mother makes on a child is that which results from the food and oxygen which she supplies.

Reasons for Popularity of Belief in Maternal Impressions

With all this evidence to the contrary why is the belief in maternal markings such a popular superstition? Its popularity might be based, in part at least, on the fact that people are rather reluctant to admit that they may carry any sort of hereditary defect. When a defective child develops, there is likely to be an effort to establish an environmental explanation.

A favorite explanation for a mentally defective offspring has always been that the nurse "dropped him on his head when he was a baby," or that "he got kicked in the head by a mule," or that some similar catastrophe occurred. In this way the parents feel that somehow they are absolved from any taint of defective ancestry. Maternal impressions also offer an easy "out" for the parents regarding any abnormalities which are present at birth.

There is no need for such a guilty feeling about abnormalities when the principles of heredity are better understood. As a matter of fact, there is probably not one among us who does not carry quite a number of hereditary factors for rather serious defects which we do not express. By the law of chance, some of these variations will occasionally appear in children of perfectly normal parents. Also, there are certain embryonic "accidents" which may occur while any woman is carrying a child and result in abnormalities in the offspring which are not inherited. These are not conditioned by anything the woman sees or thinks or does. Hence, there is no reason why causes for abnormalities should be sought in the external environment. However, parents aware of congenital defects in their ancestry should seek professional advice before having children.

CHAPTER 5

THE MALE CARRIER

Before we inquire into the mysteries of inheritance, we must understand something about the organs which serve as carriers, processors, and transmitters of the genes. As individuals we are doomed to death—we cannot hope to live forever—but we carry within our bodies an immortal stream of protoplasm which can continue throughout the future of mankind. We are glorified carriers of this precious germ plasm. Human beings are divided into two sexes, each with a different role to play as a carrier of the genes. In this chapter we shall consider the male carrier.

The Neglected Father

When a baby makes its appearance in a home the mother and the new arrival are usually the objects of special attention while the poor father is pushed into the background and stands around like a country bumpkin feeling about as useful as a fur coat at the equator. At such times it might be well for us to remember that all this could not have happened without a man. While woman is honored, and rightly so, for her elaborate part in the process of reproduction we should not completely forget that the man has a part to play as well. As a matter of fact, he contributes just as much in the way of the all-important genes of heredity as the woman does.

Each sex has its own functions to perform in the complicated process of begetting new life, and each must have specialized organs to accomplish these functions. A man must have organs to produce sperms, to store them, and at the proper time to release them within the body of a woman in order to accomplish his reproductive function in life. A woman, on the other hand, must have organs to produce eggs, to release them at periodic intervals during the fertile period of her life, to receive the sperms from a man, and to care for the embryos which develop from fertilized eggs. To accomplish such widely diverse functions it is necessary that there be marked differences in the nature of the reproductive organs of the two sexes. We will consider now the organs of the male sex.

Assembly-Line Sperm Production

Man has achieved marvels in the mechanical world by means of assembly-line techniques. An automobile going down the line in the factory appears to be formed almost magically as the various parts are added to it while it is moving along. Within the body of every man there is an assembly-line technique which can turn out millions of intricate bodies within a 24-hour period. Here there are no strikes, no lay-offs, no time-and-a-half for overtime, no fringe benefits—day and night the workers keep this assembly line moving, requiring only room and board as recompense for their labors.

This marvelous process takes place in the male organs known as testes, two glands about the size and shape of pecans which are suspended from the body by a loose fold of skin, the scrotum. To investigate the structure of this assembly plant let us examine a testis more closely. It is covered by a tough, shining membrane with a pearly hue. Within, there are many feet of tiny coiled tubes, known scientifically as the seminiferous tubules, which look like coarse sewing thread. It is within these tubes that the sperms are produced. They start as ordinary-looking cells near the outer edge of the tubes. Let us trace one such cell. It moves toward the interior and by a series of two divisions it becomes four smaller cells. Then follows a molding and shaping which eventually results in four mature sperms, each with a long tail and ready for action. At this point, the sperms are shoved out into the cavity within the center of the tube. Here they mingle with hundreds of other sperms being extruded from the walls of the tube around them.

The Tortuous Journey

These sperms have a long way to go before they can accomplish their purpose in life. Many feet of tortuous tubes lie between them and the outside world. Furthermore, they do not move about at this stage of their existence. They have precious little food with them anyway and it must not be squandered before they even have an opportunity to fulfill their missions. The assembly-line technique continues. These tubes in which the sperms find themselves are lined with cells which bear many tiny hairs (cilia) which wave back and forth in such a manner as to keep the sperms moving along. Once they leave the testis there are still more tubes. Lying on the testis is a small organ, the epididymis through which the sperms must pass. This organ, although only about an inch long, actually contains about twenty feet of fine coiled tubing. Once the sperms have been carried through this organ, they emerge into a larger tube, the vas deferens. This tube carries the sperms up inside the body; it is about eighteen inches long, but has no smaller tubes within it. It enlarges and forms a sort of reservoir for the sperms, known as the ejaculatory duct. It is here that the sperms are stored.

A Thermostat for Developing Sperms

Man likes his comfort and much of the ingenuity of the mechanical age has been devoted to an increase in that comfort. The thermostat is one of man's inventions which contributes to his ease. As with so many of man's so-called discoveries, however, we find that nature had been using the principle long before man ever thought of it. Right in his own body there is a splendid example of a built-in thermostat. This is the scrotum which serves to hold the developing sperms at an optimum temperature level.

You may sometimes wonder, especially if you are a man, why such delicate and sensitive organs as the testes are placed outside of the body where they may be so easily injured. Any man can testify to the almost paralyzing pain that comes from a blow on the testes. Why are they not kept in a more protected position in the body? A partial explanation seems to lie in the temperature requirements for the production of sperms. The testes lie within the body cavity before birth, in a position about the same as that occupied by the ovaries of a woman, and descend into the scrotum at about the time of birth. In a few cases, the canal through which the testes must descend is blocked by an obstruction which prevents the normal descent. A person with such an obstruction may grow into a perfectly normal man, but he will be sterile, probably because the high temperature within the body is not conducive to the production of normal sperms. When such men are operated on surgically and the obstruction is removed, the testes may descend into the normal position where the temperature will be cooler; the man may then become fertile. (Undescended testes, cryptorchism, may also be caused by deficient male hormone without any obstruction.) In some men the canal may remain rather large throughout life and such persons sometimes develop inguinal hernia when a portion of the intestine descends through this canal and into the scrotum. Such hernia is rare in women because their canals are nearly always quite small.

Even outside the body, the testes are subject to temperature variations which must be accommodated for. It is just as bad for them to become too cold as it is for them to become too warm. Suppose a man is mowing his lawn in warm weather. His body is giving off a large amount of heat. The transmission of this heat to the testes is prevented because the scrotum relaxes and allows the testes to hang down several inches from the body. Now suppose the man goes in and takes a cold shower. The cold water coursing over his body soon lowers the temperature of the testes and the scrotum will contract and draw the testes up close to the body. In this position they can absorb more of the body heat and chilling is prevented. Thus, the scrotum acts as a thermostat which keeps the testes always at the best temperature for the normal development of the sperms. There have been cases where men have prevented this thermostat from working by wearing tight underwear in warm weather, and they have become temporarily sterile as a result. A change to looser clothing which allowed the testes to drop away from the body brought about a return of fertility.

Once formed, the sperms however, appear to be able to withstand greater temperature variations. They are stored in the interior of the body where the temperature is several degrees warmer than in the scrotum. Furthermore, they may even be stored in a refrigerator after having left the body and they will still retain their vitality.

Hydraulic Transmission

Let us get back to the sperms which we left stored in the ejaculatory duct ready for emission. Attached to this duct there is another organ called the seminal vesicle which produces a viscid, glycerine-like fluid which is mixed with the sperms at the time they are expelled from the body. This fluid serves as a medium to transmit the sperms to the female—a case of hydraulic transmission. The fluid also contains an activating chemical that stimulates the sperms to greater activity. Within the ejaculatory ducts the sperms are sluggish and practically immobile—they are not wasting the food which will be needed in a possible race for the egg. Once mixed with the fluid from the seminal vesicle, however, the sperms immediately become very active. The mixture of sperms and fluid is called semen.

If freshly emitted semen is examined under the microscope the sperms can be seen vigorously wiggling, threshing their tails, and propelling themselves along as rapidly as the viscid nature of the medium will permit. Due to this rapid expenditure of energy their food is exhausted within a few hours and the sperms slow down and lose their power to accomplish fertilization. It is sometimes possible to recover living sperms from within the vagina of a woman several days after a sexual relationship, but these are so exhausted that they cannot accomplish fertilization. When they are still vital it is possible to slow them down by refrigeration and, thus, conserve the food which they carry and prolong their effective period. Sperms from bulls have been kept for over a week by this method and were then used to fertilize cows. As a matter of fact, in recent years, sperms have even been frozen and kept in a deep-freeze for over a year. Many calves have been born as a result of the artificial insemination of cows with semen which had been frozen for over a year after it had been taken from the bull. This has even been extended to human sperms. Doctors at the University of Iowa Medical School have kept human semen in a deep freeze for months and then used it successfully in artificial insemination. There are several children in the country today whose paternal genes had a sojourn in a deep-freeze between the time of ejaculation and insemination. In all probability the sperms could be kept in this manner for many years. It is now possible for a man to have children long after he is dead.

Male Accessories

There are also other organs in the male system which act as accessories to the transmission of sperms. There is a testis, a vas deferens, an ejaculatory duct, and a seminal vesicle on each side of the body. At the point where they join together there is a mass of tissue known as the prostate gland. The tubes unite within this gland and form the urethra which is a tube that leads from the bladder; through this tube urine is conveyed to the outside. Thus, this tube must carry both urine and semen. Urine, however, is nearly always acid and sperms are killed by exposure to acid. Here the function of the prostate gland comes in. It secretes an alkaline fluid which flows along the tube and neutralizes the acid residue from the urine, thus providing a lubricant which gives a "greased track" for the expulsion of the semen. There is another small pair of glands, the Cowper's glands, further down the urethra, which secrete a similar fluid with the same purpose.

As the urethra leaves the body it passes through the most conspicuous accessory organ, the penis. This is truly a remarkable organ which is adapted for the introduction of the semen into the vagina of a woman. Externally, the penis is composed of a sensitive glans at the tip, followed by the body which is covered with a loose skin. Part of this skin, the foreskin or prepuce, normally overlaps the glans, but this is commonly removed in an early operation, called a circumcision. Internally, the penis is composed of three bodies of spongy tissue, the corpora cavernosa. These are connected by blood vessels and may become engorged with blood under sexual stimulation.

John and Mary

Now that we have some concept of the nature of the organs of reproduction in man, let us see how these organs function to fulfil their *raison d'etre*. The testes begin to produce sperms in a boy at about the time the physical and psychological changes of adolescence make their appearance. They continue to be released throughout young manhood, middle age, and even into old age in some cases. There will be some variation in the number produced according to the seasons and according to a man's general physical condition. A man whose body is weakened by disease, malnutrition, or old age will not produce sperms as abundantly as a man who is in good physical condition.

The preparation of the reproductive organs for use and the emission of the sperms is controlled by a special set of nerves which are a part of the autonomic nervous system. This system is not under direct control of our conscious mind. The nervous system involuntarily affecting reproduction is stimulated by certain emotions and responds to physical manipulation of the penis. Whenever there is a strong sexual stimulation these nerves bring about many changes in the body of a man. Let us use an incident to illustrate what happens.

Suppose there is a young man, let us call him John, who is sitting alone on a sofa in the living room, wondering how long it will be until dinnertime. A door opens and in walks a lovely young lady, let us call her Mary, who impresses John as being a very attractive young lady. She sits beside him —almost immediately his heart begins beating faster and stronger. She moves closer—a bit of her hair brushes his cheek—John becomes conscious of a pleasing perfume—he forgets all about dinner. His autonomic nerves have started their work—they stop the secretions in his stomach that were making him hungry and increase the rate of heartbeat; his blood pressure rises. John reaches over and grasps the young lady's hand—he has a peculiar tingling sensation all over. Mary squeezes his hand gently in return—his breathing becomes deeper and faster. None of these responses occur directly in the reproductive organs, yet all are a part of the grand preparation for a possible culmination of the emotion manifested in John. The autonomic nerves have no way of knowing whether John is married to the girl who is generating all these reactions, nor how far he intends to progress. They are automatic in their response to stimuli and prepare him for any eventuality. By this time, the prostate and Cowper's glands have probably become active and are releasing their clear, viscid, alkaline fluids into the urethra, thus sweeping away all traces of acid residue which may have remained from the urine that has passed through this tube and paving the way for the possible ejaculation of semen.

Mission Accomplished

Events may progress no further—moral or legal barriers may intervene to bring a halt. In marriage however, these responses may culminate in a delicate relationship which is known as sexual intercourse. Under the stimulation of intimate love-making which precedes such an act the autonomic nerves cause a dilation of the arteries entering the penis. This, coupled with the increased blood pressure and rapid heartbeat, causes a greatly increased blood supply to accumulate in this organ, for the veins leaving the penis have valves which slow the exit of blood. As a result, the blood fills the spongy tissue and the penis becomes enlarged and firm and may be used to penetrate the female. At this time the penis is very sensitive to physical stimulation. In the act of sexual intercourse this physical stimulation, together with the powerful emotion of the act, will, in time, bring about an emotional explosion, known as an orgasm, which climaxes the reproductive drive. The climax is accompanied by a release (the ejaculation) of semen. The autonomic nerves cause a rhythmic contraction of the seminal vesicles. This forces their fluid out and it mixes with the sperms—the ejaculatory ducts also contract rhythmically and force this newly formed semen out of the urethra in a series of spurts. There will be about four or five cubic centimeters of this fluid in a normal ejaculation. An orgasm is a unique body reaction which gives a pleasurable sensation, but which is very hard to explain. In a way, it is like a sneeze—if sufficient stimulation is received to start the reaction, then the full orgasm and ejaculation will take place.

After the orgasm the body gradually returns to a more normal state as the stimulation of the autonomic nerves subsides. Man thus completes his part in gene transmission.

CHAPTER 6

ETERNAL WOMAN

A man's part in procreation is completed within an extremely short time, but a woman's part extends over a much longer period. A woman must not only produce reproductive cells and have organs which make possible their union with reproductive cells from the opposite sex, but must also provide for all the needs of the embryo which is to develop in her body for a period of about nine months, and, in addition, must usually provide for food and protection for the baby for some time after its birth. As a result of these extensive requirements, a woman's part in the process of reproduction is somewhat more complex than that of a man.

The Cradle of Humanity

A little girl, on first seeing the productive organs of a boy, sometimes feels as if nature has discriminated against girls by not providing them with organs which are as distinctive as those of boys. As she learns more about the organs of reproduction, however, she may be consoled by the fact that these organs are actually more extensive in girls—they are just placed in a position within the body so that they are not externally evident. A girl has ovaries which are comparable to the testes of a boy, but, while the testes of a boy descend at about the time of birth so that they can be seen externally, a girl's ovaries remain within her body. In a mature woman each of these ovaries is about the size of a shelled almond. There is one on either side of the abdomen, in the lower region, and they are held in place chiefly by a broad ligament. The eggs are formed in a layer of tissue (the germinal epithelium) which lies around the outside of the ovaries, but they move toward the interior of the ovaries to complete their development. At first, a number of smaller cells (the follicle cells) will form around each egg. Then a fluid (the follicular fluid) will accumulate between the cells. Eventually, there will be so much of this fluid that the entire structure, now known as a Graafian follicle, will bulge out and make a bump on the ovary. The egg is now mature and ready to be released. One of these Graafian follicles will break open about every 28 days and release the fluid together with the egg and the corona of follicle cells which surround it. This process is known as ovulation, and it is at this time that fertilization is likely to occur if there is a sexual relationship about the same time. Sometimes a woman feels a sudden sharp pain on one side of her back or the other at the time this rupture takes place. It normally occurs about 14 days before menstruation. The follicular fluid contains an important hormone which helps regulate the reproductive cycle of a woman.

The ovaries are almost surrounded by finger-like processes extending out from the open end of a tube, the Fallopian tube. The hair-like cilia which line this tube pull the egg in and move it slowly along the tube. It is in this tube that the sperms of the man usually contact the egg and accomplish fertilization. Fertilized or not the egg continues its journey down the tube and enters the uterus (womb) which is the place where the embryo develops; this is, truly, the cradle of humanity. The uterus is an organ about the size and shape of a pear. It consists of thick muscular tissue which is capable of great distension to provide for the embryo which may develop inside. The neck (cervix) of the uterus opens into a passage, the vagina, which is about three inches long. This is the tube into which the semen is ejected.

Female Accessories

Externally there is a pad of fatty tissue (the mons pubis) in the front of the genital region of a woman. This becomes covered with a mass of pubic hair at adolescence. This fatty tissue extends backwards and forms two large lips (the labia majora) which inclose the region of the more delicate reproductive organs. The opening of the vagina lies at the posterior part of this region. At birth this opening is partially closed by a thin membrane (the hymen) which usually is unperforated until it is broken by sexual intercourse. It should be pointed out, however, that the hymen may be broken by various types of injuries during girlhood, so a broken hymen is not necessarily an indication that a woman is not a virgin. Just in front of the opening of the vagina is the opening of the tube from the urinary bladder (the urethra) through which the urine is expelled. While in a man the urethra carries the semen as well as the urine; there is no like dual function of this tube in a woman. Both the opening of the vagina and the urethra are inclosed in a smaller pair of lips (labia minora). Just in front of these lips is a small organ called the clitoris which is like a small male penis. This organ has the same type of spongy tissue as the penis and becomes firm during sexual excitement. It, also, is very sensitive to physical stimulation at such a time. There is a mass of similar spongy tissue on either side of the opening of the vagina. This tissue also becomes enlarged during sexual stimulation and spreads apart the lips opening into the vagina. Within this tissue there are two glands (the greater vestibular glands) which secrete a viscid alkaline fluid during sexual stimulation which provides a lubricating medium for sexual intercourse and also neutralizes any trace of acid residue from the urine.

A woman will usually experience the same sort of emotional explosion (orgasm) as a man at the climax of intercourse, but there is no sudden expulsion of fluid as in man at this time. Woman is much more variable than man in this regard—some women may experience several orgasms during one intercourse while some reach the emotional heights necessary for orgasm infrequently, and there are a few women who never experience it.

The female breasts should also be included in a discussion

of reproductive organs for they play a definite role in the whole process, since under primitive conditions, at least, a baby could not live after birth without nursing. The breasts of a girl become enlarged during adolescence due to the accumulation of fatty tissue and the enlargement of the milk-secreting glands. There are from fifteen to twenty-five of these glands with slender ducts which connect with the nipple of the breast, which radiate out from the nipple like the spokes of a wheel. These glands do not secrete milk, however, until childbirth. The breasts of a boy do not normally become so enlarged, but they have the same basic structure and it is actually possible to induce milk production in the male by injecting the proper hormones. While such experiments are not done on human beings, big tomcats have been so treated and have nursed kittens with all the maternal solicitude of a natural mother. The female breasts are definitely associated with sexual stimulation and the nipples may become firm and sensitive to physical manipulation during sexual excitement.

One Woman's Cycle

Woman is notably a creature of varying moods and emotions—at one time perhaps sweet and coy, only to display a temperament more like a daughter of the old man with the forked tail at other times. In part we can justify such inconsistency by the cyclic changes in her body which are a part of the normal functioning of the female reproductive system. There is a rhythmic ebb and flow of hormones, which, in turn, induce her organs to become prepared for possible pregnancy and to regress if the pregnancy does not materialize. Throughout the years of her life when she is fertile there will be a continuous recurrence of this sequence of events about every 28 days interrupted only by pregnancy, which brings about a more extended cycle of hormonal changes which covers approximately nine months.

A cycle is a circle and a circle has no beginning nor ending. Hence, it is hard to know just where to begin a survey of a cycle such as the reproductive cycle of a woman. We could start at any point. Suppose we choose ovulation, the release of an egg from an ovary as a starting point. Rather than generalizing, let us take a specific instance. On one bright spring morning, let us say that the date is May 1, there is a housewife, Mary, who is busy preparing lunch. She reaches into an upper shelf of a cabinet for a dish and feels a sudden pain on the lower left side of her back. Mary has felt such pains before and goes on about her work without giving it a second thought. An important event has taken place in her body, however. The outer wall of the Graafian follicle on her left ovary has ruptured, releasing the follicular fluid and the egg within it. Some of the smaller blood vessels in the vicinity are broken and there will be some bleeding. Some of this blood may make its way down her Fallopian tubes and show up later in the day as a slight discharge from her vagina. The finger-like processes around the funnel-like opening of the Fallopian tube catch the precious egg as it comes out of the ovary and carry it down into the tube by the action of the hairlike cilia which line the tube. Ovulation has occurred.

Mary is now in the fertile period of her reproductive cycle. The egg will remain in the Fallopian tube and be receptive to fertilization by a sperm for a period of about 48 hours. Let us assume that she has no intercourse during this period or that some measures are taken to prevent sperms from entering the uterus and making their way to the egg. In this event, the egg loses its power to initiate new life. It may stay in the Fallopian tube for several days longer, but, even though sperms reach it, there is no fertilization. Eventually, it will reach the uterus and then will be shed through the vagina, but is so small that the woman will have no knowledge of its passage.

The preparation for ovulation and possible pregnancy actually started about 10 days before it occurred (April 21). At about that time Mary's last menstrual period ceased and there began an enlargement of the Graafian follicle which was to burst. It produced a gradually increasing amount of female hormone (estrogen) which brought about a great thickening of the inner lining of the uterus or womb and an increased blood supply to this organ. This preparation for a possible developing embryo, provided a sufficient blood supply for the nourishment of a new life. Within a day or so after ovulation the cells of the ovary where the egg broke out become enlarged and form a yellow body, the corpus luteum. They now begin secreting a second very important hormone (progesterone) which continues the preparation of the lining of the uterus for an embryo. This hormone stimulates the secretion of a viscid mucous within the swollen lining of the uterus which probably furnishes the first nutritive substance for an embryo.

The Weeping of a Frustrated Womb

There is no embryo this month and all this preparation for pregnancy is to no avail. In such an event there is a regression of the corpus luteum and a decrease in the hormone which it secretes. This would be evident about May 12. The regression and reduction of the hormone is often accompanied by a feeling of depression and increased irritability. On May 14 Mary begins another phase of her reproductive cycle, menstruation. This comes about because there is a sloughing off of the swollen lining of the uterus, a liberation of the accumulated mucous within, and some bleeding due to the rupture of some of the small capillaries within the lining of the uterus. Poetically, menstruation might be called the "weeping of a frustrated womb." All of the elaborate preparations for the reception and nourishment of a new life have been in vain and there is now a breakdown of the prepared tissue. Mary's organs have no way of knowing in which month she will hang out the welcome mat for the stork however, so they continue the cycle of ovulation and the other stages of the reproductive cycle so that she will be ready when that time comes.

Mary marks the date menstruation began on her calendar

for she has learned that she can expect a recurrence of the event in about 28 days, in this case, about June 11. For two days there is a rather heavy flow of the menstrual fluid then it begins to taper off and by May 19 there is no longer any evidence of flow. Her uterine lining is now very thin, as the uterus has shed the outer cells and regressed when the blood supply was reduced. For a few days it will remain thin, repairing tissues which were broken during menstruation. At the same time, however, another Graafian follicle is enlarging in one of her ovaries and it is producing increasing quantities of estrogen. This hormone stimulates the lining of her uterus to begin growth and the preparation for a possible pregnancy is again under way. On May 28 Mary feels another sudden pain in the lower region of her back and again ovulation has taken place. The cycle of events is now complete—during 28 days we have come from one ovulation to another. This woman is again in the fertile period of her cycle.

Of course, the sequence of events of the cycle is by no means always as regular as we have described it. While a 28-day cycle is the most common, there may be considerable variation among different women. There are some who accomplish the series of events in about 21 days and others who have a regular cycle of about 35 days. Most women range somewhere between these two. In some the cycle may be very irregular, however, ranging from two weeks to several months in duration. Such variations and irregularities are based on the hormones which govern the various events in the cycle.

Two Halves Make a Whole

But to get back to Mary who has just ovulated on May 28. Let us suppose that she and her husband have decided that it is now about time for them to start a family. On the evening of this day they have intercourse. The sperms are released in the woman's body during a mutual orgasm and the couple then go to sleep. Within Mary's body, however, there is great activity. The sperms, activated by the seminal vesicle fluid,

YOUR BABY'S TIMETABLE

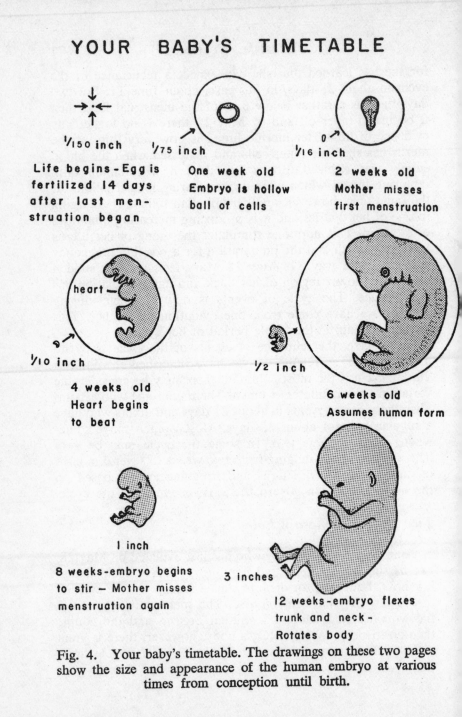

1/150 inch

Life begins - Egg is fertilized 14 days after last menstruation began

1/75 inch

One week old Embryo is hollow ball of cells

1/16 inch

2 weeks old Mother misses first menstruation

heart

1/10 inch

4 weeks old Heart begins to beat

1/2 inch

6 weeks old Assumes human form

1 inch

8 weeks - embryo begins to stir — Mother misses menstruation again

3 inches

12 weeks - embryo flexes trunk and neck - Rotates body

Fig. 4.   Your baby's timetable. The drawings on these two pages show the size and appearance of the human embryo at various times from conception until birth.

YOUR BABY'S TIMETABLE (Cont.)

Size reduced
to one-fifth

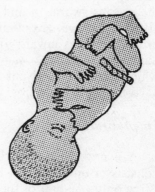

7 inches

20 weeks - Becomes
more active - Mother
feels movements of the
embryo

5 inches

16 weeks
Embryo blinks - Moves lips
Swallows - Clenches fist

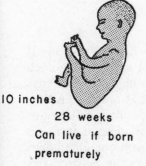

10 inches

28 weeks
Can live if born
prematurely

40 weeks—Time for arrival-
Turns so head points down-
Is crowded - Seems to rebel
at restricted movements

Fig. 4.

are threshing and wiggling as they make their way along in the secretions which cover the wall of the vagina. They tend to congregate at the entrance to the uterus and try to force their way inside. They find, however, that their way is blocked by a plug of rather thick mucous which must first be dissolved. They carry a special enzyme for this very purpose. Any one sperm has only a small bit of the enzyme, but through the combined action of many of them the plug is dissolved and the sperms are free to make their way inside the uterus. Once inside they make their way up this organ and some of them will enter the Fallopian tube and start out toward the egg which was released that morning and is now in the tube on its way toward the uterus. It is here that the two meet. Remember, however, that the egg is still covered by a mass of follicular cells which the sperms must tear away before they can reach the egg. These cells are held together with an intercellular cement. The sperms again use another specific enzyme which dissolves this cement and in time these cells fall away. Then the sperms swarm in and attempt to penetrate the outer covering of the egg. Eventually, one succeeds in getting his head in and migrates inward to mingle with the nucleus of the egg. Simultaneously, the egg forms a membrane around itself which seems to prevent any more sperms from getting in. Two half cells have now made a whole cell.

Implantation

We now have a fertilized egg—a new life has begun. It consists of only one cell now for the sperm and the egg each carry only one-half of the number of genes and chromosomes that are found in human body cells, and it is only when they are united that a complete cell is formed. This cell begins division within a few hours and continues dividing as it makes its way along the Fallopian tube. It takes about eight days for it to reach the uterus and by that time the cells of this young embryo have formed into a hollow ball. As it enters the uterus it reaches a crucial point in its development. Up

to this time it has· been existing on the stored food that was
present in the original egg. There has been cell division, but
very little increase in size. If it is to continue to live and to
grow it must now form an attachment to the lining of the
uterus so that it may be nourished by the mother. Fortunately,
nature has made provision so that the attachment is easy. The
walls of the uterus are swollen and filled with nutritive mucous
which invites implantation. As the ball of cells touches this
lining it sticks and actually begins sinking down into it. It
is not always thus, however, for there are many cases where
the embryo begins its life, but fails to make the proper connection with the uterus and is shed from the woman's body
just as an unfertilized egg would be shed. In Mary's case
everything goes well and the embryo, now firmly implanted
in the uterus, begins absorbing nourishment.

The Baby's Timetable

As yet, Mary has no knowledge of the successful fertilization and implantation that have taken place. The date
is now June 5 and another critical time is approaching—
June 11 is the time that Mary expects her next menstrual
period. If menstruation occurs the lining of the uterus together
with this newly formed embryo will be expelled although it
will be so small that Mary will have no knowledge of its
passage and will never even know that she had become pregnant. Many early pregnancies terminate in this manner. In
an attempt to head off such a catastrophe, there are important
things taking place in Mary's body during the six days preceding the expected menstrual period. The developing embryo
begins the production of a special hormone which is spread
over the woman's body by her blood and causes the yellow
cells of the corpus luteum to continue their secretions which
will keep the uterine lining receptive to the embryo and will
thereby inhibit menstruation. This corpus luteum hormone
also prevents the development of more Graafian follicles and
ovulation in future months. This is very important—otherwise

it would be possible to have fertilization of·new eggs after one
embryo started development and embryos of different ages
would be in the uterus at the same time.

June 11 comes and goes without menstruation. The young
woman whose private life we are exploring so intimately thinks
nothing of it, for it is quite common for her to have a slight
variation in the exact day of menstruation. By June 14 Mary
begins to wonder, and when she wakes up on the morning of
June 16 feeling somewhat nauseated she suspects that she is
pregnant. With each succeeding day the nausea becomes more
acute. Within her body there is a conflict—a conflict between
the forces which usually cause menstruation to occur and
between the forces which are now striving to protect and hold
the new embryo. Mary's doctor may give her injections of
corpus luteum hormone which has been extracted from the
ovaries of pregnant sows that have been killed at slaughter-
houses. This tends to aid the secretion of this hormone from
her own body and relieves the nausea to some extent.

The embryo is now growing rapidly. The genes are forming
the shapeless mass of cells into an orderly arrangement which
gradually becomes distinguishable as a human being. The
embryo is very soft and delicate during this time, but it
develops around itself a membrane filled with fluid in which
it floats as it grows. A placenta is formed which is firmly
attached to the uterus. Food and oxygen are readily absorbed
by this organ and passed down to the embryo by way of the
umbilical cord. Let us keep in mind the fact that it is the
genes which are the sculptors which take this food and
convert it into protoplasm and form the organs in the manner
consistent with that which they have used on countless
occasions in past generations. Fig. 4 illustrates much better
than words can describe just how a human being is formed
from a shapeless mass of cells by the action of these genes.

By September, Mary finds that she has difficulty zipping
up some of her dresses and must begin thinking about a
maternity wardrobe. Her breasts have enlarged considerably
due to the action of the pregnancy hormones which are

causing the milk-secreting glands to become larger. There is no milk in these glands yet, however, and there will not be until after the birth of her baby. She finds that she has a ravenous appetite and at times has a very strong craving for certain foods. Many well-meaning, but often misinformed neighbors drop in and give her all sorts of advice. Mary is a very sensible girl and takes all this advice with a "grain of salt." She depends upon her doctor for directions which will lead to the most satisfactory progress of her pregnancy.

On October 15, just when everything seems to be going so nicely, Mary begins to feel pains in her abdomen which, from what she has been told, resemble the labor pains of birth. She calls her doctor immediately and he diagnoses the condition as a threatened abortion. She is put to bed and given extra injections of corpus luteum hormone and by the next day all pains have subsided and the crisis is past. After this the days and weeks pass uneventfully until the time for birth approaches. This crisis, however, is unusual in all normal pregnancies.

The Blessed Event

Mary has been told that the normal term of pregnancy is about nine months as reckoned from the time of the beginning of her last menstrual period. On this basis she counts from May 14 and obtains February 14 as the date of the expected birth. Her doctor tells her, however, that it actually takes about ten cycles of 28 days, or 280 days. This would place the date at February 18. The actual age of the embryo at birth is about 266 days, for fertilization does not occur until about 14 days after the beginning of the last menstrual period. February 14 comes and goes, however, and February 18 comes and goes—still nothing happens. Mary begins to wonder if the baby will ever be born. She has gained 25 pounds and for weeks now she has felt big and awkward. She has often thought how nice it will be when she can once again see her toes and walk without raring back on her heels to keep from falling forward. Then too, her baby has been so active lately—she has felt its movements ever since about the third month of pregnancy, but now they have become so pronounced that they keep her awake for long hours at night when she wishes to sleep so much.

Then it happens—early on the morning of February 20 she feels a sudden tightening of the muscles of her uterus and there seems to be a slight downward movement of the embryo. Then it stops. Can this be the beginning of labor or is it just a false alarm? Within about fifteen minutes, however, a second and more severe contraction occurs. The contractions continue to come at regular intervals, but the intervals between them become shorter during mid-morning, and her doctor decides that it is time for her to go to the hospital. Upon her arrival in the labor room the contractions are coming at five-minute intervals and are so severe as to be quite painful. By noon they are only about one minute apart and seem to merge into one another so there is almost continuous contraction. By this time she has been prepared by the nurses and is taken to the delivery room.

She is placed on an odd-looking contraption which holds her legs elevated and spread wide apart and her hands are placed in straps upon which she can pull as she sets herself to the serious business of getting her baby into the world. She struggles bravely for a few minutes and then can feel her baby's head at the entrance of her vagina. The orifice seems to be distending wider and wider yet there seems to be no further outward movement of the baby. It is quite painful, but the doctor has given her some drugs which help relieve the pain although she is still conscious. Finally, the doctor decides that it is time to make a small incision at the outer rim of the vaginal orifice and thus hasten delivery. This is done and the baby's head passes out fairly easily, followed by the rest of the body. The head is the largest part of an embryo's body and once it has passed the rest of the body follows easily.

At about this time Mary hears the first cry of her newborn

baby. She had so hoped that her baby would not have to be spanked into taking its first breath of life-sustaining air, and her hopes were rewarded. Within her body the baby's lungs were collapsed and filled with fluid. Upon birth it can no longer depend upon the mother's blood to bring it oxygen so must begin breathing for itself. The cry of a newborn baby is the signal that the first breath has been taken. Although her mind was still somewhat foggy, Mary heard the doctor say, "It's a fine baby girl." She was happy—she had determined not to fix her desire on either sex and hoped only that the baby would be healthy, which it was.

The climax had passed, but the events attendant to birth were by no means over. The umbilical cord was still attached to the placenta inside her body and to the baby outside. The doctor tied and cut the cord close to the baby's body and placed the infant on its right side to aid in the changes which must take place in the circulation of a newborn baby. A valve in the heart must close and send the blood circulating in a different pattern if the baby is to receive oxygen from the lungs rather than from the placenta which supplied it before birth. Improper closure of this valve results in "blue babies."

Now an important self-performing surgical operation is taking place in Mary's body. The placenta and the other membranes which surrounded the embryo are a part of the embryo's tissue and not a part of Mary's body. Hence, they must be separated from the close connection which they form with her body and expelled. With some smaller labor pains this tissue is expelled and the ordeal is over. The doctor quickly sews up the small incision in the edge of the vagina and Mary is soon back in her hospital room.

The baby is brought in for nursing the next morning, but there will be no true milk production for about three days after the birth. There is a fluid produced during this time, colostrum, which aids the infant in preparation of its digestive organs to take over the function of obtaining and digesting its own food, a function which its mother's digestive organs have carried on for the first nine months of its life.

CHAPTER 7

THE BRIDGE OF LIFE

Each of us—male or female, short or tall, handsome or homely, brilliant or dull—began life as a tiny pinpoint of protoplasm, a fertilized egg. Contained within this cell were all of the hereditary potentialities which caused you to develop into a human being with characteristics of the race to which your parents belong and with individual characteristics which distinguish you from other members of your race. This cell was formed by the union of a sperm from your father with an egg from your mother. The sperm was so small that a thousand of them could be lined up side by side across the head of a pin with room to spare. Yet this was your only hereditary link with your father—within the tiny head of this sperm there were all of the factors for the characteristics which you have inherited from him. A child may show great similarity in appearance, mannerisms, and aptitudes to a father whom he has never even seen because of the inheritance transmitted over this tiny bridge of heredity. The egg from your mother was very small also, no larger than the period at the end of this sentence; even so, its volume was thousands of times greater than that of the sperm. However, this does not mean that you inherited more characteristics from your mother, for most of the egg is composed of yolk which you used as food during that critical stage of your existence before you formed an attachment to your mother's womb and could begin obtaining food from her blood. The factors of heredity are contained in a tiny nucleus of the egg and are no more numerous than those that are concentrated in the head of the sperm.

These two cells—the sperm cell and the egg cell—form the bridge of life which connects the generations of the past with those of today and it is such cells that will carry on characteristics to yet unborn generations after we have departed this earth. Over this slender protoplasmic bridge all the hopes of the past and prospects for the future of mankind must pass.

Sperms as Big as Watermelons

By now you may begin to wonder how this is all possible. How can the tiny head of a sperm and the nucleus of an egg possibly carry sufficient material to account for the countless characteristics which stamp you as an animal instead of a plant, an animal with a backbone instead of an earthworm or an insect, a warm-blooded mammal instead of a cold-blooded frog or a snake, a human being instead of a cow, a member of a certain race, and a son or daughter of your parents? To understand this we must be prepared to deal with a world of extreme smallness—smallness almost beyond our conception. Perhaps it will help us to visualize it if we assume that we can greatly enlarge the reproductive cells and look at them as we would view an object which easily comes within the range of our natural vision.

Suppose we discover some marvelous chemical which can enlarge any living thing ten times every time we apply it. Let us begin with a single human sperm. Delicate microscopic measurements have shown us that the sperm head is about one five-thousandth of an inch in length. We will treat it with the magic chemical and it becomes ten times larger—one five-hundredth of an inch in length—still far too small to see with the naked eye. A second treatment makes it one-fiftieth of an inch in length, and a third makes it one-fifth of an inch—it is now visible, but much too small for the study of its details. A fourth treatment brings it up to two inches in length and a fifth treatment makes it twenty inches, about the size of a fairly large watermelon.

In case you have failed to realize the great enlargement

which this sperm has undergone, let us suppose that you spilled some of the chemical on yourself each time it was applied to the sperm. Assume that you started as a small person, only five feet tall, you would jump to 50, 500, 5,000, 50,000 and end up towering 500,000 feet in the air (about 95 miles). Our high-altitude planes could barely reach the lower part of the calf of your leg. If you put your foot down in the New York area you could crush Newark, Manhattan, the Bronx, Queens, and Brooklyn with your toes lapping over in the Atlantic Ocean. You could wade the deepest oceans without getting your knees wet and could easily step over the world's highest mountains. It would take a man of this size to produce sperms with heads the size of watermelons if we assume that they were in proportion to the size of the rest of the body. One seminal emission from such a Gargantua would shower the earth with over a billion gallons of semen filled with these huge wiggling sperms. It would be a flood of no mean proportions.

Now that we have some conception of the tremendous degree of enlargement which we have accomplished, let us examine this huge sperm. The sperm has a head at one end, connected to a middle piece of about the same length, and terminates in a long tail which extends about sixteen feet with a diameter of only about four inches. The head appears to be egg-shaped when we look at it from above, but as we change our position and see it from the side we notice that it is flattened and somewhat thinner at the front. This gives it a wedge-shape from a side view. Within this head there are packed all of the genes of heredity. Also, at the very front end of the head there is an area which is somewhat transparent. This contains the enzymes which are so necessary for the sperms to penetrate the mucous and the cemented cells which bar the way to the egg. The enzymes are held in place by a thin, transparent membrane which fits over the head of the sperm somewhat like a bathing cap. When we examine the middle section we can see that there are two thick cables, each of which is composed of many smaller strands twisted together, which run from the head and extend into the tail. Surrounding these cables there is a spiral body wound around them something like the insulation which is wound around electric cables. This intricate mechanism in the middle piece is the motor which gives the power of movement to the sperm. It is through the activity of this motor that the movements of the tail are possible.

It is the head, however, with which we are most concerned. Let us dissect it so we can learn more about its contents. We carefully slice open the outer covering. The fluid at the front containing the enzymes spills out. We can now see that most of the head is filled with tightly packed coils. We reach in and pull on one of the coils and it comes out of the sperm's head as a long snake-like body which varies in diameter along its length. This is what is known as a chromosome; there are 23 of these within the sperm head. As an integral part of this string we will find the individual units of heredity, genes, in a linear order. Here we are reaching an area which is so small in its normal size that even the highest-powered electron microscopes cannot easily penetrate it—a size comparable to large protein molecules. In fact, it is very likely that the genes are actually very large protein molecules. According to the most reliable information, however, these ultimate units of heredity would appear to be about one-eighth of an inch in diameter in the tremendously enlarged condition we are considering, although they will vary somewhat in size.

The 23 chromosomes will be of different lengths and will carry different numbers of genes, but if we happen to pull out one of average length we will probably find about 870 genes on it, for our best estimates place the total number of genes carried by a sperm at 20,000. Here we find our ultimate explanation of heredity—the genes are the sculptors which take food, from whatever source it may come, and convert it into protoplasm in accordance with the pattern which they have established over many generations.

It is the fabulous genes that form your cells into shapes which eventually assumed a human form. If you have brown eyes it is they that produce the brown pigment in the irises. It is they that molded the shape of your nose and gave it familial characteristics. If you have musical aptitude, you may thank your genes, for they molded the many phases of your total being to enable you to have this ability. Yes, the genes not only account for all the many inherited physical characteristics, but also influence the less noticeable characteristics of the nervous and glandular systems which result in more intangible qualities such as intelligence, aptitudes, temperament, and even minor mannerisms. A fond mother may be determined to make a musical genius out of her daughter, yet no amount of study and practice can produce an outstanding musician unless the child has inherited an aptitude for music. It takes aptitude plus study and practice to make a great musician.

The Egg and You

Were we to enlarge a human egg in proportion to this sperm we would have to get in a rather large auditorium with a high ceiling for it would become a huge globe about fifty feet in diameter—too large to crowd into an ordinary room. Yet, if we were to cut into such an egg and work our way through the tons of rich yolk we would find a nucleus near the center, and within the nucleus there would again be 23 chromosomes containing a total of about 20,000 genes— the same as in the sperm. These, then, are the carriers of heredity. Let us now return them to their normal size and learn how they propagate themselves as they pass through the generations.

Gene Duplication

At the time of fertilization the head of a sperm penetrates the outer covering of the egg, makes its way through the yolk, and unites with the egg nucleus. Consequently, there are now 46 of these gene strings (chromosomes) in the cell, which now contains approximately 40,000 genes. In order to make a human body, however, this cell must divide over and over again before it can produce the billions of cells which we know are to be found in a mature body. But it is not enough for the cell to divide—if the genes are to influence the development of the entire body they must be present in all parts of the body. The genes and the chromosomes must divide each time the cell divides. Division is not a good word for this process, however; duplication would be better, for when this cell splits we find that each of the two cells produced contains 46 chromosomes and each chromosome has the full number of genes which were present in the original cell.

This is the most remarkable process that ever occurs— the very foundation of life itself. Think of it, here we have 46 strings of genes; the cell prepares to divide; the genes and the strings then duplicate themselves so that we actually have 92 such strings in the cell for a short time. It is as if we cut apples in two, but instead of getting half apples we obtain whole apples and each of the whole apples is exactly like the one which was cut to form it. If you have a gene which produces brown eyes on one of your chromosomes, when this gene divides (duplicates itself) there are two genes for brown eyes, each with the same power to form brown eyes as the first gene possessed. In some ways each gene is able to take food from its surroundings and construct an exact duplicate of itself. That is the reason genes can continue from one generation to the next through centuries without change.

Thus it was that the genes within the cell which was to form your body were duplicated in preparation for the first cell division. The duplicated gene strings adhered together at first and became rather tightly coiled to form the short, thick chromosomes which can easily be seen microscopically in dividing cells. Fig. 5 shows how these chromosomes arranged themselves in the center of the cell and were pulled apart so that, when the cell split in two, each cell formed contained one of each of the kinds of genes which were present in the first cell. This process is known as mitosis. In a short time each of these two cells divided again to give four cells, each with the full set of genes and so on until your entire body was formed. It is possible to take cells from certain parts of your body today and demonstrate the 46 chromosomes which descended from the fertilized egg through repeated cell divisions of this nature.

Cell Duplication

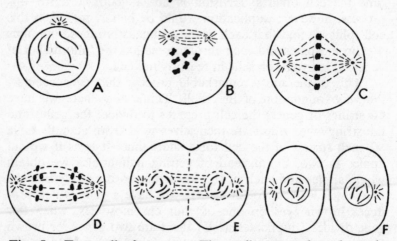

Fig. 5. Two cells from one. These diagrams show how the chromosomes become doubled and shortened (B) and arrange themselves in the center of a spindle-shaped figure (C). The double portions of the chromosomes separate (D) and then become elongated (E). The cell splits in two and two complete cells are formed. These diagrams show only six chromosomes; in man the number is 46, but they go through the same process shown here.

You Could Have Been Twins

Occasionally an embryological accident happens which gives us the best proof possible that the genes actually duplicate themselves with each cell division. Sometimes, the early embryo will separate into two parts, but when this happens each of the two parts can go on to produce a complete person and identical twins are born. Furthermore, identical twins always have identical genes—they will always be the same sex, have the same color eyes, and express all the same inherited characteristics. This gives us a definite indication of the exactness of the duplication of the genes which precedes cell division. Every person could have had an identical twin from the same mass of protoplasm from which he was formed. You may not have a twin because you stuck together when you were just a tiny ball of cells, but, had those cells broken apart to form two embryos, there would have been another being exactly like you, yet it would have taken nothing from you in the way of heredity.

To avoid confusion we should state at this point that there are two types of twins, as illustrated in Fig. 6. First, there are the identical twins, which we have just discussed, and then there are the fraternal twins which originate from two separate cells to begin with. Occasionally a woman will release two eggs in one fertile period and both will become fertilized. The twins which result from such an event will be no more alike than children of the same parents born at different times

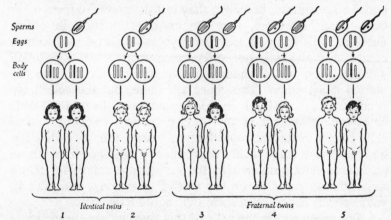

Fig. 6. How the different kinds of twins are formed. Identical twins are formed from one sperm and one egg. They are always of the same sex and with the same heredity. Fraternal twins are formed from two sperms and two eggs and they can be of different sexes and with some differences in heredity. They are no more alike than brothers and sisters born at different times.

(After Clyde Keeler)

as far as heredity goes. They may be of different sex, and may show differences in variable physical characteristics.

Studies of identical twins offer us an excellent opportunity to determine the effects of heredity and environment. Since identical twins have identical genes, it stands to reason that any differences between them must be due to environment. In a few cases such twins have been separated at birth and raised in different environments and these have been very valuable in such studies. This is discussed more thoroughly in Chapter 21.

The Precious Germ Plasm

As you developed in the early stages of your life your cells all looked somewhat alike, but, as you grew larger, certain cells were stimulated by certain genes to form your brain, others made your heart, stomach, lungs, kidneys, and the other specialized body organs which are a necessary part of a complex organism like the human body. As these cells became specialized, however, they lost the power to form other body parts; therefore, they cannot now function in reproduction. Cells from an early embryo can split off and form a complete individual, but cells taken from your skin today will not grow into a human being if transplanted into the uterus of a woman. The genes are there, but the cells have become so specialized in form that they have lost their embryo-development power. It is necessary, then, that some cells be set aside for reproduction before this specialization has reached a stage where reproduction is impossible. These particular cells remained in the embryonic condition, living somewhat as parasites on the rest of your body, and later in your growth began producing the reproductive cells.

The genes within the cells of this germ plasm are identical with the ones received from your parents, and are transmitted through generations without change, with the rare exception of mutations which may alter the nature of a gene. You can do whatever you wish to the billions of cells which make up the main part of your body, but you cannot tamper with the contents of the germ plasm which you carry. The genes of the germ plasm are sealed off in their own special envelope to be delivered to the generations of the future without alteration. They are much too important to be subject to the whims and weaknesses of the deliverymen and deliverywomen who carry them. You can refuse to deliver them (not have children) or destroy them, but you cannot break the seal and alter the contents according to your desires.

The Inexhaustible Sperms

Can the supply of sperms become exhausted? Some people believe that they can—that the testes which are formed during childhood have just so many cells which can produce sperms and that when these are all gone, permanent sterility will follow. A man releases about 400 million sperms with each seminal emission and it may appear logical that some day they would all be used up. Within the testes, however, there is a system of sperm production which provides an inexhaustible supply. In the outer portion of the little tubes within the testes is the germ plasm. Here there are cells which are potential sperm producers; they can produce sperms by the millions; yet their numbers are never depleted. Here is the way it is done. One of these outer cells will divide by mitosis—this gives two cells like the original one. Let us call them Cell A and Cell B. Cell B will begin migrating in toward the center of the tube. As it moves, it divides and makes two cells. As these continue inward each divides again and there are now four cells. Each of these cells forms a sperm. In the meantime, Cell A is growing in size as it absorbs food from the blood flowing past. Soon it will be ready for another division and again one of the two cells formed will migrate down and form four sperms while one stays in place.

Thus, we can see that it is impossible for a man to use up his sperms. Of course, the rate at which the sperms can be produced is limited and excessive emission of seminal fluid will reduce the number of sperms in the semen. The quantity of semen in a normal ejaculation will be four or five cubic centimeters and will contain about 100,000,000 sperms per cubic centimeter. After repeated ejaculations within a limited period of time, the quantity may drop to less than two cubic centimeters, possibly with less than 25,000,000 sperms per cubic centimeter. This does not influence the germ plasm, for it still contains the same number of cells as before. With advancing age and the general deterioration of the body organs there will, of course, be a corresponding deterioration of the tissue of the testes and the sperm production will slow down. The age at which this occurs varies greatly and depends upon the general health of the man to a great extent. There are actually authenticated cases where men of ninety years of age have fathered children.

The Virgin Egg

When you speak of eggs, the average person probably thinks of the large products of domestic chickens which have come to be a standard bill of fare on the American breakfast table. These are eggs all right, but many animals produce eggs which are much smaller. The mammals do not need a large egg which contains a rich food supply sufficient to nourish the embryo until it can obtain its own food. The mammal embryo is nourished through a connection with its mother after it has grown large enough to form a connection with her. Also, we need to clear up another point. To the average person eggs are eggs, no matter whether they have been fertilized or not. An infertile hen's egg looks just like a fertile egg. There is a big difference, however—the fertile egg has twice as many chromosomes as the infertile egg. Half of these have been brought in by the sperm. In this discussion we are talking about the infertile egg; to distinguish it, let us call it the virgin egg.

If you happen to be a female, your germ plasm will be in the outer part of your ovaries. Here egg production begins. As in the case of the sperm-forming cells there is a division (mitosis) which produces two cells and only one of these goes on to produce an egg. This cell migrates inward and soon

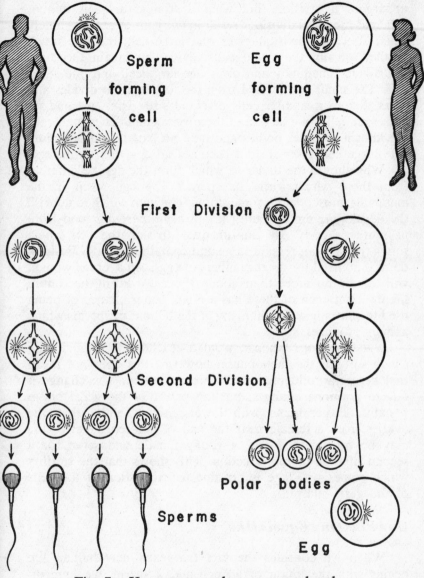

Fig. 7.   How sperms and eggs are produced.

(Adapted from Winchester, GENETICS, Houghton Mifflin)

undergoes a division, but what a strange division this is. Whereas most cell divisions result in two cells of approximately equal size, this division gives one large cell and one much smaller. Again, these two cells divide, but again the large cell divides unequally and gives one large cell and one small one. The small cell formed from the first division divides and gives two even smaller cells of equal size. Thus, we end up with four cells, one large and three very small. The small cells are known as polar bodies and take no part in reproduction. The large cell goes on and becomes an egg, the virgin egg.

Why should the divisions which form the egg be different from those which form the sperm? The egg, even in the mammals, must contain some stored food with which to nourish the developing embryo until it can begin deriving food from its mother's body. By this unequal division the cell which forms the egg can remain large and contain this food. Besides, there is no need for great numbers of eggs. An average woman will release no more than about 350 eggs during her entire lifetime, but each of these has a much better chance of being used to start a new life than any of the billions of sperms which a man produces.

Ovulation stops when a woman reaches the stage in life which we call the menopause; however, this does not mean that her egg-producing powers are exhausted. The change is due to hormone changes, but the power of the germ plasm remains. Experiments with lower animals show that the ovaries from a female near the end of her reproductive life may be transplanted into a young female and serve for a second lifetime of reproduction. This shows that the sterility which comes with age is not due to exhaustion of the cells of the germ plasm.

One Plus One Equals One

When we consider the fact that each new human life begins with the union of an egg and a sperm, we immediately run into a mathematical problem which must be solved.

Arithmetic teaches us that one plus one equals two, but somehow in the process of fertilization, one plus one must equal one. Two cells unite, but only one cell results and this cell has the same number of chromosomes as do the body cells of each of the parents from which the two cells came. How can this be? Human body cells contain 46 chromosomes and if two of these united we would have 92 chromosomes in the cell which was formed. The next generation would have twice this number and so on until an impossible number was reached. We know, however, that the number remains 46 for each generation.

This is accomplished by an ingenious type of cell division which causes the sperm and the egg to receive only one-half of the chromosomes carried by the body cells of each parent. When the sperm-forming or the egg-forming cell prepares for division it starts with a doubling of the 46 (23 double) chromosomes as with any other division. But then, when the chromosomes line up, ready for separation, there is something different. The chromosomes are in pairs. There are 23 *pairs* of the double chromosomes (46 chromosomes). When the cell divides, one of each pair goes to each of the two cells which are formed, so there are now only 23 double chromosomes in each cell. These are double chromosomes; however, another division follows which separates the doubles and we end up with four cells, each with 23 single chromosomes. This unusual double division is known as meiosis (a lessening). When a sperm and an egg unite, each contributes 23 chromosomes and a cell is formed with the normal number of 46 chromosomes. The human body has devious ways its wonders to perform.

Genes and Ancestry

We have now completed the cycle of the genes in your body from their origin in the reproductive cells of your parents to their presence in your own reproductive cells. Any children you may have will receive only one-half of your chromosomes and the genes which they contain. You received 23 from each of your parents and you can transmit only 23 to each of your children. Since you have 46 chromosomes it is obvious that no one child which you may have can inherit all of your genes. You can only give him one-half of them. The others are irretrievably lost. You may have great mathematical aptitude, yet have a child who cannot count above ten without taking off his shoes. Perhaps there was some gene necessary for this aptitude that got lost in a sperm that wasn't used or was in a polar body rather than an egg that was released on the month in which conception occurred.

One-half of the genes in ancestry are lost each generation. Since you received only one-half of your parents' genes, it is obvious that your child will receive about one-fourth of his genes from each of your parents. Your child's children will receive only one-eighth of your parents' genes and so on. Of course the division is not exact, for in the shuffling of chromosomes which takes place when reproductive cells are formed, it is possible that some of the sperms (or eggs) produced in your body will receive a greater proportion of chromosomes and genes from your mother than from your father. A child formed from such a reproductive cell would be somewhat more like his grandmother than his grandfather on your side. You may have a second child, however, who would be just the reverse. It is this shuffling of the genes that causes variety among children of the same parents.

Some people take great pride in their ancestry, a highly commendable attitude, for after all we received all that we possess in the way of genes from our ancestors, no matter how many generations back we may go. We are not justified, however, in placing too great a stress on one or several very distinguished persons in our distant ancestry, for we must remember that we inherit just as much from the undistinguished members. You carry just as many genes from the horse thieves, drunkards, and slave traders in your ancestry as from the governors, generals, and senators to whom you may point with pride. The shuffling chromosomes play no favorites.

CHAPTER 8

OUR GAMBLING GENES

Life is a game of chance—everyday events over which we have no control place their imprint upon our beings and shape our future destinies. A chance meeting may determine with whom you will share your future life; chance associations may influence your choice of a lifetime vocation; chance happenings may play a great part in your financial success in life. If you stop to think of all the small chance happenings which have played a vital role in your life, you can readily understand that if you lived your life over again there is not one chance in a trillion that it would come out exactly the same way a second time. In this sense life is one great gamble after another.

The most important gamble of all, however, took place before you were even in existence. That gamble involved the shuffling and assortment of genes in the reproductive cells of your parents—cells which later were to unite to produce you. These genes which, by chance, were assorted into the exact combination received by these reproductive cells have a greater influence over the many varied aspects of your life than any other chance happenings. You may change your vocation, you may change your geographical location, you may even change your marriage partner, but you can never change your genes—they remain with you throughout life with far-reaching influence on your personality, your appearance, your health, your abilities, and your temperament. Once your gene combination has been determined it is fixed once and for all. It is quite plain, therefore, why we can say that the most important gamble of your life took place before you actually existed as a unified individual.

Let us investigate the shuffling and assortment of genes and see how knowledge of these events can be used to explain the pattern of transmission of hereditary traits. Also, how it may be used to predict the hereditary characteristics of children yet to be born. There are many genes in human cells— the best estimates place the number at about 40,000 in each cell—so it is readily apparent that we cannot hope to follow the intricate course of all of these genes at once as they go from one generation to the next. It is possible, however, for us to consider the behavior of a single pair of genes at a time and, thus, gain an insight into the behavior of all of them, for they all follow a similar pattern of distribution. So this is the plan we will follow.

Dominant and Recessive Genes

The skip-generation transmission of inherited traits is one of the most mysterious manifestations of heredity in the minds of many who are not familiar with the nature of genes and their method of transmission in reproduction. A man with flaming red hair marries a woman with dark hair and all their children have dark hair, but when these children mature and marry, lo and behold, some of their children show the carrot-topped condition of their grandfather. What happened to the genes for red hair in the first generation? It is quite evident that they were somehow suppressed only to come to full expression in some of the children of the second generation.

It will probably be easier for us to understand this by a cross with lower animals. Many principles of heredity are discovered by such crosses since people are such poor subjects for experiments of this nature. People are so slow about reproducing, they have so few children, and above all they have the stubborn habit of wanting to decide for themselves whom they will marry and how many children they will have. Rabbits, on the other hand, will breed like—well, rabbits—if we just keep them well-fed and cared for, and allow the two sexes to mingle freely with one another. We know that the

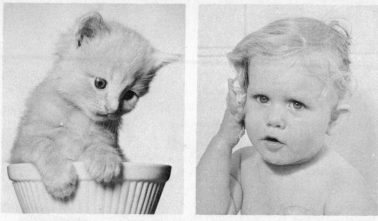

Plate Ia. Two babies formed from the same raw materials. The marvelous gene sculptors can take the same food, yet one set of these sculptors forms it into a soft, fluffy baby kitten, while another set forms it into a human baby.

Plate Ib. The discoverer of human sperms and his wife. This is a modern artist's conception of Anton van Leeuwenhoek holding one of his primitive microscopes with which he discovered the sperms in human semen.

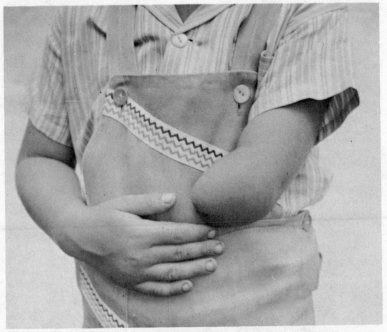

Photo by author

Plate II. A marked child? The mother of this child witnessed the results of a serious automobile accident late in her pregnancy. The child was born without a left hand as shown above. Some friends have influenced the mother to believe that she marked the child and caused this deformity by viewing the accident.

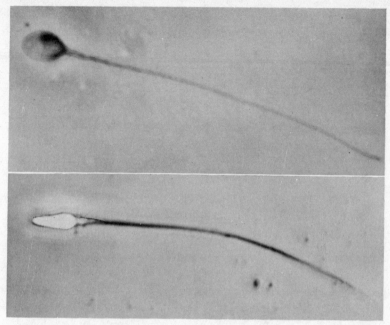

Plate IIIa. Living human sperms magnified about 2,000 diameters. In the top view the head is lying flat, while at the bottom the head is turned on its side.

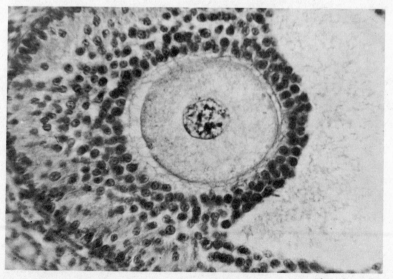

Photo IIIb. The human egg within a Graafian follicle.

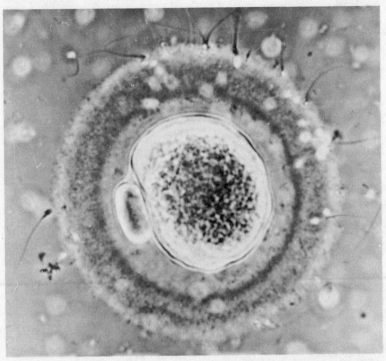

Photo courtesy Dr. Landrum R. Shettles

Plate IV. Human fertilization. This remarkable photograph shows a living human egg with living sperms attacking the corona of follicular cells. Note the polar body to the left of the egg.

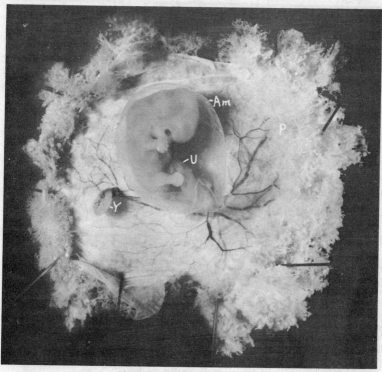

Photo by Chester Reather, Carnegie Institute of Washington

Plate V. Human embryo about 42 days after conception. The placenta (P) has been cut open to show the embryo floating in the protective fluid within its membranous sac, the amnion (Am). The umbilical cord (U) can be seen leading from the embryo and connecting to the placenta. Note that even at this early age the fingers and toes are already formed. This embryo is about one-half inch long.

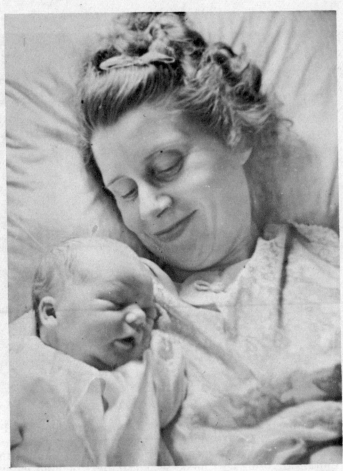

Plate VI. The blessed event. All of the inconveniences
and worries of pregnancy are quickly forgotten when a
new mother sees her baby for the first time.

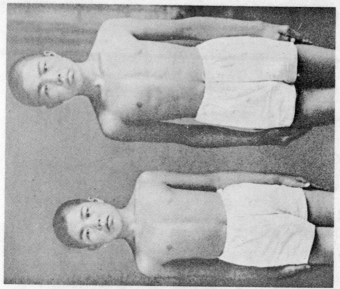

From Taku Komai & G. Fukooka in Journal of Heredity

Plate VIIb. "Identical" twins are not always identical. These were the same size until five years of age when the one on the left developed a disease which caused some deterioration of his pituitary gland. Now, at fifteen, he weighs 31 pounds less than his brother.

Photo by author

Plate VIIa. Two girls from one egg. These identical twin girls started life as a single fertilized egg. Later the embryo separated into two parts and each part made a complete girl.

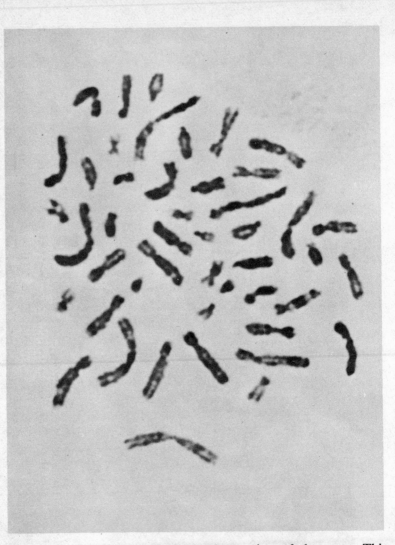

Plate VIII. Human chromosomes, the carriers of the genes. This photograph was made when the cell was in an early stage of preparation for division and when the chromosomes had already become double. Each of the 46 chromosomes can be clearly seen. It was this photograph, and many others that have been made since, that showed that the chromosome number of man is 46.

method of gene transmission in man follows a similar pattern, so we can breed rabbits (or other animals) and then apply the principles learned to heredity in man.

Let us see if we can learn how a single gene is transmitted through several generations by crossing rabbits which show a clearly distinguished physical difference which is due to a difference in one gene. Suppose we obtain a group of rabbits with brown fur that have descended from pure brown ancestors. Then let us obtain another group of rabbits with black fur who have descended from pure black ancestors. Here we have a difference which can be easily distinguished by anyone who can see. What happens when we cross these two types of rabbits?

We select five virgin females with brown fur and allow them to mate with five of the black males. Then, to see if sex has anything to do with the inheritance of coat color, let us mate five of the black females with five of the brown males. In about thirty-two days each female bears from four to seven offspring. When these little, naked, blind offspring begin to develop fur we find that it is black in every case. Not one brown rabbit is obtained from all the crosses, but all these black rabbits carry the gene for brown fur—the gene is just not expressed. We allow these black rabbits to mature and breed freely among themselves. (This is the equivalent of brother-sister matings.) Hundreds of offspring are produced from these matings and there are both brown and black rabbits among them. If we separate and count them we will find that about one-fourth of these are brown and the other three-fourths are black. Thus it is apparent that the gene for brown fur was not lost—it was carried by the first generation rabbits in a dormant state.

This brings out one of the great principles of heredity—a gene may be carried without being expressed when there is another gene in the same cell which dominates over it. Such genes are known as *recessive* genes, and the genes which dominate over them are known as *dominant* genes. It is quite evident that the gene for black fur is dominant in this case—

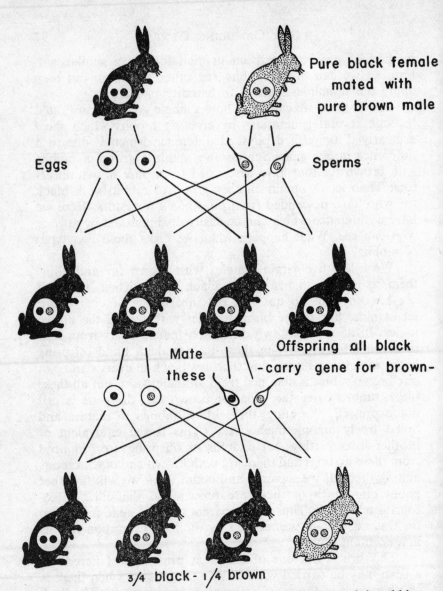

Eggs

Sperms

Pure black female
mated with
pure brown male

Mate
these

Offspring all black
-carry gene for brown-

3/4 black - 1/4 brown

Fig. 8. Skip-generation transmission of a recessive trait in rabbits.
When a pure black rabbit is mated to a pure brown rabbit, all the
offspring are black, but they carry the gene for brown. When these
are mated together the brown coat color will appear in the second
generation in about one-fourth of the offspring.

it has a greater strength than the gene for brown fur and when the two come together in a rabbit, the gene for black fur wins out in the battle for self-expression. The gene for brown is carried just the same, however, and produces a full-blown brown coat of fur when it is released from the dominance of the gene for black fur.

Fig. 8 shows how the genes are shuffled in these two generations to give the results outlined. It can be noted from this diagram that the body cells of the rabbits always carry two genes which influence this particular variation in color of the fur, but the reproductive cells carry only one. The body cells of a rabbit may carry genes of both types, but a reproductive cell may carry brown or black—not both. Pure chance determines which of these genes shall be included in any one reproductive cell. When we think of, not one pair, but thousands of pairs, of genes being shuffled in a like manner as the human reproductive cells are formed, we can understand the infinite variety of gene combinations which may result. Even though a married couple could have hundreds of children they would have no two with the same gene combination—barring identical twins, of course. There are just too many possible assortments of the different kinds of genes for this to happen. You, therefore, are an individual with a gene make-up the like of which there is no counterpart on the earth, has never been, nor will ever be again, assuming that you do not have an identical twin. You are, indeed, an individual.

Intermediate Expression of Genes

Whenever two athletes are pitted against each other in a test of skill and strength, one or the other usually wins the contest. Let us assume that it is a wrestling match—one of the contestants is usually stronger or more skillful, and that one wins. There are some matches, however, in which the strength and skill of the two is so nearly the same that the bout will end in a draw with both athletes sharing the honors.

In a similar manner whenever two genes for different expressions come together in the body of a newly formed human being, we might say that a contest ensues—a contest for supremacy and the right to expression. In most cases, one of the two genes will be stronger than its opponent in the contest and that one wins out and expresses itself—it is dominant, the loser is recessive. If we think of genes as having varying degrees of strength, however, it is quite natural that there will be some cases where two opposing genes will come together which have about equal strength. In such instances neither will win out, and both genes express·themselves to a

INTERMEDIATE INHERITANCE IN CATTLE

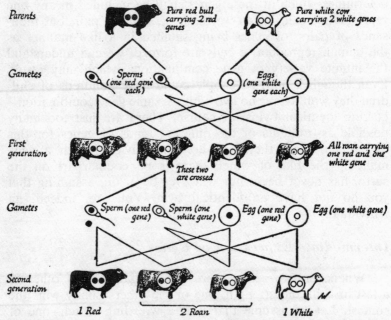

Fig. 9.   Intermediate inheritance in cattle. When a red short-horned bull is crossed to a white short-horned cow the offspring are all roan, an in between color. Red and white can come out again, however, in the second generation as shown.

(From Winchester, BIOLOGY, Van Nostrand)

certain degree, rather than one being dominant and the other recessive. Thus, the characteristic resulting will have an expression that is a compromise. It will be unlike that brought about by either gene when it is not competing with the other.

We can easily understand how this works by considering a cross in shorthorned cattle. Whenever we cross a red bull with a white cow the resulting calves show an in-between color called roan. This means that the gene which causes the red pigment to appear and the gene which causes a lack of red pigment (white) have shared the honors and we have an intermediate color expression. When roan cattle are bred with each other we get calves which are white, roan, and red in the ration of 1:\`:1. You can understand how this happens by a study of Fig. 9.

As an example in man we will take the curliness of the hair in the Caucasian race. Studies of family pedigrees indicate that slightly curly or wavy hair is an intermediate expression of the gene for curly and the gene for straight hair. In other words, marriages between a man with straight hair and a woman with curly hair (assuming that it is not a beauty-parlor curl) will have children all with wavy hair. Two persons with wavy hair could expect children with curly, wavy, or straight hair with the chance for wavy being twice that for either of the other two. In a study of a large number of marriages in which both parents had wavy hair one investigator found that the children could be grouped into 22 curly, 51 wavy, and 27 straight. This is very close to the ratio of 1:2:1 which is expected in the case of intermediate genes.

Inheritance of Characters Which Differ Quantitatively

There are many human traits which are influenced by heredity, yet do not fall into sharply defined classifications. They show a wide number of variations from one extreme to another. Such a character is body height—we cannot group all people into tall and short as might be expected if only a dominant and a recessive gene were involved. Neither could we assume that the genes are intermediate and divide people into short, medium, and tall classifications. In this case and in many others we find that there may be variation in quite a number of gene pairs which may cause the inheritance of

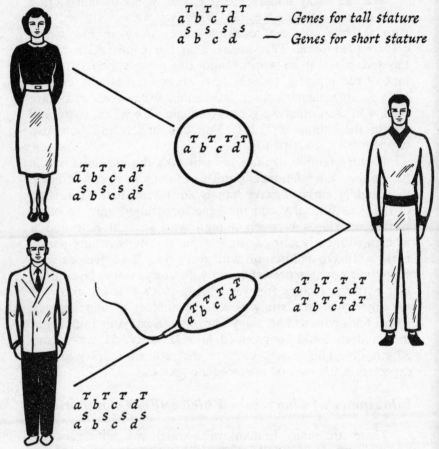

$a^T b^T c^T d^T$ — *Genes for tall stature*
$a^s b^s c^s d^s$ — *Genes for short stature*

Fig. 10. A tall child from medium-sized parents. There are a number of genes which influence body stature and medium-sized parents may carry several genes for tall stature. When these happen to segregate out into a sperm and an egg which unite in conception, a child is produced which will be well above average in stature.

(From Winchester, GENETICS, Houghton, Mifflin)

different degrees of body height. Many genes are involved in the formation of most body characteristics, but, when there is variation in only one of the pairs of these genes, we can trace a simple dominant-recessive or intermediate type of inheritance. When there is variation of more than one pair of the genes involved, however, we must consider the inheritance on a quantitative basis.

Let us look more fully into the inheritance of body height as an example. Of course, environment plays an important role here—diet, disease, and other environmental factors all have their effects in the attainment of hereditary potentialities of stature, but everyone can testify to the effects of heredity on this trait through common observation. Let us assume that there are four pairs of genes which may influence stature in man and that all are intermediate in their effects. (Actually, there are more than this, and they include some dominant, some recessive, and some intermediate, but this number will illustrate the point very well.) If two medium-sized persons married, each with four genes for tallness and four for shortness, they could have nine different gene combinations for height in their children. These would include those considerably taller and considerably shorter than the parents. Thus, we can see how children of the same parents may show such variation, even though they have similar environments.

Inheritance of skin color is another human characteristic which may vary considerably as a result of variation in a number of different genes. As in the case of body stature we see many gradations in the color of the skin from very dark to extremely fair, even among the members of the Caucasian race. Environment again plays its part and the tanning effects of sunlight must be taken into account in any studies of inheritance of skin color. We must take areas of the body which are commonly covered when the body is exposed to the sun, although we must admit that modern bathing suits leave only sparse areas of epidermis in this category. Studies of the skin-color genes which distinguish the Negro race from the Caucasian race indicate that differences in about four pairs of genes account for the skin-color differences between the two races. These are intermediate in their expression, so the children which result from a mixture of the two races are intermediate in skin color (mulatto). When two mulattoes marry, however, their children can show many degrees of skin color from the typical negroid to the so-called white skin of Caucasian race. The proportions of each of these is shown in Fig. 11.

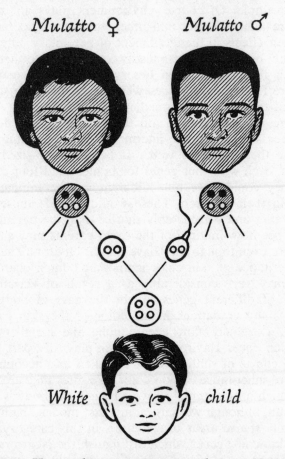

Fig. 11.   How mulatto parents can produce a white child.

It is apparent from the discussions in this chapter that all inherited characteristics are not transmitted in exactly the same manner. In addition to those ways which we have described in this chapter, there are some characteristics which are influenced by sex—these are discussed in Chapter 12. We should keep in mind, however, that all genes go through a shuffling process as they go into the reproductive cells and, regardless of which of the various methods of inheritance apply to any particular character, a gamble is involved in the transmission from parents to children—the greatest gamble of our lives.

CHAPTER 9

WHICH SEX WILL IT BE?

When a woman first begins to feel the changes in her body which portend an imminent visit from that well-known bird with the long bill, one of the first questions to enter her mind is, "Which sex will it be?" So much of life is predestined by sex that it is easy to understand why such a question would be uppermost in the minds of both prospective parents. To a great extent the way we dress, our occupations, our hobbies, and our personal interests are conditioned by sex. Even the lives of parents are greatly influenced by the sex of their children. Hence, there is little wonder that the question of sex-determination should be foremost in the minds of those preparing to introduce a new life into the world.

Boy and Girl Sperms

Sometimes an overanxious (and inconsiderate) father, who wants a son to carry on the family name and, perhaps, be a future partner in his business, will be deeply disappointed when the doctor announces, "It's a girl." He may even berate his wife for bearing a daughter when she knew that he especially wanted a son. With a little knowledge of sex-determination, however, the wife might well turn to him and tell him it was all his own fault—that she had nothing to do with it. The eggs produced by a woman's ovaries are all alike so far as the potential sex of a child is concerned—each egg can produce a child of either sex. Not so with the sperms—they are

106

of two types with respect to sex-determining potentialities. Half of them will produce boys and the other half will produce girls. Therefore, it is truly the man (or at least his reproductive cells) which determine the sex of every child that is conceived by a woman.

How Sex Is Determined

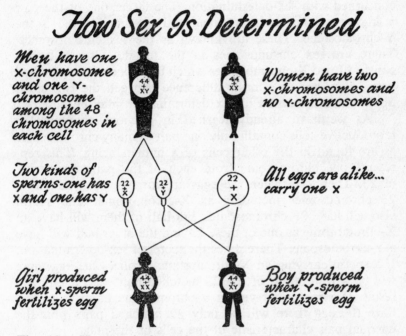

Men have one x-chromosome and one Y-chromosome among the 48 chromosomes in each cell

Women have two x-chromosomes and no Y-chromosomes

Two kinds of sperms-one has x and one has Y

All eggs are alike... carry one x

Girl produced when x-sperm fertilizes egg

Boy produced when Y-sperm fertilizes egg

Fig. 12.   How sex is determined. There are two kinds of sperms, one carrying an X-chromosome and one carrying a Y-chromosome, and the sex of a child depends upon which of the two fertilizes the egg.

To understand how this can be, let us get a picture of the nature of the cells in the body of a man and of a woman. In every cell there is a difference between men and women. In the body cells of a woman there will be 46 of the rod-like bodies known as chromosomes. These are composed of 23 pairs—for every chromosome of one type in the cell there will be another of the same size and shape to accompany it. The body cells of a man also have 46 chromosomes, but there are only 22 matched pairs—the 23rd pair consists of one large chromosome and one small chromosome. This is true of *each* cell in the male and female. It is this unmatched pair that is concerned with sex-determination. The larger one of the pair is known as the X-chromosome and the smaller one is the Y-chromosome. These are known as the sex chromosomes. There are sex chromosomes in the female, also, but they consist of two X-chromosomes which form one of the matched pairs. Now here is a basic difference between the two sexes upon which a method of sex determination may be based.

As we have already learned in previous chapters the reproductive cells contain only one-half as many chromosomes as are found in the other cells of a human being. This represents one chromosome from each of the pairs or a total of 23. Therefore, when the eggs are formed, each will have 23 chromosomes including an X-chromosome. The sperm also will have 23 chromosomes, but half of them will have an X-chromosome as one of these 23 and the other half will have a Y-chromosome. Therein lies the secret of sex-determination. If a sperm carrying an X-chromosome fertilizes the egg there will be a restoration of the 23 matched pairs and a girl will result. If a sperm carrying a Y-chromosome happens to fertilize the egg there will be only 22 matched pairs plus the unequal pair characteristic of the cells of the male.

This somewhat simplifies things—here we have two types of sperms, one male-determining and one female-determining. Within the body of the female there is an egg awaiting fertilization; it can form either sex. The sperms are released near the neck of the womb and the race is on—wiggling and squirming they make their way toward the egg. Eventually, one sperm successfully penetrates the egg and fertilization is accomplished. If that sperm carries the X-chromosome the child will be a girl, while a Y-chromosome-carrying sperm will result in a boy.

Inequalities of the Sex Ratio

Since a sperm carrying a Y-chromosome is produced every time one is produced which carries an X-chromosome, there will be one-half of each kind in the male semen. Consequently, we should expect girls one-half of the time and boys one-half. Of course, there will be cases where the proportion of the sexes in any one family will be far from equally distributed. Families exist where eight girls have been born in succession. This does not mean that there is anything wrong with the method of sex-determination in these cases, but such families had a "run," as a gambler would say. If you toss a penny in the air, the chance that it lands heads is one-half; but it is possible, if you toss long enough, that you may toss eight heads in a row. Families with an unequal distribution of sexes usually represent similar chance results. There are a few cases, however, when it must be admitted that something besides chance must be operating. This is when there is a predominance of one sex for several generations in a row. Experiments on such cases in lower animals indicate that this can be due to certain hereditary factors which cause the death of the embryos of one sex, leaving only those of the opposite sex to be born alive.

The Weaker Sex

There has probably been many a person approaching marriageable age who has wondered if there were enough members of the opposite sex to go around. Such persons may be reassured by a reference to statistics which show that among people between twenty and thirty years old, the sexes are almost exactly equal. There are geographical variations, however. For instance, there is an excess of males on the west coast and some deficiency of males in the New England States at the present time in the United States. Such variations, however, may be explained by population migration and are not due to any difference in the over-all proportion of the sexes in

THE DWINDLING MALES
NUMBER OF MALES FOR EACH 100 FEMALES

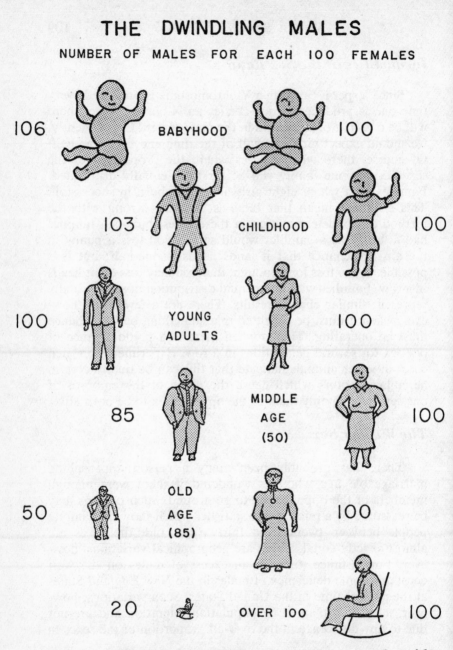

Fig. 13. The weaker sex. At birth boy babies outnumber girl babies, but the death rate is greater for the males at every stage of life until at 100 years there are only about 20 males for each 100 females.

the country as a whole. (Apparently, too many young men have taken Horace Greeley's advice, "Go west young man.")

Strange to say, when we examine the statistical records of live births in the United States we find that the sexes are not born in exactly equal numbers—there are about 106 boys for every 100 girls. How can this be, when the male-determining and female-determining sperms are produced in equal quantities? One might assume at first that the female embryos are weaker than the male embryos and a smaller proportion of them survive the rigors of embryonic development. We know that from 16 to 20 per cent of all conceptions terminate in the death of the embryo before or at the time of birth. Perhaps there are more girl babies among the group. A study of some of these embryos, however, does not bear out such a premise. At the great laboratory of the Carnegie Institution of Washington there is a collection of a large number of embryos which have died in all stages of development up to and including birth. There is actually a slightly greater number of males among this group. This holds true for those found in the earliest stages in which sex can be distinguished up to the normal time of birth.

Then how can we explain the excess of males among the live births? To begin with, we must assume that more male embryos are formed in the first place. With the two different kinds of sperms produced in equal numbers, it is evident that the male-determining sperms must have some superiority over the female-determining sperms in the race to reach the egg or in penetrating it. To such a small body as a sperm, with its limited food supply, the trip through the reproductive organs of a woman must be an arduous journey indeed. To put it in human terms we might compare it to a race of about sixty-four miles by men on foot over a course beset with many obstacles along the way. We get this figure by comparing the length of a sperm to the distance to be traveled with the height of a man and a proportionate distance on the ground. If a group of men started on such a grueling race, the slightest advantage would make a tremendous difference in the chances of winning. But what advantage could the Y-carrying sperms have over the X-carrying sperms? For one thing they might be lighter; true the difference could only be very minute, but the Y-chromosome is smaller than the X-chromosome and it must, therefore, weigh somewhat less. A few pounds of weight makes a great difference in a horse race; perhaps this relative variation makes a difference in the sperm race. Furthermore, it is conceivable that the Y-sperms may have a slight advantage in penetrating the egg after they have completed the journey. They may be very slightly smaller in diameter because of their smaller size. At any rate we know that a few more eggs are fertilized by sperms carrying this Y-chromosome than by those carrying the X-chromosome.

This excess of boy babies would seem to give the girls an advantage in the marriage mart—they should have a larger number of potential mates to choose from. We have already pointed out, however, that at the time for marriage the proportion of the two sexes is approximately equal. This is because of the viability differential which begins operating early in life and kills off the boys faster than the girls, so that there is numerical equality at the time of life when such equality is most important. Sad to say, boys, the male is actually the weaker sex. The boys just do not survive the diseases and dangers of childhood as well as girls. This predestined weakness of the male continues to manifest itself throughout life. It is best demonstrated by the cold facts of insurance statistics—a woman receiving an annuity upon retirement will have smaller monthly payments than a man of the same age because of her greater chances for a longer life. At fifty years of age we find that the males have shrunk from equality at twenty to the point where there will be only about eighty-five men to every hundred women. At eighty-five, the women outnumber men almost two to one and at one hundred, there are about five times as many women as men. Men may well claim superiority in muscular power, but in terms of physical qualifications for survival we must concede the advantage to the ladies.

Sex of War Babies

There is a common belief that during times of war more boy babies will be born to replenish the stock of males that are being destroyed in the conflict. Of course, we could easily dismiss this apparently groundless belief by saying that the sperms have no way of knowing that there is a war going on, and, even if they did, we could hardly imagine the female-determining sperms moving aside so as to let the male-determining sperms accomplish fertilization in a greater proportion of the cases. No, the business of fertilization still goes on according to the same rules of chance in spite of war, storm, famine, or plague. Yet, strange to say, statistics show that there actually are a few more boys born during wartime. True, the difference is slight, but with the great number of births which occurred in the United States during World War II we can hardly say that it has no significance. During the five years preceding this war, the ratio was 105.8 boys to each 100 girls. During the war itself the ratio was 106.1 to 100.

There is a perfectly logical explanation for this. We have already mentioned the fact that the male is the weaker of the two sexes. As a result of this fact, the ratio is dependent somewhat on the chances for survival of embryos of all types—the higher the survival rate, the greater the proportion of boys. We know that there is a higher number of boys born to women in the higher economic groups than to those who are low in the economic scale. This is probably due to the fact that a pregnant woman from the first group will receive better pre-natal care, better diet, and better attention at the birth of her child. Hence, each embryo has a maximum chance of survival. In the lower-income group, on the other hand, there will be more embryonic deaths, and since the males are weaker than the females there will be more males among these prenatal fatalities and, consequently, a greater proportion of girls among the live births. This concept is supported by studies of the sex ratio of live births in different countries. Invariably, in those countries where the general standard of living is high, the ratio of boy babies is higher than in those countries where the general level of living is on a very low scale. In India, for instance, where a great segment of the population lives on the brink of starvation, there are actually more girl babies. The ratio is 98.7 boys to each 100 girls among the live births.

Also, it has been found that young women bear more boys than older women. Between the ages of eighteen and twenty-two there may be as many as 120 boys born for every 100 girls. Between thirty-eight and forty-two, on the other hand, the number seems to be no higher than 90 to 100. This is correlated with the fact that there are more embryonic deaths among the older mothers—they are not as well-adapted to motherhood as their younger sisters.

In further support of this viewpoint, it is known that there is a smaller ratio of boys among multiple births than among single births. This would be expected, since the more crowded conditions found where more than one embryo must develop in the same womb at the same time would cause more embryonic deaths in the weaker males and, consequently, result in more girls among the live births. For twins in the United States the ratio is 103.5 boys to 100 girls, for triplets it is about 98 to 100, and for quadruplets it is about 70 to 100. All of these show more girls than the 106 to 100 ratio for all births, and it can be seen that the ratio of boys drops as the number of embryos in the womb increases.

Also, statistics show that there is a slightly greater chance of a boy among first children. This might be due, in part, to the fact that the mothers are younger when they have their first child. Furthermore, when children are borne in rapid succession the general health of the mother is impaired and there are more deaths among embryos after the first child.

We now have a basis for an explanation of the slightly greater number of boy babies born during wartime. For one thing, there are earlier marriages, earlier pregnancies, and more pregnancies among the younger women. Many who would postpone marriage and child-bearing under normal conditions decide not to wait during the urgent times of war.

There are more first babies born during wartime because there are more of such marriages. Also, during wartime, those in the lower economic positions commonly have more money and live better than during peacetime. These factors combine to give embryos a slightly greater chance of surviving the rigors of pregnancy and birth, hence the small increase in the proportion of boy babies.

Predetermination of Sex

This question has intrigued man since the dawn of history. In many former societies (and even some present ones) women were considered as inferior or second-rate human beings, fit only to carry out the duties of the home and to bear children. In such societies the birth of a boy baby was an occasion for great rejoicing, while that of a girl baby would result in sadness. We even read of women of ancient Egypt tossing girl babies to the crocodiles of the Nile River in their shame at so greatly disappointing their husbands by bearing a child that could never hope to attain the lordly state of a male. In any such society one is certain to find a great desire to insure the birth of a boy. Just how the population could be maintained if such a method were to be discovered has apparently never occurred to them. Even in our own society where we are generally satisfied with whichever sex our babies happen to be, many persons would still like to know of a method of predetermining sex so they could have their families according to a definite plan or sequence of sexes.

The actual method of sex-determination makes it extremely unlikely that any method will ever be discovered by means of which a child can be produced which will definitely be of one sex or the other. Of course, any method, or no method, will result in the desired sex about one-half of the time, since the sexes are normally produced in about equal numbers. A woman may be told that she will be sure to have a boy baby if she will sleep on her right side during the term of her pregnancy. She may follow this suggestion and, sure enough, a boy baby is born. She may then become an enthusiastic advocate of this method without stopping to reason that the child could have been a boy no matter which side she slept on.

In royal families, where the birth of a male heir to the throne is of such great concern to an entire nation, history shows that almost every conceivable method has been tried to insure the delivery of a boy. Many a royal queen of medieval times was subjected to unpleasant and even painful treatments by the midwives and medicine men during her pregnancy in an effort to produce a boy. Many a doctor lost his head because his particular method failed. Perhaps a doctor had gone to great lengths to obtain a magical potion that was sure to produce a boy—blood from the heart of a male lion, the extract of boiled comb and wattles from a rooster, tissue fluid squeezed from the testes of a bull—these he had blended and administered to the young queen. Yet a girl was born—the doctor was a fake—off with his head! At the next pregnancy another doctor perhaps treated the queen with equally revolting concoctions and possibly added the extra frills of burning incense while murmuring his magical incantations. And this time the child was a boy, and this doctor received great rewards for his impressive powers. His method, too, failed when tried again and was supplanted by still others. Over two hundred years ago Drelincourt, in France, collected and tabulated the various methods which had been advocated as means to predetermine the sex of unconceived as well as conceived but still unborn children. He found two hundred sixty-two theories, each of which has been found to have no basis in fact and entirely worthless.

In spite of the extensive list of past failures, new techniques continue to be proposed. A few of these which have been advocated in pseudoscientific books and magazines in the past few decades deserve mention because there are people of today who go to great trouble and expense to follow some of these techniques even though they have no value. One such theory holds that the time of conception in relation to the menstrual cycle determines the sex of the child—conception during the first few days after the menstrual flow ceases is supposed to result in a boy, whereas conception which occurs later during the intermenstrual period would produce a girl. Modern scientific observations have shown that the time of any conception must be within the rather restricted period of not more than about two days (some say only several hours) which comes somewhere near the middle of the time between menstrual periods. Not discouraged by this discovery, the champions of this method merely narrowed the time saying that boys result when fertilization occurs at the first part of this fertile period and girls at the latter part of the period. Knowing what we do about the X- and the Y-chromosomes, and their relation to sex-determination, we can see that such theories are entirely false.

Another sure-fire method which has been proposed relates not to the time of month, but to the month itself. According to this, a boy will result if conception occurs during one monthly cycle, but a girl will be produced if conception occurs the next month and so on—boy one month, girl the next, alternating throughout the reproductive life of a woman. In order for her to know which cycle is which, however, she must bear one child first; let us assume that it is a boy. In the future, if she wants another boy she should conceive during even monthly cycles; if she wants a girl, conception should be timed to occur during an odd monthly cycle. A pseudo-scientific explanation is even offered for this theory. It is based on the assumption that the left ovary produces eggs which always result in girl babies and the right ovary produces eggs which always result in boy babies. Furthermore, the ovaries are supposed to alternate in producing eggs—left ovary one month, right ovary the next. The only difficulty lies in the fact that these assumptions are false. First of all, there is no regular pattern of alternation in the release of eggs—the left ovary may release several eggs on successive months or the right may do the same. Second, children of both sexes may be produced from eggs from either ovary. This has been proved by a number of cases where women have had one ovary removed surgically and later have borne children of both sexes. Attractive as it may sound, this is just another of the many unfounded theories which we must relegate to the pile of unjustified speculations.

Other theories have even less basis in fact. One which is believed rather widely has to do with diet—if the prospective mother eats large quantities of meat during pregnancy the child will be a boy, while sweets will produce a girl. Some even hold that a woman's very thoughts can, in some vague way, influence the developing embryo inside her to become one sex or the other. Since we know that sex is determined before a woman even realizes that she is pregnant, we can ignore all such theories.

There was one recent theory which created quite a bit of interest because it at least recognized the fact that sex was determined by sperms carrying two different types of sex-chromosomes. This is the acid-alkali technique. According to this, if a woman wants to have a girl she should take a vaginal douche of lactic acid and water before the act to produce a child. On the other hand, she should substitute bicarbonate of soda if a boy is desired. This theory was proposed by a German doctor who claimed about 85 per cent effectiveness for it. He said that the two types of sperms possessed different chemical affinities which made those that would produce boys sensitive to acid and those that would produce girls sensitive to alkali. Therefore, he concluded that the use of an acid or alkaline douche before sexual intercourse would create a condition in the reproductive tract of the female favorable to sperms of one type and unfavorable to those of the other type. All of this seemed logical and some accepted it. A research laboratory in New Jersey began large-scale experiments with rats to test the theory and their first results seemed to support it. One of the large New York newspapers gave daily reports of the progress of the experiments and two of the employees, a married couple, became so enthusiastic that they began a private test of their own. Readers of their columns were informed of this, but they were all disappointed when a girl made her appearance at the blessed event instead of the expected boy. As other evidence accumulated it again became evident that this was just another of the many theories which could not stand up under experimental analysis.

So it is that man finds himself without any known means of predetermining the sex of his offspring and in all probability will continue to accept the stork's little bundle without any control over its sex. Theoretically, predetermination of sex is possible—if only some way could be found to separate the two different kinds of sperms. There seems to be no chemical difference between the two, but there may be a very slight difference in weight as we have already pointed out. A very delicate centrifuge conceivably might throw the heavier female-determining sperms with their large X-chromosome toward the bottom of a tube. These might then be separated and used in artificial insemination to achieve the desired sex. The difference in weight, however, is so very slight (if it even exists at all) and there are probably overlapping weights in the two groups so there seems little likelihood that the method will ever succeed.

It is probably good that the method of sex-determination is beyond man's control. Even in the United States, where boys do not enjoy the favored status found in some sections of the world, it would not be for the best. At this writing, adoption agencies report that there is a much greater demand for girl babies than for boy babies. This illustrates the fact that there might be fads for having one sex or the other at different times. There might be a fad for having girls at one period, or in one section of the country, and at another time or place the fad might favor boys and the carefully balanced mechanism which gives us an equal distribution of sexes at the age when mating is most common would be upset. In a small city there might be a group of girls which would mature to find very few of the opposite sex in their age group. Perhaps their mothers thought it would be so nice to have girls so they could be playmates with the neighborhood children. There might be a nice crop of boys coming along in the grade schools which were born at a time when the pendulum had swung in the opposite direction, but you could hardly expect a young lady of twenty to become enamored over a ten-year-old boy and wait for him to grow up and marry her. Social and economic problems would arise which, as the atom bomb has, would make us wish we had never made the discovery.

CHAPTER 10

SEX GENES AND HORMONES

To open this chapter let us set the scene at Idlewild Airport in New York City. A large transoceanic plane is landing. As it taxis in to discharge its passengers a great crowd of newspaper reporters, television technicians, and movie cameramen gather around. When the plane doors are finally opened, out steps a slender, attractive, blonde woman, dressed in the latest Paris fashion. She is immediately besieged by the reporters striving for interviews and photographs. Now pretty women arrive in New York every day by the thousands—what had this one done to warrant all this attention? Had she achieved some great success in the theater? opera? or perhaps in art? or writing? Not at all, this person had done nothing extraordinary and had not even been known outside of her personal acquaintances up until a few weeks before her arrival in New York. Then why all the excitement? The remarkable thing was that this person left the United States only two years previously as a man and was now returning as a very feminine-looking woman to all outward appearances.

A few years ago this person, Chris Jorgensen, was a normal man in body build and general appearance. He was not a person of mixed sex as some believe when they read reports of his transformation. He served for a time in the U.S. Army, which would certainly never have accepted any person who showed any signs of abnormal sex organs. It happened, however, that Chris was the psychological type of man

121

who admired women's clothing and enjoyed wearing such
apparel. This is a condition that is not too uncommon in
men—it is known as transvestism. In time, this desire became
so strong that Chris thought it would be more pleasant if he
were a woman instead of a man; then he could wear women's
clothing all the time. Other men have had similar desires, but
Chris was one of the first who had the initiative and courage
to do something about it. He learned of the advanced work
on sex and hormones which was being carried on in a Denmark hospital and decided to go there to have the transformation made. During a period of two years he underwent
treatment and operations before returning to the United States
with name changed to Christine Jorgensen. And the feminine
name was warranted. You may have wondered just what went
on during those two years and just how much of a woman
Christine is today. First of all, let us see exactly what determines whether a person is a male or a female; then we can
learn to what degree these natural characteristics can be
reversed by scientific application of this knowledge.

Sex Differences

Men and women are creatures which show considerable
differences from one another—that no one would deny—but
these differences are more extensive than is generally realized.
Of course, we first think of the differences in the primary sex
organs which have to do directly with reproduction and the
nursing of the young. These are obvious and easily distinguishable; but there are other sexual characteristics which have
nothing to do with reproduction, although they stand out
clearly as distinctions between the sexes. For instance, typical
masculine characteristics include a heavy growth of hair on
the face and other body parts, an angular body build, and a
deep voice. On the other hand, a smooth skin, flowing curves,
and a higher-pitched voice are typical feminine characteristics.
What many do not realize, however, is the fact that sexual
differences go far deeper than this— they extend to every part
of the body—the blood, the muscles, the skin, the bones—

there is hardly any part of the body that does not show distinctions characteristic of the sex of the individual.

The Sex Genes

How can these great differences be explained—how is it possible that children of the same parents can exhibit such a great number of variations as exist between the male and the female? We learned in the previous chapter that a sperm carrying a Y-chromosome will produce a male while an X-chromosome-carrying sperm will result in a female; but how can this rather minor difference in one chromosome out of twenty-four in the sperms account for the far-reaching differences between the sexes? First of all, let us understand that all persons carry all the potentialities for both sexes. Within your body now, no matter whether you are male or female, you carry all the genes necessary to produce all of the characteristics of both sexes. If you are a man you have all the genes necessary to produce fully-formed feminine breasts, yet such breasts have not developed, for there has been no realization of the potentialities of these genes, A woman, on the other hand, has genes for a fully formed beard, yet a beard normally does not develop. This knowledge makes the problem of sex-determination much simpler—now all we have to do is find a way to inhibit the genes for the characteristics of one sex and stimulate those for the opposite sex to full expression and we can effect the sexual differences. Sometimes, we know that the inhibition of genes may not be complete. We may see a lady with a beard in a circus side show who may be a perfectly normal woman in other respects. Also, there are numerous cases of men who develop feminine breasts, but are fully masculine otherwise. Such cases are rare, of course, but serve effectively to illustrate the fact that genes for both sexes are present in all of us.

The Trigger

We might compare this double dose of genes to a double-barreled shotgun, fully loaded and cocked. Let us assume that the shell in one barrel contains coarse buckshot while that in the other barrel contains fine birdshot. Here we have a bipotential shotgun; it can deliver a charge either of buckshot or birdshot—it all depends upon which trigger is pulled. Likewise, a tiny human embryo has a bipotential charge; it can deliver either male or female characteristics—it all depends upon which trigger is pulled. The sex chromosomes pull the trigger; the genes do the rest.

Recent studies have given us some clues or insights as to how this process is accomplished.

It is possible to take some actively dividing cells from the bone marrow of the breast bone and to grow them on special media in test tubes. These are the cells which produce the various types of blood cells. When the culture is growing well, there will be many cells in various stages of mitosis (cell division) during which the chromosomes show most clearly. Some of these cells can be removed, stained, and placed under the microscope for observation. By studying the chromosomes of cells taken in this manner from persons with sexual abnormalities, we have been able to draw some conclusions about the role the chromosomes play in normal sex determination.

Kleinfelter's syndrome is a condition in which an apparent male is sterile, has underdeveloped sex organs, abnormal breast enlargement and fat deposits and hair growth which are typically female in nature. Studies of the cells of such persons show that they have two X-chromosomes, but that there is also a Y-chromosome present. This situation could be caused by an abnormal distribution of both X- and Y-chromosomes to one sperm, or it could be due to abnormal egg formation in which both X-chromosomes go to one egg and there is fertilization by a Y-chromosome sperm. These are rare accidents, but they are known to occur in other forms of animal life. The resulting syndrome, in any case, seems to indicate that the X-chromosomes carry genes which trigger the development of femaleness and the Y-chromosomes carry genes which trigger the development of maleness. The individual is a male because of the presence of the Y-chromosome, but the two X-chromosomes bring out some of the female characteristics.

Another sexual abnormality known as Turner's syndrome bears out this interpretation. A person with this condition is a female, but the female characteristics are not fully developed and the reproduction organs are not sufficiently mature to function in childbirth. There is only one X-chromosome in such persons. This condition could arise if an egg which received no X-chromosomes was fertilized by an X-chromosome sperm, or if a normal egg was fertilized by a sperm carrying neither a X- nor a Y-chromosome. The characteristics expressed in this case again suggest that the trigger for the female characteristics is on the X-chromosome, but that a single X-chromosome is unable to bring out the full expression of all the female traits.

Hormones and Sex

Although hormones are rather recent scientific discoveries, it has been known for a long time that there is a close relationship between the sex glands of the male and the sexual characteristics which appear in all parts of his body. A boy castrated before adolescence fails to develop the beard, the musculature, and the voice of a man. He will not manifest any interest in females as such, nor will he stimulate a responsive chord of admiration in women. He will become, actually, a person without sex. True, he will retain the male reproductive organ which was already formed when he was castrated, but it will remain infantile in nature. In past centuries choir boys were castrated to prevent the loss of the fine quality of their soprano voices when they reached adolescence. Some religious sects required the castration of men who joined their orders so that they might not be subject to the temptations that would accompany normal masculinity. Fabulous oriental rulers had many eunuchs as slaves so they could feel assured that the ladies of the harem would be safe from sensual temptations.

In the case of the female, the knowledge of the relationship of the ovaries to sex came later. As surgery developed to the point where removal of the ovaries was possible, it became evident that a relationship similar to that in the male between these glands and sex exists. In those cases where removal of the ovaries from an immature girl was necessary, the child would grow into an adult devoid of the many feminine characteristics which normally come with womanhood.

Continued studies have shown that these relationships are due to hormones secreted by the reproductive glands. This means that the reproductive glands have two functions. The testes of a man not only produce the sperms, but also secrete the male hormone upon which his masculine characteristics are largely dependent. A woman's ovaries produce the eggs for reproduction and also the female hormones which not only account for her feminine characteristics, but also regulate the complex cycle of ovulation, menstruation, and pregnancy.

But how can we correlate these established facts about the influence of hormones on sexual characteristics with the equally well proven facts about the role of the sex chromosomes in determining sex? There is no conflict between the two concepts—both are correct. It seems as if the sex chromosomes get things started and pull the trigger which releases the hormones of one sex or the other and these hormones carry on from there.

Suppose we look at the genital region of a group of very young human embryos, say about eight weeks of age. We will find that the reproductive organs are present, but they all look alike regardless of which sex the embryos would have been had they survived. This similarity exists until rather late stages of embryonic development in some forms of life—any of you who have tried to distinguish sex in newborn puppies or kittens realize how much alike the sex organs may be even as late as birth itself. In the early human embryo there is a genital tubercle and two folds of skin on either side of a single opening. Then, if the embryo is to form a boy the tubercle will enlarge and surround this single opening to form the primary male reproductive organ (the penis). The folds of skin become loose and receive the male glands which descend from within the body at about the time of birth. If the embryo is to form a girl the tubercle will remain small and becomes the clitoris, the folds of skin will form the labia (or lips) of the female organs, and the single opening will become divided to form two—one opening into the vagina and the other opening into the tube from the bladder.

Thus, from a common beginning the external reproductive organs of one of the two sexes are formed. Internally, there is a similar situation. There is a pair of reproductive glands which may become either testes or ovaries. There are, however, two different sets of tubes—one of which becomes functional if the embryo becomes a male and the other set becomes functional if a female results. The glands contain an inner portion made up of tissue like the male testes and an outer shell of tissue like the female ovaries. It seems as if the chromosome balance determines which of these two types of tissue shall gain the advantage in growth. With the XY combination, the testicular type of tissue enlarges and secretes the male hormone which can then account for the expression of most of the male characteristics. On the other hand, the XX combination of chromosomes causes enlargement of the ovarian type of tissue and the glands become ovaries with their female hormones which account for the expression of most of the female genes.

Remarkable things can be done through artificial injection of hormones to bring out the dormant traits of the opposite sex. Amazing as it may seem, big tomcats have been injected with female hormones which actually causes them to secrete milk and nurse kittens with all the maternal solicitude of a natural mother.

Sex Transformation

Possessing this knowledge of the method of production of one sex or another in the normal course of events, to what extent can man use it to alter this normal course and achieve a transformation of sex from one to the other? Some of the earlier experiments along this line were done with chickens. The ovaries can be removed from young female chicks and testes from male chicks can be transplanted into their bodies. Such chicks mature into roosters which are indistinguishable from those that started their lives as males. Of course, they are sterile because the tubes to carry the sperms are not properly connected to the transplanted glands. This shows the powerful effect of the sex hormones in stimulating the expression of the genes for one sex and the inhibition of the genes of the opposite sex.

But what about human beings? Up until the case of Chris (or Christine) Jorgensen, there is no record of any attempt at transformation of sex. Here, however, we have a positive demonstration of how far transformation can go even in a mature human being through the manipulation of hormones. The exact nature of the operations performed on Chris will probably remain a professional secret of the doctors in charge, but we know that first of all they must have removed the testes in order to remove the source of male hormone which kept the male side dominant. With these gone, Chris would have tended to slip into a neuter sex—such as the eunuchs which have been made since the dawn of history. Female hormones could be administered, however, to bring out those latent feminine characteristics which had been present all the time, but had lain dormant in the absence of the female hormones. These hormones would cause the muscles to become more feminine in contour and the breasts to enlarge. The individual's feelings toward the sexes would change and emotional reactions would be more feminine in nature. There are many respects, however, in which the transformation would be incomplete. For instance, there would be little effect on the beard for it had already developed, and Christine will have to make daily use of her razor or depend upon more complicated methods of removing hair to keep a feminine-looking facial complexion. Also, the voice had already changed although it was not a low-pitched voice for a man. Those who have heard Christine on television or in the movies know that

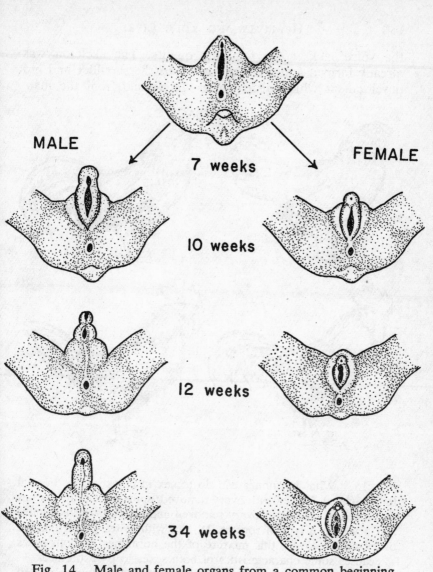

MALE   7 weeks   FEMALE

10 weeks

12 weeks

34 weeks

Fig. 14. Male and female organs from a common beginning.
The sex organs of all babies are alike at seven weeks of age, but
by ten weeks a difference is evident. The organs of both sexes are
formed from the same original structures.

the voice lacks some feminine quality. The skeleton was already formed and there can never be the shoulder and hip development which distinguishes the female from the male

Fig. 15. What hormones can do to sex in chickens. A, normal female (hen). B, hen with ovary removed; some male plumage has developed. C, hen with ovary removed and testes engrafted; looks and acts like a typical rooster. D, hen with testes engrafted, but ovary not removed; this mixture of the hormones of both sexes causes some characteristics of both sexes to b expressed.

(From Winchester, GENETICS, Houghton, Mifflin)

skeleton. In spite of these drawbacks, however, beauty parlor treatments on the hair and cosmetics on the face coupled with the latest styles in clothing give an over-all feminine appearance that would make Christine acceptable as a woman anywhere.

The question now arises: is this person really to be classified as a woman, or is this a man in whom some of the latent feminine characteristics have been brought to the surface with an erasure of some masculine traits and appendages? This is a very important question, and there may be some terrific legal tangles involved before it is settled. For instance, one promoter has offered Christine $100,000 to become a lady wrestler. Now, should she be allowed to compete with women in wrestling, or any other sport, for that matter? If not, should she (or he) be classified as a man in regard to insurance and in other cases where sex makes a difference in rates and payments?

Basically Christine is still a man. The cells of the body still contain the single X-chromosome and the Y-chromosome which are characteristic of the cells of the male. More important, however, is the fact that there could not have been a transformation in reproductive organs themselves. The testes certainly were removed, and the penis also, but there is no way in which female organs could be produced to replace the male organs. Some people have even asked if it would be possible for Christine to have a child. Such is completely out of the question. It might be that ovaries were transplanted into Christine's body, for this has been done successfully in other mammals, such as rats. Ovaries are often removed surgically in hospitals and would be available for such transplantations. It is more likely, however, that Christine must depend upon daily doses of female hormones in tablet form to maintain her feminine characteristics. But even if the transplantations were successful they will furnish only the hormone—in the absence of any other female organs they could not function in any other way.

It would have been better if Chris had made up his mind before adolescence, for then he would have retained the high-pitched voice of childhood which would have been more convincingly feminine. Also, the skeleton would have assumed female proportions to a great extent as it matured, the beard would never have developed, and the penis would have remained small. It will be interesting to trace this case through future years.

It would also be possible to accomplish a degree of transformation in the other direction—from female to male. If the ovaries of a baby girl were removed and regular injections of male hormone given, a person would result who would be masculine in outward physical appearance and who could compete physically with other men. Again, however, there could not be a change-over in the sex organs because of the rather advanced state of their development at birth, but there could be some changes in the case of this type of transformation. The female clitoris would enlarge and form a penis-like organ and the vagina would remain infantile although it would still be present in adulthood. If a mature woman should attempt a transformation the degree of change would be considerably less pronounced.

Medical Use of Sex Hormones

Through the proper use of sex hormones many people are able to live happy, well-adjusted lives who otherwise would be social misfits. A man may lack the masculine musculature, deep voice, and typical male aggressiveness which would enable him to compete on even terms with other men in everyday life. A deficiency in the secretion of male hormone from his testes may be the cause of this and he may benefit greatly from administration of extra male hormone or of a hormone which will stimulate his own testes to function more efficiently. There have even been a few cases where testes from one man have been surgically transplanted into another man who was deficient in this hormone. We must hasten to add, however, that there cannot be successful transplantation of the testes of other animals such as goats and monkeys. Some years ago there was a national scandal over the wholesale transplantation of animal glands into human beings by a doctor in Missouri who was ostracized by the medical profession because of his unethical practices. Investigations showed that none of his transplantations grew in the bodies of his gullible patients. Some actually claimed noticeable results from this treatment, but whatever rejuvenation they experienced was due to psychological, rather than to physiological, reasons. There can be no more hope for success of such transferrence of testicular tissue than there could be for the successful transfusion of blood from some lower animal to man. The tissues of animals of different species differ too widely to offer hope of success.

The use of sex hormones may also be of value to women. When there is a deficiency of the female hormone there may be an infantile underdevelopment of the sexual organs and consequent sterility. In some cases treatment with female hormone may induce these organs to complete development and become normally functional. Also, they are often of value during the menopause of any woman. At this time of life there is a diminution of the secretions of the ovaries, and a consequent physical and mental adjustment that may bring about unpleasant symptoms. The intelligent use of extra female hormones may often relieve many of the difficulties that are experienced during this transitional period of life.

There are a few cases on record where there have been oversecretions of sex hormones to produce precocious sexual development. A few years ago, it was announced that a five-year-old girl in Peru had given birth to a normal son. Investigation revealed that the child had begun menstruating at three and had full breast development. Her baby was delivered through a Caesarian operation and she now believes that her

son is her brother. The administration of extra sex hormones
to the young of some animals can induce precocious sexual
development, and it seems probable that this child had an
oversecretion of hormones from her own body. This, coupled
with a family life on an extremely low scale of morality, made
the pregnancy possible.

CHAPTER 11

SEXUAL ABNORMALITIES

The mechanism of sex determination is intricate as we have seen and, as would be expected with such a delicate balance between the sexes, it does not always go according to plan. On certain occasions there may be a deflection somewhere along the way which results in abnormal sexual development. The unfortunate deviates find it difficult to fit themselves into a society composed mainly of men and women with normal sexuality. In this chapter we will learn what some of these sex deviations are, how they are produced, and possible measures which may be taken to bring them within the bounds of normal sexuality.

Undersexed and Oversexed Individuals

There is considerable variation in the degree of sexuality of persons who are within the bounds of normalcy. Stop a moment and think of several men with whom you are acquainted—you can readily realize how great this variation may be. Some men are strongly masculine in both appearance and actions, some are on the feminine side, and others would be classified somewhere in between. The same variations are easily recognized in women. These variations make it difficult sometimes to decide just where normalcy ends and abnormality begins. There is a continuous variation from one extreme to the other and the dividing line is arbitrary in nature. Nevertheless, it is quite clear that at the extremes there are those who are abnormal in their sexual development. Hormones seem to be at the base of these variations.

Let us consider an undersexed man first. He may have rounded hips, soft muscles, a rather high-pitched voice, and a somewhat timid disposition which makes him no match for normal male aggressiveness in social and business associations. Such a man should not be confused with the pseudohermaphrodite who exhibits characteristics of both sexes. The type of man we are discussing now is entirely male with completely formed testes, but these testes may be of a small size or deficient in the type of tissue which produces the male hormone. Hence, the secondary male characteristics are not accentuated to the degree normally found. In some cases, the testes of such a man will not descend from the body cavity, but will remain located in a position similar to that occupied by the ovaries of a woman.

Very striking results have been obtained by administering male hormone to such persons or by administering pituitary hormone which stimulates the man's own testes to develop more fully. There is an almost immediate development of masculine attitudes and an increasing interest in women, which may have been almost completely lacking previously. In time, there will be changes of a physical nature which will make the person more masculine in appearance. If the testes are undescended they may come down to a normal position under the influence of the extra male hormone. There was one interesting case of a man, just returned from a midwinter Florida vacation, who did not develop the mannish coat of tan which other men exhibited. His doctor began giving him injections of male hormone and—lo and behold—a beautiful tan developed in New York in midwinter, complete with a swim-suit outline of fairer skin. It seems that the pigment-forming cells of a man will not function properly without a full amount of the male hormone. Sad to say, a few men have become somewhat bald after receiving such hormone treatment. This is due to the fact that some men may inherit baldness, but their hair remains in (like a woman's) unless there is a full supply of male hormone.

In striking contrast to the timid soul just described we have the oversexed man who is just as aberrated. In addition to abnormal desires for sexual gratification—desires which no normal woman can satisfy—such a man may also have difficulty in adjusting to normal living conditions. There may be an excess of aggressiveness which can lead to various forms of crime. There was an interesting case in Atlanta, Georgia, when such a young man was constantly getting into trouble because of his sexual overdevelopment. By his own consent, one of his testes was removed to lower the amount of male hormone in his body, and he settled down to a more normal pattern of life.

Women may have an abnormally low female hormone production and, thus, may be low in the scale of femininity. Their sex organs may remain infantile in nature and be incapable of conceiving and bearing children. They are likely to be very low in sexual libido and frigid in their responses to sexual stimulations. Treatment with female hormone may bring such a person closer to the normal state of sexual interest and permit child-bearing.

At the other extreme we find the oversexed woman who has an overdeveloped sexual desire which may be so strong as to result in nymphomania. In such a female, the desire for sexual gratification is so strong it overpowers all other considerations.

Homosexuality

It is common to think of men who appear feminine and women who appear masculine as possible homosexuals, but extensive studies of homosexuality do not bear out this assumption. Strong, virile-looking men and some women who would appear to be even on the voluptuous side may confine their sexual interests to members of their own sex.

There is a bar in Miami Beach which looks very much like other bars at first sight, but if you go inside and stay awhile you will become aware of unusual things going on. The place is patronized almost exclusively by men who may appear normal, but you will notice flirtations going on between them which very closely resemble the pattern of courtship between members of opposite sexes. Coquettishness, shy smiles, and lifted eyebrows are common as new acquaintances are made. These are homosexuals who know this is a common meeting place. Such persons seem to have a normal supply of sex hormones—they have an interest in sex which is unusual when there is a deficiency of sex hormones. For some reason, however, their interest has been diverted to members of their own sex rather than to the opposite sex. Such persons have sometimes been treated with sex hormones in an effort to divert these interests to more normal channels, but extra male hormones given to a homosexual man only increases his interest in having affairs with other men, and the results are similar when homosexual women are treated. Thus, it seems not to be a hormone deficiency, but a diversion of interest which is involved.

This is not too hard to understand when we go back to our original premise that all persons are potentially both sexes. Sometimes, some of the characters of the opposite sex will break through and be expressed although the basic sex of the person is not affected—as with the bearded lady or the man with the feminine breasts. Likewise, we can understand how some persons may have normal sexual development and normal sex drive, but with that drive directed to members of the same sex. Just why this should occur in some cases is not too clearly understood, but we do know that training has something to do with it. A child who develops an abnormal attachment to a parent of the same sex and comes to fear those of the opposite sex is a potential homosexual. Also, it seems as if heredity plays its part. Studies of identical and fraternal twins, where one member of the pair was homosexual, showed that among identical twins the other member of the pair was much more likely to be homosexual than in the fraternal group. In conclusion, it might be said that it appears as if heredity conditions certain persons so that they have the potentiality of being homosexual. Couple this with an environment that develops this potential trait and the person may find it impossible to direct his sexual interests to members of the opposite sex.

Half-Man and Half-Woman

At a carnival or circus side show one may sometimes view a strange-looking individual which is purported to be "half-man and half-woman." The barker, in very convincing, scientific-sounding terms describes this great wonder of the ages who possesses a body divided down the middle—male on one side and female on the other. With a great flourish a robe is removed and there stands a person with a heavy muscular leg on one side and a delicate nylon-clad leg on the other; with a hairy, masculine chest clad in a leopard skin on one side and a silk brassiere which appears to hold a feminine breast on the other; with a stubby beard on one side, and a smooth, delicately rouged cheek on the other; with a crew haircut on one side and feminine curls on the other. The author has even seen one who would talk out of one side of the mouth in a deep, masculine voice and then switch to a higher-pitched feminine voice when talking from the other side of the mouth. Such an individual may seem to be quite authentic, but from what we have learned about hormones in this chapter we can readily see that it would be difficult to explain such a bilateral separation of sexual characteristics. Hormones are carried by the blood to all parts of the body and it is hardly conceivable that they could stimulate the genes for one set of sexual characteristics to develop on one half of the body while the other half is stimulated to produce the characteristics of the opposite sex. Such cases as those described usually are men who have a somewhat underdeveloped musculature on one side of the body—perhaps due to some affliction that prevented the normal muscle growth on that side. Starting with this it is easy to build the illusion of a bilateral sexual division of the body. A sharp razor can easily eliminate any signs of unwanted hair, as many women have discovered. In some men there may be an enlargement of the breast on one side which would help, although in these days of feminine "falsies" this would not be necessary. Carefully applied cosmetics and beauty parlor hair treatments could help complete the illusion.

Both Sexes in One Body

Not all animals are divided into separate sexes as is the case with human beings. If you go out on a dark summer night when it is damp and misty and shine a flashlight on the ground you may see earthworms on the surface in the act of mating. If you watch long enough, however, you may notice a strange thing—any two earthworms can mate. There is no need for them to seek a member of the opposite sex because all earthworms have the complete sex organs of both sexes and can serve as male as well as female at the same time. In other words, each worm will transfer sperms from the male parts of the body to the body of its partner and will receive sperms from its partner into the female organs. This has certain advantages, but the great disadvantage lies in the fact that all the individuals must have all the organs and be capable of acting both as male and female. In the vertebrate animals (those with a backbone) the sexes are separate so that each individual is specialized to serve as one sex, and does not need the organs of the other. There are times, however, when the method of sex-determination goes wrong and a vertebrate will be produced with sex organs of both sexes. Almost any animal breeder can tell you of a few cases which he has run across in goats, pigs, et cetera, which were of this mixed nature.

It is even possible for human beings to combine both sexes in one body. Remember that all of us begin life with the same organs and a potential development into either sex. In a few rare cases both sets of organs develop side by side and result in mixed sex. A person of this nature is known as an hermaphrodite, or more properly a pseudohermaphrodite,

since the term hermaphrodite technically refers to some of
the lower forms of life (such as the earthworm) which serve
normally as both males and females in reproduction. In the
human pseudohermaphrodite there will be development of
the organs of both sexes and the secondary sexual characteristics will be somewhat intermediate between the two sexes.

Let us look in on a home in a rural community in
Oklahoma on a dark night near the turn of the century. This
was a special night and the lights burned brightly in the home.
A doctor's buggy stood outside. The cry of a newborn baby
suddenly broke the stillness of the night to announce the
arrival of a new life. At first the doctor was somewhat
puzzled—he adjusted his glasses and peered carefully at the
squirming baby. Then he told the anxious couple that they
were the parents of a baby girl—they took his word for it
and dressed and treated the child accordingly. As adolescence
approached, however, this person decided that she—rather,
he—was not a girl and began dressing and acting like a boy.
Masculine characters developed to some extent, but not to
the degree which would be expected in a normal man. At the
age of twenty-four this person married a normal woman and
lived a normal married life as a man. At the age of forty-two,
this individual was examined by the author and was found
to have fully developed sex organs of both sexes. The genital
tubercle had formed a penis about one-half the size of the
normal male organ, but there was also a fully formed vagina.
The reproductive glands, in which probably both testicular
and ovarian tissue had developed, were inside the body and
not descended like the male testes. (It has already been noted
that there are some undersexed men in which the testes remain
within the body cavity and do not descend.) The breast development of this person was that of a girl of about fifteen and
regular menstruation had been taking place for several years
preceding the examination. The voice was intermediate in
quality. The beard growth was light, but required regular
shaving. It was quite confusing to talk to such a person—at
times it would seem as if it were a man—then, due to a certain

expression or mannerism, the impression of a woman would be uppermost.

Just what causes such persons to be produced is still open to question. Studies of the anatomy of such forms in pigs has led to the theory that these pseudohermaphrodites begin life with the XY chromosome combination which normally produces males. In certain rare cases, however, it seems as if the genes for femaleness get a head start on the male genes and proceed to develop some of the ovarian tissue before the chromosome combination for maleness succeeds in inhibiting them. The front part of the gland develops first and this is like the ovary. Then, the rest of the gland develops the testicular portion; so we find both male and female hormones being produced in the same body. As a result, both sets of sex genes are stimulated to partial expression and the peculiar combination of sexes in one body results.

At a large hospital in Birmingham, a few years ago, a case was reported that strongly substantiates this theory. A human hermaphrodite came to the doctors for help. This person, quite naturally, found it very difficult to fit into a society which is divided into males and females. Such minor matters, for instance, as a trip to a public rest room became a major problem. Questionnaires for employment, college entrance, or even to obtain a driver's license invariably had a space to be filled in, indicating sex. In an effort to improve this person's psychological adjustment to life, a group of the doctors asked the person to decide which sex was preferable. The male sex was chosen, and the doctors then performed an operation to remove the ovarian type of tissue which was producing female hormones. Within two years this person was a well-adjusted member of society, although he (we can now use the masculine pronoun) still has the non-functional parts of the female organs which he developed before his transformation.

CHAPTER 12

HEREDITY INFLUENCED BY SEX

A few years ago Prince Alfonso, the crown prince of the deposed Spanish dynasty, was living in Miami, Florida, in exile from his native land. Late one night he was driving down one of the main boulevards of the city in a high-powered automobile. A sudden emergency arose as another car pulled in from a side road. There was a screeching of brakes, a sudden crash, and the tinkle of shattered glass on the pavement when the cars collided. It was not a serious collision, as automobile collisions go, but Prince Alfonso was cut by the flying glass. The cuts were not of a serious nature; however, he began to bleed profusely and continued bleeding long after the normal time for blood coagulation. Ambulances arrived and the Prince was rushed to a hospital, but too late. The loss of blood had been so great that he died before any treatment could be given.

A Royal Affliction

This event called to mind the unusual "bleeder's disease," hemophilia, that has plagued the royal families of Europe for many years. Persons with this disease have blood that does not clot properly; even small injuries assume major importance as blood continues to pour from wounds for hours after an injury. There is some factor lacking in the blood of such persons which is essential for normal clotting. Whereas normal blood clots within two to eight minutes after flowing from a blood vessel, in persons having hemophilia the time may be prolonged from thirty minutes to twenty-four hours.

143

This condition is inherited and was perpetuated in the royal families of Europe because of close intermarriages necessitated by the fact that royalty could marry only royalty. Poor little Prince Alexis of the ill-fated Romanoff dynasty of Russia had many a close brush with death during his brief life because of this disease—although it was the revolution rather than the disease which finally ended his life. Rasputin, the mad monk of Russia, obtained his strong hold on the government partly because of his apparently successful treatment of the little Tsarevitch during one of these bleeding attacks. Rasputin's unscrupulous use of his power was a notable factor in the precipitation of the Russian revolution. When we consider how the recent history of the world has been influenced by this revolution, we may ponder how far-reaching can be the effects of a single gene.

Hemophilia is an ancient human affliction. Among the Hebrews of antiquity there were cases reported of male infants who bled to death after circumcision. An Arabian surgeon of the eleventh century, Albucasis, described boys in a village who bled to death if their gums were rubbed harshly, and men who bled to death from slight wounds. Strangely, however, in all of the accounts of the disease it seems to have appeared only in the male members of a family, and pedigrees show that it follows an unusual "skip-generation" pattern of inheritance. What is there about this gene (which results in hemophilia) that is different from other genes which affect both sexes with equal frequency?

Sex-Linked Genes

The unusual method of inheritance of hemophilia is explained by the fact that it results from the expression of a gene which lies on the X-chromosome. Any gene on the X-chromosome is said to be sex-linked because this chromosome is involved in the determination of sex and will, therefore, have a pattern of heredity which is different according to sex. Remember that males carry only one X-chromosome, while females have two. Hence, males will express the genes which lie on their single X-chromosome. Even those genes which otherwise would be recessive will be expressed because there are no dominant genes to suppress them. In the female, however, there are the two X-chromosomes, and if a gene is recessive it must be present on both of these chromosomes if the characteristic involved is to be expressed. This means that a man will show a recessive character which he receives through a single gene from his mother, but a woman must receive such a gene from both father and mother in order to express it. If the character is relatively infrequent in occurrence, as is the case with hemophilia, there is very little likelihood that any female will ever receive the gene from both parents. Hence, it may appear to show only in the males, but this is because there have been no marriages between a man and a woman who both carry the gene. This is all expressed in the diagram in Fig. 17.

Some recent work seems to indicate that the blood of a woman who carries the gene for hemophilia is somewhat slower in its clotting time than the blood of a woman who does not carry the gene. There is not enough difference to have any significance with respect to serious bleeding; however, this information may make it possible to identify women who carry this gene and, thus, to determine if they might be potential breeders of hemophilic boys.

Fig. 16 shows how hemophilia was transmitted through the royal families of Europe. Note that the boys always inherited the abnormality through their mothers and never through their fathers. This is due to the fact that boys always receive their single X-chromosome from their mothers and receive the Y-chromosome from their fathers. The Y-chromosome is largely devoid of genes so it is not involved in the transmission of this character. The gene for hemophilia in the royal families of Europe seems to have arisen with Queen Victoria of Great Britain, probably as a mutation, and to have been spread as shown by the pedigree chart.

Color blindness is another character which comes about

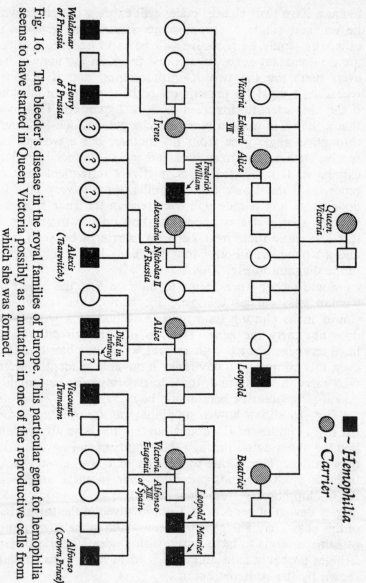

■ ~ *Hemophilia.*

◐ ~ *Carrier*

Fig. 16. The bleeder's disease in the royal families of Europe. This particular gene for hemophilia seems to have started in Queen Victoria possibly as a mutation in one of the reproductive cells from which she was formed.

(From Winchester, GENETICS, Houghton, Mifflin)

as a result of the effect of a recessive sex-linked gene. There is a gene on the X-chromosome which plays a part in the formation of the color-sensitive cells in the retina, which are necessary for the distinction of red and green colors. One recessive form of this gene fails to do its job properly and results in red-green color blindness. It is difficult for a person

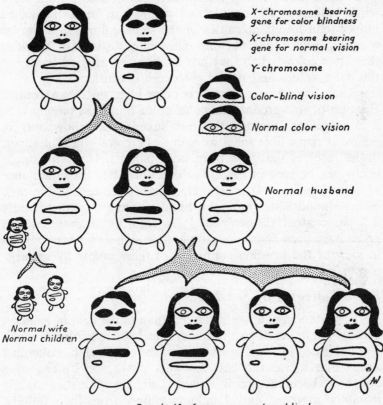

One-half of sons are color-blind

Fig. 17.   Sex-linked inheritance of color blindness. When a recessive gene is carried on the X-chromosome all the males who carry it show the trait, but the females must receive it from both parents in order to show it.

(From Winchester, ZOOLOGY, Van Nostrand)

with normal vision to realize what the world looks like to a color-blind person since we cannot get a word picture of this condition because colors cannot be described. It has been suggested, however, that normal vision at twilight is somewhat like the vision of a color-blind person. As darkness falls one may notice that reds and greens gradually become less distinct, while blues and yellows retain their characteristic hues for a while longer. Brilliant reds and greens can be distinguished longer than lower intensities of the same colors. In a similar manner, color-blind persons can often distinguish between these two colors when they are intense and in good light, but the paler values and poor light cause confusion.

There are a great many more color-blind men than women. Because of this predominance of color blindness among men it is sometimes thought that sex-linked genes show only in males. It is possible for a woman to be color-blind, however, if she receives the gene from both parents. How this might occur can be seen in Fig. 17 which illustrates the inheritance of color blindness. It is estimated that 8 per cent of the men in the United States are color-blind to some degree, but only 0.5 per cent of the women. It is unfortunate that red and green have been chosen as stop and go signals for traffic lights in view of the possible confusion of these colors by so large a proportion of our population.

False Concepts of Sex-Linkage

Some time ago a world-famous man in the field of aviation became the father of a son. In a syndicated news column which was published in newspapers all over the country, the columnist stated that it was too bad that this was a son instead of a daughter, because sons inherited their characteristics mainly from the mothers, and daughters mainly from their fathers. Had it been a daughter it would have received the genes for the genius of the father, but these would be lost in a son. This illustrates a popular misconception about sex-linkage which should be corrected at this point. This is one case among many where a scientific fact is misinterpreted and expanded into a belief which is quite false. It is true that a man receives all of his sex-linked genes from his mother and none from his father, but this represents only about one twenty-fourth of his total inheritance—certainly not a significant proportion. Girls receive exactly the same number of chromosomes and genes from each of their parents so no distinction of this kind can exist in their inheritance.

It is also common to falsely interpret the results of sex-linkage to mean that sex-linked characteristics are always more prevalent in men than women. This is certainly true for hemophilia and color blindness, but if the characteristic happens to be due to a dominant gene it will be more prevalent in women. For instance, one dominant sex-linked gene produces defective enamel of the teeth, and persons having this condition wear down their teeth so that they are usually just stubs protruding from the gums. A woman, having two X-chromosomes, has twice the chance of receiving this gene as a man with his single X-chromosome. Thus, women show this condition about twice as frequently as men.

Sex-Influenced Genes

In addition to the genes which are located on the X-chromosome, there are other genes on the other chromosomes which are influenced, to some extent at least, by the sex of the individual.

As one sits in the balcony of a theater and looks over the audience below, one may be impressed by the rather large number of bald heads which are so prominent in a gathering. Various environmental factors are often mentioned as possible causes of baldness, but, as a matter of fact, the great majority of bald people are that way because they inherit a genic combination which produces, baldness. The character is certainly more prevalent in men, although a greater number of women are bald than is commonly believed—for they can hide it more easily. At first sight, such a condition would suggest recessive sex-linked inheritance, such as we find for color blindness. Investigation of the inheritance of baldness, however, definitely shows that it does not follow the pattern of sex-linked genes, for sons often inherit the condition from their fathers. It is due to one of those genes which are called sex-influenced genes. This particular gene is dominant in men and recessive in women. This accounts for the preponderance of the expression of this character in men as compared to women, for a man is bald if he has only one gene for baldness, whereas a woman must receive two such genes to be bald. It seems that a single gene can operate only in the presence of the male hormone. One interesting case which indicated that this was true was that of an undersexed man who began taking treatments with male hormone. He obtained the desired masculinity, but he lost his hair. This man was evidently of the type that carries one gene for baldness and one for normal hair growth, and he previously had not had enough male hormone to cause the single gene to express itself. In any studies of the inheritance of baldness, however, we must keep in mind the fact that the condition may be induced by such diseases as syphilis, infectious seborrhea, or thyroid disease. Baldness from disease is not inherited and appears with equal frequency in either sex.

Sex-Limited Genes

Sex-limited genes are those which normally express themselves in only one sex. These are the genes which determine the expression of the characteristics associated with sex. For instance, all women have genes for a full beard development, but these usually do not develop in the absence of the male hormone. A man can inherit the type of beard he has through his mother even though her face has no trace of such a beard. Likewise, breast development is limited to women, but hormone imbalance may cause feminine breast development in man. Such genes, which depend upon the sex hormone balance for expression, are sex-limited genes. It is these genes which are responsible for the many distinctions between the sexes which were discussed in Chapter 9.

CHAPTER 13

WHAT WILL YOUR CHILD BE LIKE?

All prospective parents are understandably interested in knowing what they might expect in their children in the way of inherited characteristics. In some cases this is much more important than the simple curiosity which gives each of us a desire to have a peek into the future. One or both of some couples planning to marry express some serious defect which they fear might be transmitted to possible children. Or, they both are entirely normal, but there is some serious hereditary defect in the immediate family of one or both of them. Sometimes the decision as to whether to have any children or not rests upon an understanding of the possibility of the transmission of such a defect. In the preceding chapters we have learned how the genes are assorted and transmitted to the reproductive cells, how sex is determined, and how sex influences heredity. In this chapter we hope to show how this information can be used in predicting inheritance.

Predictions and Probabilities

There are cases where we can say definitely what the children of a couple will be like with regard to some specific characteristic. More often, however, we can only say that a certain characteristic will appear in a certain proportion of the children. For instance, we can say that it can be expected to appear in one-fourth of the children (that one child out of four is expected to show it), but we cannot say with any certainty that it will appear or not appear at any one birth. The element of chance is involved, and it is no easier to predict than chance happenings of an inanimate nature.

To illustrate with an inanimate example: we know that the chance of obtaining a head when we toss a penny is fifty per cent (one out of two), but we cannot say for certain that a head will appear at any particular toss. In a similar way, we must realize that the same laws of chance govern the transmission of genes to each child, regardless of the genes which may have been expressed in previous children.

This principle is often misunderstood by people just beginning to learn the principles of heredity. A young couple recently consulted a geneticist about an heredity problem which confronted them. They were both normal, but had one child who was an albino (a pigment deficiency resulting in very fair skin, almost white hair, and pink eyes). Albinos are handicapped in their vision because of the lack of pigment in the eyes and must avoid even short exposures to sunlight because their skins burn so easily. This couple wanted to know what the chances were that their future children would show the same condition. Albinism is due to a recessive gene, so it was evident that both parents carried this gene, since recessive genes must come from both parents if they are to be expressed. It was also evident that both carried a gene for normal pigmentation which was dominant over the gene for albinism, otherwise they would have been albinos.

The geneticist carefully explained this to them and showed them why about one-fourth of their children would be expected to be albinos. Then the woman's face brightened as she thought she understood his implications. She said, "Oh, I'm so glad to know that; now that we have already had the albino, the next three children we have will be normal." Unfortunately, however, the genes in their shuffling around have no foreknowledge that this couple have had an albino child, therefore, it is possible that the sperm and egg carrying the gene for albinism will come together again at the second conception as they did at the first. Consequently, while we can say that about one-fourth of the children of such a couple will show the recessive characteristic, it would be possible for them to have three more children and all three could show it. If we study a large number of families of this nature, however, we will find almost exactly one-fourth of the offspring will show the recessive characteristic and three-fourths will show the dominant characteristic.

This shows the difficulties which we encounter when we attempt to make absolute predictions about the expression of hereditary traits in any particular child. Nevertheless, if a man has some serious hereditary defect and, after studying his ancestry, we can tell him that the chances of transmission of the defect to his children are fifty per cent, he may decide that such odds are too great against the little gamblers and forego fatherhood.

Dominant and Recessive Traits

Odds such as the above can be calculated for those characters which have been studied enough so that we know the nature of the genes which produce them. Let us first of all see how this can be done for those characters which change according to the variation of a single pair of genes which are dominant and recessive in nature. It will be easier to follow if we take a specific case as an example, so we will continue with the character of albinism. Sufficient families have been studied in which this character is found to tell us that the gene for albinism is recessive, while the gene for normal pigmentation is dominant over it. Now, let us see how many different kinds of marriages we may have which involve combinations of these genes. First of all, there may be a marriage between two albinos. The children from such a marriage will all be albinos, for each parent must carry one gene for this recessive character in order to express it. Each sperm and each egg, therefore, will carry a gene for albinism, and there is no way for a child to receive a gene for normal pigmentation from such parents. This, then, is one case where we can predict accurately what the children will be like for they will all be the same.

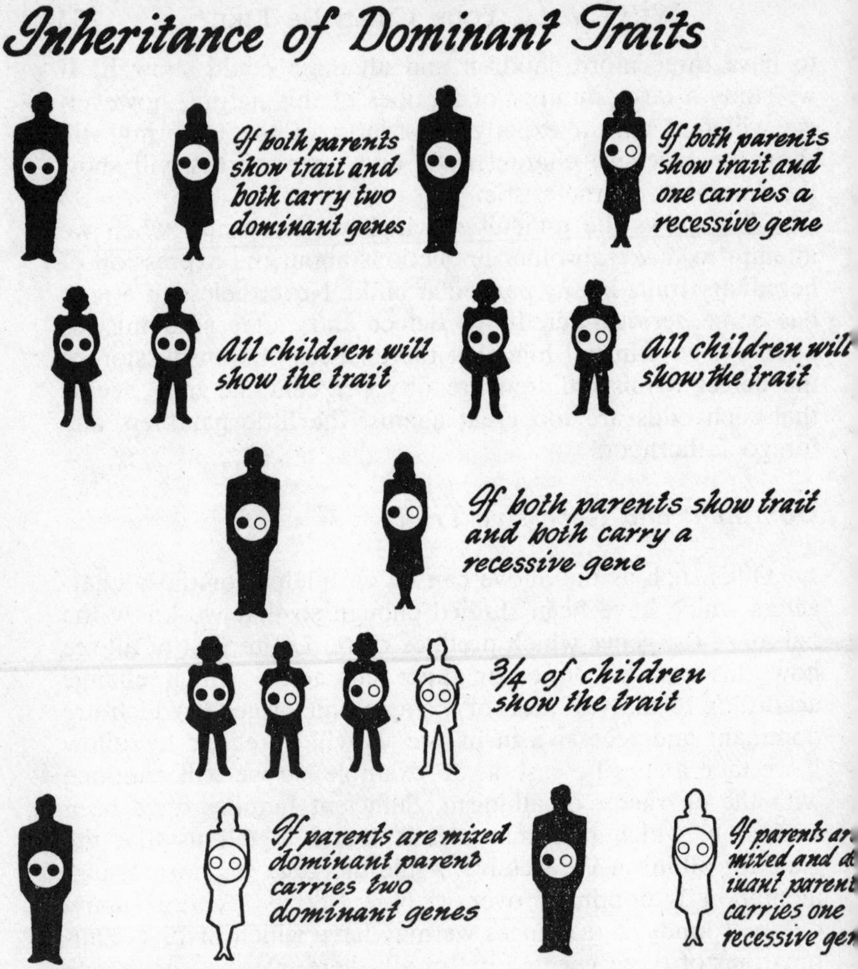

Inheritance of Dominant Traits

If both parents show trait and both carry two dominant genes

If both parents show trait and one carries a recessive gene

All children will show the trait

All children will show the trait

If both parents show trait and both carry a recessive gene

¾ of children show the trait

If parents are mixed dominant parent carries two dominant genes

If parents are mixed and d__iuant parent carries one recessive gen__

All children will show the trait

½ of childre__ show the trai__

Fig. 18. Inheritance prediction chart for dominant traits.

The second type of marriage may be between an albino and a normally pigmented person. What can we expect in the children of such a couple? To answer this we must find out more about the normal member of the couple. We know that he has at least one gene for normal pigmentation, but what about the other gene of this pair? It may be of either type. If either of his parents was an albino then we know that the person carries the albino gene. If his parents were both normal, but there were several albinos in his immediate ancestry there is a good chance that he carries the gene. There is no way to be absolutely sure. If, on the basis of the available information, we conclude that the normal person probably carries the gene for albinism then we will expect that about one-half of his children will be albinos. On the other hand, if a careful study of the ancestry of this normally pigmented person reveals that there are no cases of albinism, then we may conclude that there is a very little possibility that an albino gene is present. In such an event, all of the children will be normal, even though one of the parents is an albino. All of these children will carry the gene for albinism, however, and can pass the characteristic on to their children if they marry persons who also carry the gene.

The third type of marriage will be between two persons with normal pigmentation. Again we must examine the ancestry of these persons and try to determine if they carry the gene. If both of them carry the gene then we will expect albinos in one-fourth of their children—the rest will have normal pigmentation. If one carries the gene, but the other does not, then all of the children will be normal. If neither carries the gene, which is the case in most such marriages, then all children will have normal pigmentation and none of them can ever have an albino child.

All of these possibilities can be more easily understood by reference to the inheritance prediction charts. These charts show all possible types of marriage involving a character which is inherited as a dominant or as a recessive. You can apply the charts to your own family by substituting one of your characteristics in the proper chart. In this way it is possible to predict what your child will be like, keeping in mind, of course, that in many cases the prediction must be expressed in terms of chance.

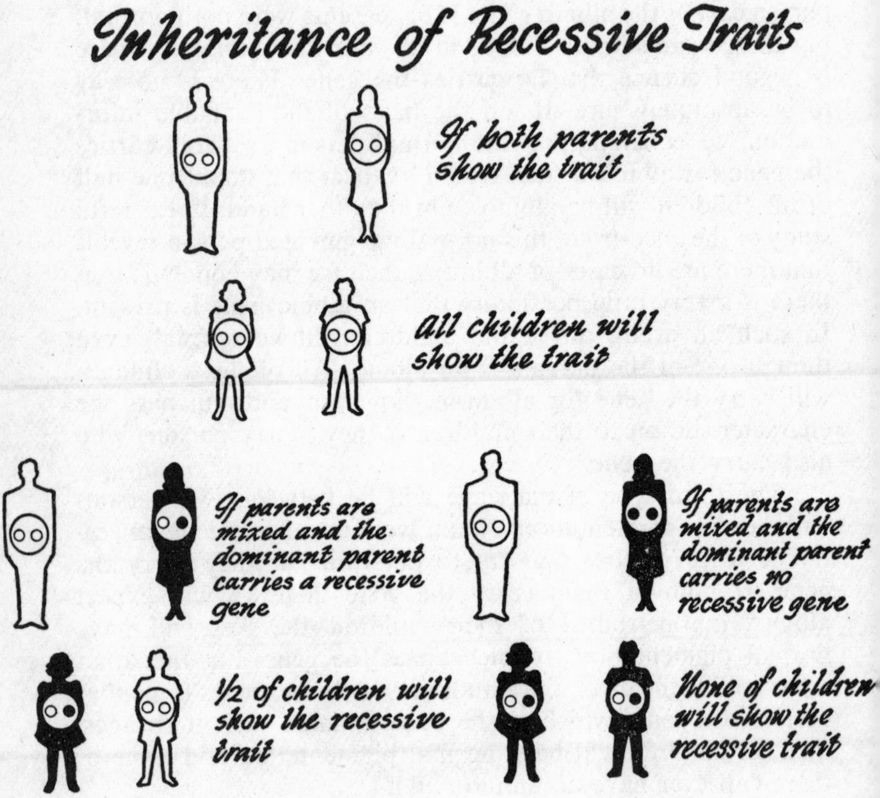

Inheritance of Recessive Traits

If both parents show the trait

All children will show the trait

If parents are mixed and the dominant parent carries a recessive gene

½ of children will show the recessive trait

If parents are mixed and the dominant parent carries no recessive gene

None of children will show the recessive trait

Fig. 19. Inheritance prediction chart for recessive traits.

Application of the Inheritance Prediction Chart

Let us take a hypothetical case and see how it works. Suppose you are a man with ear lobes that hang free, but your wife has ears that are attached directly to the side of her head without any free-hanging lobes. This characteristic has been studied sufficiently in other families to indicate that the free-hanging ear lobes are present whenever a person carries a certain dominant gene for this condition. Now, you want to know what kind of ear lobes you can expect in your children. We refer to the chart which includes marriages between a person who shows a character due to a dominant gene and a person who shows a character due to a recessive gene. There ares two possibilities in this chart; one in which the person showing the dominant character carries the recessive gene, and one in which he does not. How are we to know into which category your marriage falls? Well, you know that your wife carries two genes for the attached lobes, else her lobes would not be attached. You also know that you carry at least one gene for free ear lobes, but what about the other gene of the pair which affects ear lobes? It may be either kind. Suppose you find that your mother had attached ears—that solves the problem—you know that she transmitted the gene for this condition to you for all the eggs which she produced carried this gene. Your father is certain to have had free ear lobes under these condtions and he transmitted this dominant gene to you. Since you carry the gene we know that you fit into the first possibility on this chart. As we trace the assortment of genes in this combination we find that one-half of the children are expected to show the recessive character and one-half show the dominant character. This means that one-half of your children should have free ear lobes and the other half should have ears attached directly to their heads, according to this ratio.

If you have a large family, it is likely that your children will fit the ratio rather closely, but it is entirely a matter of chance with each child. Just as it is possible to toss three heads in a row with a penny, it is possible that you will "have a run" as the gamblers say and have several children with the same type of ears. The chart shows the ratio to be expected when large numbers of offspring are considered. No chart can show definitely what any one child will be unless there is only one type of child possible.

The greatest difficulty in using the chart comes when you try to decide whether a person who shows a dominant character carries a recessive gene. In the illustration which we have just used it was easy, for when one parent shows a recessive character then it is certain that the gene for this character will be passed on to all children. In other cases, however, it is not so easy—you and both of your parents may show a certain dominant character, but one of your parents may have carried a recessive gene and transmitted it to you. You can only judge your chances for carrying a recessive gene in this instance by a more extensive study of your ancestry. If you find that the recessive character showed rather extensively in either side of your ancestry then there is a good chance that you carry the gene. The complete absence of the character would indicate that there is little likelihood that you carry it. We learn whether human traits are dominant or recessive by extensive study of family pedigrees. A tabulation of some of these findings is given in Chapters 22, 23, 24, and 26.

Intermediate Traits

In the case of intermediate genes, inheritance prediction is much simpler because there are no hidden genes. It is possible to tell the type of genes which a person carries when they are of this nature simply by observation of the person. For instance, if a member of the Caucasian race has wavy hair we know that he has a gene for curly and a gene for straight hair since waviness is the intermediate expression of these two genes. We do not need to depend upon ancestry in such cases. The types of children which may be expected when

Inheritance of Intermediate Traits

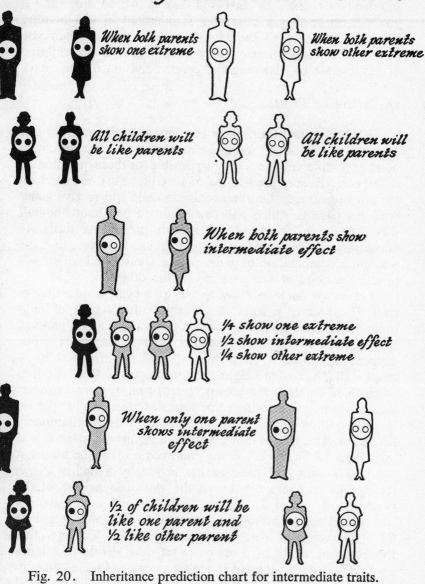

Fig. 20. Inheritance prediction chart for intermediate traits.

intermediate genes are involved are shown in Fig. 20. If you determine that a character is inherited in this manner (through reference to tabulations of inheritance) then you may predict the expression of this character in the children of any couple by choosing the proper division of the chart.

Quantitative Traits

When inherited traits show continuous variation from one extreme to the other, we must assume that variations in a number of different genes are responsible for these quantitative differences. Hence, predictions of heredity must be based on the law of averages. On the average, a child will receive genes from his parents which will cause him to be about one-half way in between his parents when such quantitative traits are concerned. There is always the possibility, however, that the particular combination of genes will be transmitted which will produce a child at one extreme or the other.

Let us go back to body height as a typical quantitative trait. In order to predict the average adult height of children, one merely takes the average height of the two parents, making due allowance for sex, of course. As an example, suppose a woman is 63 inches tall and her husband is 74 inches tall. Now what height can they expect in their children when these children are grown? First of all, we must convert the female height into the same terms as male height. We do this by multiplying 63 by 1.08. This gives us approximately 68 inches. This means that the woman in this marriage would have been 68 inches tall if she had been a man—the fact that she is a woman has reduced her height by 5 inches. Now, let us take an average between the two male heights of the parents and we get 71 inches. If this couple should have a son, therefore, he would be expected to attain a height of 71 inches when he reaches physical maturity. To determine the expected height of a daughter we must divide this figure by 1.08 in order to convert it back into terms of female height. When this is done we find that a daughter would be expected

United Press Photo

Plate IXa. This attractive young lady (?) created quite a bit of excitement when she arrived at a New York airport. She had left the United States just two years previously as a man, Chris Jorgensen, but had undergone sex-transforming operations in Denmark and was returning as a woman with name changed to Christine. Such cases show the influence of hormones on sex determination.

Plate IXb. Chris Jorgensen as a man before sex-transforming operations.

Plate X. Some male genes are expressed in a female. Miss Frances Murphy of New York City is a perfectly normal woman except for the fully developed masculine characteristic of a beard. This is a case where some genes of the opposite sex are expressed.

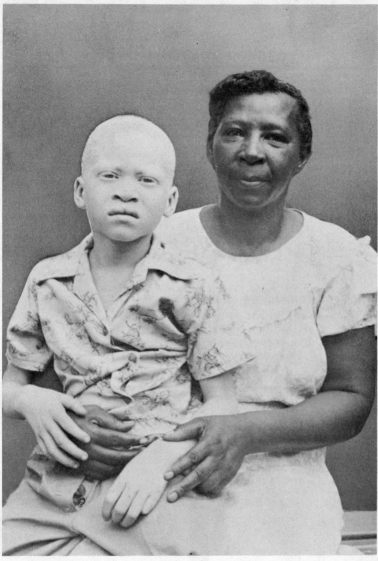

Photo by author

Plate XI. An albino Negro boy with mother. Both parents of
this boy have normal Negroid skin pigmentation, yet they both
carry a gene for albinism which interferes with the formation of
melanin in the skin. The chance of this couple having such a
child is one-fourth, but it is possible for their next child to be
an albino also.

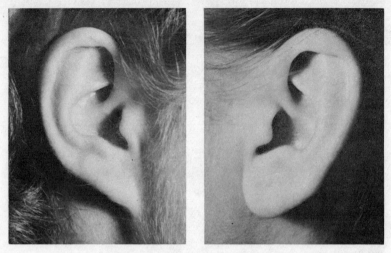

Photos by author

Plate XIIa. What kind of ear lobes will your child have? The attached ear lobes on the left result from the action of a pair of recessive genes, while the free-hanging ear lobes are found when a certain recessive ear lobe is present.

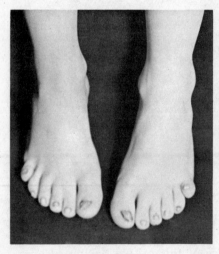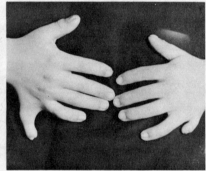

Photos by C. Nash Herndon, Department of Medical Genetics, Bowman Gray Medical School

Plate XIIb. Polydactyly of hands and feet.

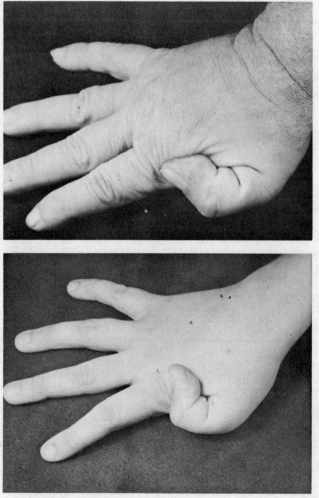

Photos by author

Plate XIII. Like father, like daughter. Family pedigrees enable us to trace the inheritance of interesting family characteristics such as extreme flexibility of the thumb joints illustrated here. The father is shown above and a daughter below.

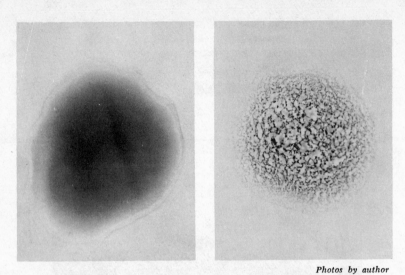

Photos by author

Plate XIVa. Compatible and incompatible blood mixtures.

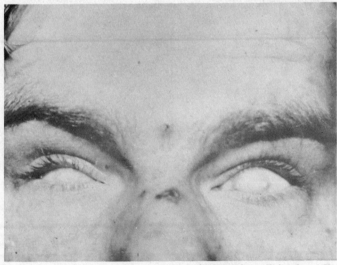

From F. E. Stephens, University of Utah

Plate XIVb. A sex-linked recessive outlaw gene causes the production of small, non-functional eyes, *microphthalmia*. It was traced through four generations of a family in Utah by Dr. F. E. Stephens.

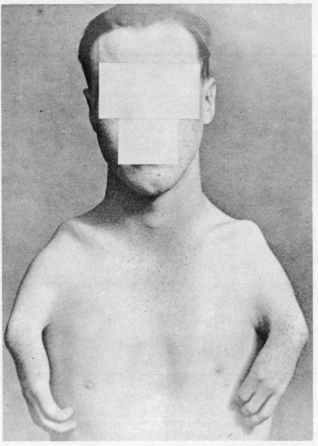

From Karl Stiles in the Journal of Heredity

Plate XV. An outlaw gene is expressed. These flipper-like arms result from the action of a dominant outlaw gene which is somewhat variable in the degree of deformity which it produces.

Plate XVI. Albino brother and sister with parents who are first cousins. Three other children in the family are normal. This is one of the recessive traits which has a much greater chance of appearing when a married couple is closely related. About 17 per cent of the albinos born in the United States have parents who are first cousins, but only about one-half of one per cent of the marriages are cousin marriages. This girl and boy are squinting even though the picture was made in the shade, because they lack the protective melanin in their eyes.

to be about 65 3/4 inches in height. Well, certainly everyone knows that this is not going to come out exactly—we have variations in height among children of the same sex born to the same parents. If they have a large family, however, the average height of their children will come very close to the figure obtained by this method of calculation.

There is another factor which we must consider carefully in this particular case. Environment plays a considerable part in physical development; therefore, this figure will be accurate only if both parents and children had diets and other environmental conditions which influence physical development that were similar. If the children have better conditions under which to develop, then we would expect them to exceed their parents' average. Statistics show that there has been a steady gain in average height among Americans for the past several generations. When we visit the old homes in which some of our forefathers lived we may be surprised by the short beds which they had during those days and wonder how they slept comfortably in them. As a matter of fact, they slept very well because their average height was below that for Americans today. There has certainly been no change of the genes to produce this difference; it is explained by the tremendous strides which have been made in our knowledge of public health and nutrition. The genes have been there all of the time, but they have a greater chance for expression today.

Other quantitative characteristics fall into this same general pattern of inheritance prediction, although environment may be less important in some of them.

Sex-Linked Traits

When traits are sex-linked (due to variations of genes on the X-chromosomes) we must use a chart which makes allowance for the fact that a man carries only one such gene. Since color blindness is a very common sex-linked trait let us use it as an example. Suppose a man is color-blind and his wife has normal vision and they want to know the chances of their children being color-blind. We know that the man carries a single gene for this character. His wife, on the other hand, carries two genes which influence color vision (since she has two X-chromosomes while a man has only one). We know that one of these two genes is for normal vision. The other gene could be either kind, since the gene for color blindness is recessive to the gene for normal vision. We must try to determine the nature of this other gene by a study of the ancestry of this woman. Have there been any color-blind people in the past two or three generations? If not, then we are safe in concluding that both of her genes are for normal vision. In this case, as can be seen by the chart, none of the children will be color-blind. If on the other hand, her father proves to be color-blind, we know that she carries a gene for this condition and we would expect half of the daughters and half of the sons to be color-blind. If her mother's father was color-blind, or there was considerable color blindness among the close relatives on her mother's side, then there is a good chance that she carries the gene even though her father has normal vision.

If we reverse the situation and assume that a color-blind woman marries a man with normal vision, then our problem of prediction is much easier. In this case we can say with certainty that all of the sons will be color-blind, but all of the daughters will be normal. Thus, we see that it is somewhat easier to predict heredity when genes are sex-linked than when they are located on the other chromosomes.

Sex-Influenced Traits

There are relatively few human traits that come under this heading. Baldness is the only one which is commonly observed. This trait is inherited as a dominant in men and as a recessive in women. We can use the charts for dominant and recessive characters for this. To determine the heredity of daughters, we treat the trait as a recessive and to determine the heredity of sons we treat it as a dominant. Thus, a woman may carry the gene for baldness without showing it, and she will pass it on to one-half of her children. The sons who receive the gene will become bald, but the daughters will have normal hair growth (provided, of course, that their father gives them the normal gene). A bald man, on the other hand, may have only one gene for baldness and, in this case, one-half of his sons will be bald, but all daughters will be normal (assuming that the mother carries normal genes). Other combinations of genes for this trait can be worked out by reference to the charts given in the first part of this chapter.

CHAPTER 14

FAMILY PEDIGREES

The influence of heredity on family traits for one or two generations is usually clearly recognized, but we often fail to realize that our genes of heredity have come down through the centuries in the bodies of countless ancestors. Time and space dull our interest in those past ancestors and we often have no record of the pattern of the inherited traits which have come through them. Sometimes they may be discovered accidentally as is illustrated by an interesting case which occurred in England in 1914.

There is an ancient cathedral in England known as Shrewsbury Cathedral which had been built over the remains of the first Earl of Shrewsbury, John Talbot. John Talbot was not an outstanding man of history, but the records show that in 1453 he took part in a battle with the French army which had been led by Joan of Arc. During this battle he was knocked from his horse and broke his thigh in the fall. In this helpless condition he was finished off by a French battle-axe which split his skull. His body was brought back to England and buried in the Cathedral which bore his name from that day to this.

Extensive repairs were undertaken on this cathedral in 1914 and in the course of the repairs it became necessary to excavate the region in which the remains of John Talbot lay. By coincidence the foreman in charge of the repairs of the cathedral was a direct descendant of John Talbot. When the remains were carefully removed from their resting place, this foreman stepped up to examine the skeleton of his distant ancestor, five centuries removed. He noted the broken thigh bone and the split skull which confirmed the identification of the skeleton. Then he uttered a cry of surprise for he saw that the joints of two fingers of each hand of this skeleton were fused. The surprise was occasioned by the fact that he, himself, had fingers fused in exactly the same way. This fusion of bones had always caused these fingers to be stiff and to lack the flexibility of normal fingers. We know this condition comes about as a result of the action of a dominant gene. The important point is that this gene had come down through fourteen generations over five centuries of time, no doubt spreading itself to literally hundreds of people during this time, yet it was just the same in its effects as in 1453. (All descendants of John Talbot, of course, did not show the characteristic since only one-half of a person's children receive any one gene; however, many of them did.)

The Importance of a Woman's Yes

This unusual coincidence emphasizes the fact that we represent a synthesis of the genes from our ancestry. Those of our more recent ancestry will, of course, contribute more genes than those more remote in time, but any genes which you may happen to have received from one of your ancestors living during the time of Shakespeare will influence you just as strongly as they influenced that distant ancestor. This knowledge may cause us to have a greater interest in our distant ancestors whom we may know today only from faded photographs or oil portraits. One anonymous poet was moved to write a whimsical verse as he looked at a portrait of his great-great-grandmother—a verse speculating on the far-reaching importance of a woman's yes in answer to that all important question.

Oh Damsel Dorothy, Dorothy Q.,
Strange is the gift that I owe to you;
What if a hundred years ago
Those close-shut lips had answered "No,"
Should I be I, or would it be
One-tenth another, to nine-tenths me?

Soft is the breath of a maiden's yes;
Not the light gossamer stirs with less;
But never a cable that holds so fast,
Through all the battles of wave and blast;
And never an echo of speech or song,
That lives in the babbling air so long.
There were tones in the voice that whispered them,
You may hear today in a hundred men.

Tracing Inheritance Through Pedigrees

Through family pedigrees it is possible for us to trace some of our inherited characteristics into past generations, thus to learn more about the method of inheritance of these characteristics. Unfortunately, many family pedigrees which have been kept for hundreds of years include only those persons who bear the family name and those who were distinguished. Also, these pedigrees often list only the accomplishments of the individuals along with their names, without giving much information about characteristics which we may wish to study from the standpoint of heredity. Such pedigrees are of limited value because they omit so many of the less desirable ancestors who influence our heredity just as much as those who are listed, and because of their failure to include the characteristics which we may wish to study. It is often possible, however, to obtain pedigrees of several generations which give us the information which we need to determine the method of inheritance of some specific character.

When we have this information it is necessary to get it down in some way which will make it convenient to study. The method which has generally been accepted is illustrated in Fig. 21. It can be noted from this that the men are represented by squares and the women by circles, marriage is indicated by a horizontal line connecting a man and a woman, and children are shown as offshoots of a vertical line leading down from the couple. When some specific character is under study, such as the ability to roll the tongue, we then represent all persons who show this character with a solid square or circle and leave those squares and circles blank when the character is not shown. By a glance at this type of chart it is possible to tell which persons show and which do not show the character, the sex of the person, and the possible method

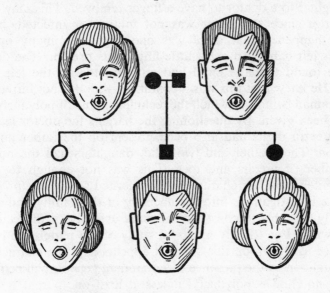

● ■ ~ *Tongue rollers*
○ □ ~ *Cannot roll tongue*

Fig. 21.   Single family pedigree of tongue rolling.

(From Winchester, GENETICS, Houghton, Mifflin)

of inheritance of the character. In this case the ability to roll the tongue into a U-shape is due to a dominant gene, but the fact that one child cannot roll her tongue shows that both parents must also have carried the recessive gene, for inability to roll the tongue and these two genes came together in this child.

Family pedigrees are much more valuable when they

include more than a single family. The more aunts, uncles, grandparents, great-aunts, great-uncles, great-grandparents, and other more distant ancestors we can include, the more we can learn about the method of inheritance of the characteristics under survey. Some time ago a woman brought her daughter to a doctor to have a finger removed. This may seem strange since the finger was not injured or infected, but it just ·happened that there was one finger too many on the girl's left hand. An extra little finger was present. The doctor also found that the child had an extra toe on the left foot.

He knew that this was a condition, which is not infrequent in human beings, to which the technical name of polydactylism has been given. By questioning the parents the doctor learned that extra digits had also been present on the father and on a son. The mother and two other daughters had the normal number of fingers and toes. This was not enough to show definitely how the character was inherited so the doctor made more investigations into the ancestry of this family and eventually was able to construct the more extensive pedigree chart shown in Fig. 22. By a careful study of the pattern of inheritance as shown on this chart, it appears as if the character is brought on by the presence of a dominant gene. It will be noted that no child is polydactyl unless at least one parent is polydactyl, and when one parent is polydactyl there are cases of polydactylism in about one-half of the children. We cannot be sure though from a study of this one pedigree. We would have to make a much more extensive study including many other pedigrees before we could feel justified in saying definitely that it was a dominant gene.

It is through such pedigree study that geneticists determine the method of inheritance of human traits. We cannot mate a man with a woman just because they happen to have some particular traits that we wish to study and tell them to have many children so we can get a good ratio of the offspring. We can make experimental crosses of similar characteristics in some of the lower animals and get some clue as to the possible method of inheritance in human beings, but we must

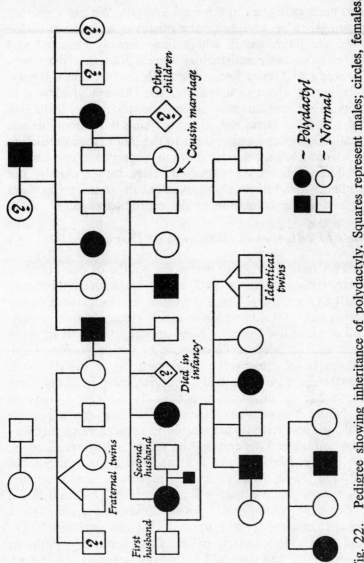

Fig. 22. Pedigree showing inheritance of polydactyly. Squares represent males; circles, females.

(From Winchester, GENETICS, Houghton, Mifflin)

● ~ Polydactyl

○ ~ Normal

■ ~ Polydactyl

□ ~ Normal

Other children

Cousin marriage

Identical twins

Fraternal twins

Died in infancy

Second husband

First husband

depend upon pedigrees in the final analysis. We can construct such pedigrees by a study of the offspring of matings of the type we are interested in which have already occurred and arrive at reasonably satisfactory conclusions in most cases.

A study of family pedigrees, such as this one on poly-dactyly, serves again to emphasize the element of chance in heredity. One person may show the character while his brothers and sisters do not. By examining the parents in any particular family and fitting them to the inheritance prediction chart we can see that the distribution of polydactylism among the children follows the expected ratios rather closely, but pure chance determines the movement of genes as they are segregated in the formation of the reproductive cells.

Value of Pedigrees in Diagnosis of Disease

We all have a curiosity about the source of our inherited characteristics and family pedigrees give us the opportunity to satisfy that curiosity. There are times, however, when family pedigrees have a value which is much greater than the satis-faction of curiosity. Heredity plays an important part in many diseases and an accurate knowledge of family pedigrees can sometimes be of great value to a physician in the diagnosis and treatment of various body abnormalities. In many cases diagnosis can be made more accurately through a study of one's family history than through elaborate and expensive laboratory tests. Also, it is possible to avoid serious mistakes in some instances. This can best be illustrated by actual cases.

Dr. Madge Macklin, who is a specialist in medical genetics at the Ohio State Medical School, reports a case of a child who was brought to a doctor for treatment. The child had a very dry skin, sparse hair, poorly developed teeth, and a tendency to become feverish upon the slightest exertion. Hypo-thyroidism (undersecretion of the thyroid gland) results in such symptoms, and the child's condition was thus diagnosed. She was put on thyroid medication, but this treatment seemed to aggravate the condition. Another doctor was called in on the case who had had training in the principles of heredity in relation to disease. He made a study of the child's family history and constructed a pedigree. From this he found that one of the parents and a number of the other relatives showed similar, but less severe symptoms, and he recognized the disease as an inherited condition known as *ectodermal dysplasia.* Among the symptoms of this disease is an absence of normal sweat glands. In normal people the body is cooled through the evaporation of perspiration from the skin, but in persons without normal perspiration the body is easily overheated. The administration of thyroxin was the worst sort of treatment because this hormone speeds body metabolism which increases the heat output. This case shows how, through pedigree analysis, a disease may be diagnosed when the symptoms might indicate some other type of abnormality.

Another case is reported by Lawrence Snyder, the great medical geneticist at the University of Hawaii. A young man developed a serious affliction which involved spasmodic facial contortions which were very embarrassing and which also barred him from any professions which required contact with the public. A doctor diagnosed the condition as *tic douloureux,* which is a type of neuralgia that can be corrected in some instances by a delicate operation on a facial nerve. Before arranging for this operation, however, the doctor consulted another physician, who recalled that there were a number of cases of diabetes in the family of the afflicted man. Realizing that the facial contortions might be an unusual manifestation of diabetic neuritis, the consulting physician examined the patient for diabetes. These tests were positive and the patient began taking insulin as a treatment for diabetes. Soon the *tic* disappeared and the patient was saved a serious and expensive operation which would have been useless.

Family pedigrees may also have value in preventive medicine. In some cases it is possible to anticipate the development of a disease and to take appropriate steps to prevent its occurrence. A person with a family history of tuberculosis might take precautions against infection which would not be necessary for one without such a pedigree. Also, every effort might be made for early recognition of such infection and steps could be taken for the eradication of the disease before it developed fully.

There is an inherited type of anemia known as *hemolytic icterus* which furnishes an excellent example of the importance of family pedigrees in preventive medicine. During the early stages of this disease the red blood cells are abnormal in shape and extremely fragile. Later there may be a greatly enlarged spleen which removes abnormally large numbers of red blood cells from the blood. This results in serious anemia, and sometimes death. It is due to the presence of a dominant gene so about one-half of the children of a person with this condition will be expected to show the same abnormality. It is wise, therefore, to examine the blood of all children of afflicted parents in order that early symptoms of the disease may be detected. Should these symptoms be found, the spleen should be removed as a preventive measure. Snyder tells of a man who died of the disease and who had two sons showing the early symptoms of it. One was operated on and the spleen removed as a precautionary measure. The other refused to have the operation since, as he put it, he "felt sound as a dollar." A number of years later, however, this man developed the advanced form of the disease and was operated on, but it was too late—he died before his body could recover from the anemia which he had developed.

Family Pedigrees in Marriage Counseling

To those who counsel others on problems relating to marriage and childbearing, a use of family pedigrees is of great value. Prospective parents who exhibit some abnormality want to know the chances of the abnormality appearing in their children. Parents are equally interested in the possible transmission of desirable traits such as musical ability, mathematical aptitude, or attractive facial features. To answer such questions intelligently, one must usually make a study of family pedigrees, for there are many characteristics which can result from different causes. In one family there may be an abnormality which was caused by an embryonic accident which has nothing to do with heredity. In another family there may be an abnormality which is similar, but which is inherited. In some cases it is possible to distinguish between the two only by studies of the family histories.

CHAPTER 15

BLOOD WILL TELL

We all know that the patterns of fingerprints are so varied and so distinctive that it is possible to pick a criminal out of thousands of suspects solely on the basis of a fingerprint left in a compromising place at the scene of a crime. Perhaps you did not know, however, that blood may be almost as distinctive as fingerprints. If we take samples of blood from a number of different people and look at it in test tubes and under the microscope, we usually can see no difference. It is all thick and red, and contains red blood cells and white blood cells in addition to a clear liquid known as plasma. When these samples are tested for the presence of certain substances known as antigens, however, we find that there are differences. Antigens make no difference in the appearance of the blood, but they can make a great difference in its reaction with other blood. There are so many possible differences in antigen composition that there actually can be millions of different combinations of blood characteristics. Hence, it may be that some day blood samples will be used to establish identification as a supplement to the present method of fingerprint analysis.

The antigens of the blood are inherited and blood tests may be valuable in establishing the facts in cases of disputed parentage. Persons who have certain blood antigens can have children with only certain blood antigens. The old saying, "Blood will tell" was never truer than it is today.

174

Discovery of the Blood Types

In the body of a person of average size there circulates about five quarts of that precious body fluid known as blood. Blood is actually a liquid tissue, but being liquid it may be lost from the body in large quantities when a major blood vessel is cut. It is so vital to life that a loss of as much as three pints at one time is likely to result in death. Man has long recognized the vital nature of blood and crude attempts at blood transfusion to prevent death from excessive bleeding were made as early as the eighteenth century in France and England. Some of these were successful—men with dueling wounds which normally would have resulted in death from bleeding were saved by passing blood directly into their veins through metal tubes leading from the veins of other men. In other cases, however, the transfusions were made in the same way, but the persons receiving the blood died in agony.

It was noted that when blood from two different persons was mixed in a container outside the body, it was found to mix smoothly in some cases, but in other cases the blood cells would stick together in clumps and separate from the clear plasma of the blood much like milk when curdled with acid. This variation in reaction remained a puzzle for many years and proved to be a barrier against the widespread use of blood transfusions until the answer was found at about the beginning of the present century. At that time a man named Landsteiner made a very revealing series of studies on human blood. He removed the blood cells from the plasma and on some occasions recombined these two elements of the blood. He noted that a smooth combination always resulted when the cells were recombined with their own plasma, but when plasma from one person was mixed with cells from another person, the mixture would sometimes be smooth and sometimes there would be a clumping of the cells. By further experimentation along these lines he discovered the blood types. At first these

were designated by Roman numerals, but today the letter
system is used almost universally. By this system there are
four primary blood types, O, A, B, and AB, and all persons
fall into one of the four groups. But what do these letters
mean and just exactly what is the difference between the
blood types?

Inheritance of the Blood Types

The letters stand for substances, technically known as
antigens, which may be present in the red blood cells. There
are two antigens in this series, designated as A and B. A
person is typed according to the presence or absence of these
antigens. If you happen to have red blood cells which contain
neither of the antigens you are type O. If your cells contain
the A antigen then you are type A. If they contain the B
antigen you are type B. If they contain both of these antigens
then your type is known as AB. This much is simple.

Next, you may want to know where these antigens come
from. The answer is simple—they are inherited just as other
body characteristics are inherited. There is a gene which
produces the A antigen, a gene which produces the B antigen,
and a gene which does not produce either antigen. Now, if
you get two of this last type of gene, one from either parent,
then you will be blood type O. On the other hand, if you
receive a gene for antigen A from one parent then you will
have this antigen in your red blood cells regardless of what
the gene received from the other parent may be. The same
is true of B. Hence, if you receive a gene for A from one
parent and a gene for B from the other you will have both
antigens and will be blood type AB. This system of inheritance of the blood types is shown diagramatically in Table I.
From this chart it is easy to determine what types of children
can be born of any union.

TABLE I

TYPES OF CHILDREN WHICH PARENTS OF DIFFERENT BLOOD GROUP COMBINATIONS CAN HAVE

Blood groups of parents			Possible blood groups of children
O	X	O	O
O	X	A	O, A
O	X	B	O, B
O	X	AB	A, B
A	X	A	O, A
A	X	B	O, A, B, AB
A	X	AB	A, B, AB
B	X	B	O, B
B	X	AB	A, B, AB
AB	X	AB	A, B, AB

Incompatible Blood

This does not explain the incompatibility of blood, however. This is caused by substances which may be present in blood plasma. These substances are known as antibodies, and they are the villains that cause the trouble when different types of blood are mixed. For instance, if you are blood type A, then you will also have antibodies which will react with the B antigen (anti-B). Type B persons, on the other hand, will have antibodies which will react with the A antigen (anti-A). Hence, if these two bloods are mixed there will be a terrific reaction and the blood cells will form in large clumps as a result of the mixing of antigens and antibodies which are antagonistic. The complete structure of the blood with respect to antigens and antibodies is shown in Fig. 23. The antibodies, anti-A and anti-B are inherited along with the antigens. So far as we know these are the only antibodies which can be inherited. We can develop others when we are exposed to foreign antigens, but we are not born with them.

Blood is always typed before transfusions are given in order to prevent the infusion of a blood which will bring about the clumping of red cells within a person's blood stream.

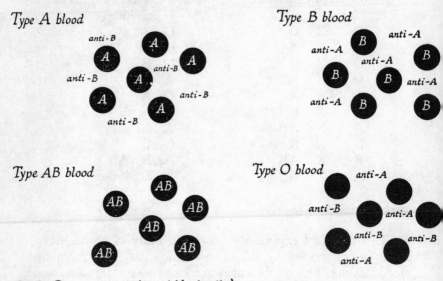

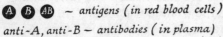

A B AB – antigens (in red blood cells)
anti-A, anti-B – antibodies (in plasma)

Fig. 23. Antigens and antibodies present in each of the four blood types. The white circles represent the red blood cells which contain the antigens and the black space in between represents the plasma which contains the antibodies.

(From Winchester, GENETICS, Houghton, Mifflin)

Table II shows the different types of blood which can be used for transfusions for each of the four major blood types. It can be seen from this table that it is possible to give a person blood of a different type, as long as this blood does not contain cells which will clump when they contact the plasma of the person receiving the transfusion. The antibodies in the plasma being

used for the transfusion are rather quickly diluted below the
danger point by the plasma that is already in the body so
these do not cause major difficulties. Because of this, it is
possible to give any plasma to anyone without typing, but
before any blood cells are infused we must test them carefully.
In actual practice, when it is available, blood which is the same
type as the recipient's is used in transfusions.

TABLE II

BLOOD GROUP TRANSFUSION TABLE

Blood group	Can give transfusion to:	Can receive transfusion from:
O	O A B AB	O
A	A AB	O A
B	B AB	O B
AB	AB	O A B AB

Thus we see that blood can actually be a fatal liquid.
Perhaps you never thought of it before, but the same blood
that now circulates through your blood vessels could cause
some other persons to die a violent death if only a little of
it were put in their veins. It is all human blood—it all looks
alike—it all performs the same functions; yet, there is an
insidious difference in the antigens and antibodies which may
make blood a deadly thing when transferred from one body
to another.

The question is often asked, "Which blood type is best?"
Well, as far as the efficiency of the blood in performing its
tasks in transporting materials within the body is concerned,
there is no apparent difference. It is only when transfusions
are needed that the nature of your blood type is of importance.
However, a recent report indicates that persons with type A
blood may have stomach cancer more often than those with
other blood types. Studies in the London area and in Sweden
both show a higher proportion of A blood types among the
patients who have stomach cancer than there is among the

general population of these areas. This is a preliminary report, but, if the finding proves to be correct, it may be that we will find that the antigens and antibodies have some effect on the body which we have not yet detected.

The Rh Factor

When a woman is going to have a baby nowadays it is common practice for the attending physician to determine whether she and her husband are Rh positive or Rh negative. Women have had children for centuries without knowing anything about the Rh factor—why should it be so important today? It has been found that many of the unexplained infant deaths which have occurred were due to a particular combination of the Rh factor in the inheritance. When a potentially dangerous combination is discovered today, it is possible to take precautions to save the baby's life.

Just what is the Rh factor? We know that it is a protein substance (antigen) which is found in the blood of all rhesus monkeys, as well as in some people. But what possible effect can this factor have on a newborn baby? To clarify its effects, let us digress for a moment and consider some interesting reactions in guinea pigs.

Suppose we use a hypodermic needle and inject a teaspoon of egg albumen (egg white) into the body of a guinea pig. We know that there is nothing poisonous about the white of an egg (most of us eat some every day without any ill effects) and we would not expect it to harm the guinea pig. This proves to be the case. If we wait about ten days and then give the guinea pig a second injection, however, the reaction will be quite different. This time it is likely that he will begin quivering as soon as the injection is completed and within a few minutes will go into convulsions and die.

What happened during this ten days that made the guinea pig react so violently? We gave him the same type injection both times; some change must have occurred in his body in between the two. Scientifically, we say that the guinea pig became sensitized, or became allergic, to the egg albumen after the first injection. If you become sensitized or allergic to the pollen of ragweed, then, when you inhale its pollen, your nose itches and becomes swollen inside and we say that you have hay fever. Something like this takes place in the guinea pig. The antigen in the egg albumen causes him to develop antibodies against it so that there is a violent reaction between the two on the second injection.

Now, to get back to the Rh factor. A number of years ago some scientists injected monkey blood cells into guinea pigs which caused them to become sensitized. Then, when clear plasma from the guinea pig's blood was mixed with the monkey blood, the red blood cells of the monkey blood clumped together in tight little balls. The antigen in the monkey red cells which caused this reaction was called the "Rh" factor from the first letters of the word Rhesus. When they mixed human blood with the sensitized guinea pig serum they found that the cells of some persons would clump (thus indicating the presence of the Rh factor) while the cells of others would not clump. They decided to call those who contained this factor, Rh positive and those whose cells lacked the factor, Rh negative.

Then it was discovered that people who did not have the Rh factor (Rh negative) could become sensitized to it just like the guinea pigs. For instance, if a person was Rh negative and was given a blood transfusion from an Rh positive person there would be no complications if this was the first such transfusion, but antibodies would develop which would sensitize the recipient of the blood. Later, if a second transfusion of positive blood were given, the cells with the Rh factor would clump and death would result. Hence, it is common practice to test blood for the Rh factor as well as the ABO types before giving a transfusion.

Maternal Complications Due to Rh Factor

There may also be maternal complications because of the Rh factor. The Rh antigen is inherited in a manner similar to the A and B antigens. There is a gene for it and if we get

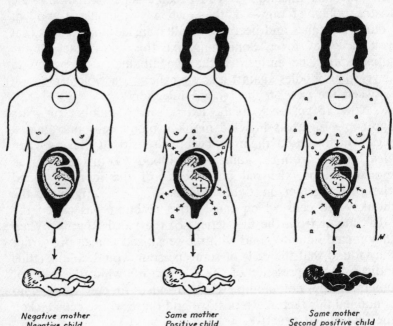

Negative mother
Negative child
Baby normal

Same mother
Positive child
Baby normal
Mother sensitized

Same mother
Second positive child
Baby born with
erythroblastosis

Fig. 24.   Maternal complications caused by the Rh factor. These
diagrams show three successive pregnancies of a negative woman
married to a positive man. The first child is negative like the
mother and all goes well. The second child inherits the positive
gene from the father and has the Rh antigens in its blood. This
sensitizes the mother's blood and causes her to produce Rh antibodies (a). In the third pregnancy the child is also positive. The
antibodies from the mother's blood seep into the embryo and
interfere with its normal blood production. It is born with
erythroblastosis.

(From Winchester, BIOLOGY, Van Nostrand)

this gene from either parent we are Rh positive. If we get the recessive gene, which does not produce this antigen, from both parents then we will be Rh negative. Thus, a person can be Rh positive and yet carry the recessive gene for the Rh negative. A man and his wife may both be positive and yet have some negative children if they both carry this recessive gene.

There is one type of marriage which is potentially dangerous from the standpoint of the children who may be conceived. This is when the man is positive and the woman is negative. At least half, and perhaps all, of the children of such a marriage will be positive (all, if the man carries two of the dominant genes for the Rh factor). In such marriages the negative woman may carry a positive child in her body for about nine months. Normally, the blood from the embryo does not enter the mother's body and there are no difficulties, but in many cases there may be a seepage of some of the blood from child to mother during the latter stages of pregnancy, when the weight of the embryo and its movements may cause small ruptures in the membranes which separate it from the mother. Enough of the embryo's blood may seep into the mother's body to cause her to produce antibodies against the Rh factor. This does not develop in time to cause any trouble at this pregnancy and this child will not be harmed. Future pregnancies, however, may result in trouble. When the second positive child develops in this negative woman, who is now sensitive to the Rh factor, there can be a diffusion of the antibodies from the mother's plasma into the child. This can cause serious abnormalities in the development of the red blood cells of the child and he may be born dead, or he may die a few days after birth because of this. The doctor will say that the child has erythroblastosis. If the doctors expect this, however, they can often save the baby's life by giving blood transfusions after birth. Also, some physicians have found that most of the damage is done to the child during the last month within its mother's body; therefore, if the child is delivered at the eighth month, instead of the ninth, it has a much better chance of survival. If the mother has received a transfusion of positive blood at some time before her first pregnancy then she will already be sensitized and the trouble may come at this first birth.

Accentuate the Negative

About eighty-five per cent of the people of the United States are Rh positive and the remaining fifteen per cent are Rh negative. This means that the negative woman has the odds against her when she selects a husband. There is the interesting case of one enterprising young lady who was a technician in a large hospital. She checked her own Rh factor and found it to be negative. Having learned something about the complications that could come if she married a positive man, she decided to take some action about it. Whenever she typed a man's blood at the hospital and it proved to be negative she made it a point to investigate and to become acquainted with the patient if he turned out to be an eligible male. Eventually, she actually married one of the men whom she selected in this way.

It would hardly be advisable for girls to place so much emphasis on this problem; however, while minimizing other factors which would enter into a successful marriage. For one thing, there is never any danger with the first child (barring previous transfusions, of course). It is only after the woman has borne one positive child that she must be careful. Then we should remember that the negative woman is not sensitized each time a positive child is born. It may be that there will not be sufficient blood seepage to cause the development of antibodies. Often negative women can bear several positive children without becoming sensitized. It is possible for a physician to test her blood for the presence of these antibodies and if they are present he can plan to take steps to prevent the fatal effect. Thus, the average negative woman can look forward to a perfectly normal and uncomplicated married life with a positive man.

Mixed Babies and False Fathers

According to the Biblical records, King Solomon, with all his glory, had his problems. At one time he was called upon to decide a case of disputed parentage. Two women claimed to be the mother of the same child and he was asked to decide who was the true mother. He decreed that they should cut the child in two and give half to each woman; however, at this point the true mother interceded and asked that the entire child be given to the other woman. Thus, Solomon solved the case satisfactorily, but had he known of blood types he might have had an easier time of it. The inheritance of blood types is so definite that it can be of great value in legal cases of disputed parentage.

A modern case of this nature came to light recently in a court trial. A young couple had taken what they supposed to be their baby home from the hospital, only to discover a tag on the child bearing the name of another woman who had borne a child on the same day. This second woman had also taken a baby home from the hospital, but she felt that she had her own child and would not consent to an exchange. You can well imagine the mental anguish which was suffered by the first couple who faced the prospect that their own child might be brought up in another home, while they would be forced to rear a child not their own. Fortunately, however, it was possible to settle the dispute by blood typing. The first baby was type O, but the couple who took this baby home from the hospital were O and AB. It would not have been possible for this couple to have a child with this blood type. The second couple had a baby with type A blood, but both parents were O. When it was proved to them that this could not be their baby, but the other one could, they were agreeable to making the exchange and everyone was satisfied.

There have been cases where such mix-ups have not been discovered so early. Dr. Weiner, who has conducted extensive studies on the blood types, relates a case in Switzerland. A father of twin boys, as his sons began to grow, was somewhat puzzled that two children born at the same time could be so different in both physical features and in temperament. When his twins were five years old this man was watching a Boy Scout parade when he saw a boy in the parade that looked amazingly like one of his twin boys. He learned who the boy was and found that this boy had been born at the same hospital and at the same time as his twins. Suspecting a possible mix-up, he asked for a blood test of the boys and the parents involved. These were first made for the ABO blood types, but this proved nothing for it happened that both sets of parents had types that could result in the types of all three boys in question. When tests were made for the Rh factor, however, it was found that there definitely had been a mix-up at the hospital and the courts of Switzerland ordered the proper exchange to be made.

When a woman bears a child there is no question about the fact that she is the true mother. As to the father, however, there sometimes may be a doubt. Paternity cases are among the hardest legal problems for the courts to rule on. A woman may sue a man for support of her child born out of wedlock claiming that he is the father—a man may sue his wife for divorce claiming that she bore a child by another man—a woman may sue for divorce from her husband claiming that he fathered a child by another woman. These are typical of the thousands of cases involving disputed paternity which come before the courts each year. Before the discovery of the system of the inheritance of blood types, the courts were forced to rely on evidence of sexual relationships between the mother of the child and the man in question at about the time conception occurred. Such evidence, even if proved, was at best only circumstantial in nature, since it is quite possible that the woman had relationships with more than one man during the period when conception could have occurred.

Today, however, there is much less likelihood of miscarried justice than there was a few years ago. At this writing there is only one state in the United States that does not accept blood-type inheritance as positive evidence. That state is California, which was unfortunate in the case of a well-known motion picture actor. A young woman resident of that state was suing the actor for the support of a child that had been born to her. The evidence of sexual relationships between the two was quite definitely established, but when the blood was typed it was found that the baby had type B, the mother had type A, and the actor had type O. This showed that he could not have been the father, but, since such evidence is not binding in California, a clever lawyer convinced the jury that there was some possibility of error and they ruled that the actor should support the child.

Sometimes it is said that blood typing may prove that a man is not the father of a child, but that it cannot prove that he is. We know that a child cannot show blood antigens unless they are present in at least one parent. Therefore, if the child has an antigen (such as the Rh factor or the A antigen), but the mother does not have this antigen, and the accused father does not have it, then it stands to reason that he could not be the father. On the other hand, it may be that the man is not the father, but he may happen to have the antigens which would be present in the true father. If this is the case, we can only say that the man might have been the father.

As we learn more about the blood antigens, however, there is a smaller and smaller chance that a man will happen to have the antigens of the father unless he is truly the father. For instance, it is possible to separate the A antigen into two groups and the Rh antigens into a rather large number of subtypes. Then, new antigens are being discovered all the time. There are now M and N antigens, an S factor, and a P factor; all of which can be used to narrow down the field of possible fathers. In fact, so many antigens have been discovered that there are now over eight million possible combinations of them. That is the reason we said at the beginning of the chapter that blood characteristics may be just as distinctive as your fingerprints.

Blood and Race

The different races of man have distinctive features of face and body which are easily recognized. The blood antigens of the different races also show racial distinctions which can be recognized by statistical studies of the blood. Take the Rh antigen, for instance. About 85 per cent of the white people of the United States have the Rh factor in their blood (are Rh positive), but if you test full-blooded natives of the Philippines for this factor you will find that all are Rh positive and none are Rh negative. On the other hand, if you test the blood of the Basques, who represent an isolated racial group in the Western Pyrenees region of France and Spain, you will find only 70 per cent with the Rh factor. These variations are also found among the other blood antigens. Only about 10 per cent of the white Americans have type B blood, but in Thailand about 35 per cent of the people have this blood type. Table III shows the percentages of some of the blood antigens in different races.

TABLE III

PERCENTAGE OF BLOOD ANTIGENS IN VARIOUS PEOPLES OF THE WORLD

Population Group	Percentage of Antigens					
	O	A	B	AB	Rh neg.	Rh pos.
Amer. Indians (Utes)	97.4	2.6	0	0	0	100
Australian Aborigines	42.6	57.4	0	0	0	100
Basques (Spain)	57.2	41.7	1.1	0	30	70
English	47.9	42.4	8.3	1.4	15.3	84.7
Polynesians (Hawaii)	36.5	60.8	2.2	.5	—	—
French	39.8	42.3	11.8	6.1	17.0	83.0
Germans	36.5	42.5	14.5	6.5	—	—
Italians	45.9	33.4	17.3	3.4	—	—
Japanese	30.1	38.4	21.9	9.7	1.3	98.7
Russians	31.9	34.4	24.9	8.8	—	—
Chinese	34.4	30.8	27.7	7.3	1.5	98.5
Javanese	30.4	24.7	37.3	7.6	—	—
U. S. A. (white)	47.0	40.0	10.0	3.0	15.0	85.0

With such figures it is possible to trace racial origins and racial blending. The distribution of the Rh factor in Europe indicates that the population once had a rather high number of Rh negative persons, but that the invading Mongols from the east brought in a large number of genes for the Rh factor. The Basques, however, were somewhat isolated by the Pyrenees and seemed to escape this invasion and the proportion of Rh negative people is still high. Thus, blood typing is helping to solve many problems of the anthropologists who have been studying various evidences for many years to unravel the riddle of the races of man.

This study is aided by the discovery that it is possible to determine the antigens present in the dried remains of people who have been dead for many centuries. Ancient Egyptian mummies, the remains of persons who lived thousands of years before blood types were known, have had their blood types determined by an analysis of dried bits of tissue from their bodies. The same has been done with mummies of American Indians. The antigens resist heating, drying, and the ravages of time and provide us with valuable clues to racial ancestry. By comparing the proportions of the various antigens in these dried remains with the blood types of the races of the same regions today it is possible to determine relationships between the ancient and modern inhabitants of the regions.

Have you ever wondered to what extent the Negroes of the United States are like the Negroes who were brought from Africa in past centuries? We know that there has been some mixing of white and Negro genes, but how much? Again blood type studies promise to answer this important racial question. Dr. Bently Glass and others of Johns Hopkins University have made a careful study of the degree of blending of the Negro and white races in the United States through blood antigen percentages. First, they took the percentage of the different antigens in the white Americans and compared that with the percentage of these same antigens in the African Negroes. As expected, there were distinctive differences between these two groups. Then they determined the percentages of these antigens in the Negroes of the Unitd States. From the samples which they studied they concluded that these Negroes had about 25 per cent of their genes from the white race. In other words, only about three-fourths of the genes in these American Negroes were the same as those brought by their ancestors from Africa. The other one-fourth of their genes have come from the white people through racial blending. This study was made primarily from Negroes in the Baltimore region and would not necessarily hold true for those living in other sections of the United States.

CHAPTER 16

WHEN GENES GO WRONG

At about the middle of the last century two young brothers, let us call them Jan and Hans, migrated to the state of Minnesota. They left behind them a family record tainted with defectives and hoped to escape the stigma associated with their family in this new environment. They changed their family name and did well in this land of new opportunities. They both married and in time children were born—ten to each brother. All appeared to be fine, healthy children. At last, it seemed as if the chain of family defects had been broken—here with a new name and a new environment they had cast off the traits that had plagued their ancestry. But they reckoned without the insidious nature of gene operation. While in his midthirties Jan began to have trouble with the muscles in his arms and legs. At times they would begin involuntary twitchings which he could not control. This became progressively worse until muscles all over the body were affected and the twitchings kept up continuously. Soon he was so helpless that he could not even hold a spoon in his hand to feed himself. Worst of all, his mind began to fail and in the course of time he was a shaking, helpless, mentally defective man. He was sent to a mental institution where he died at the age of forty-two.

The Curse of the Gene

This is a typical case of Huntington's chorea which is a disease that comes to those who receive a certain dominant gene from one of their parents. The gene will remain dormant during babyhood, childhood, adolescence and the twenties, but typically in the early thirties it begins to make its influence felt—damaging the nerves of the body more seriously than the worst germ diseases. Tragic muscular twitching, mental deterioration, and early death result.

Jan's children matured, married, and became parents, but the curse of the gene went with them. Four of his children developed the familiar muscular twitchings in their early thirties and ended their lives in the same tragic manner that characterized their father's demise, but only after they had propagated children with the same gene. Down through the generations this gene has taken its ruthless toll. Nineteen times the terrible disease has struck and among Jan's 716 living descendants it will surely strike many times more as the younger ones in this group reach the fateful age. A study of this family pedigree shows that approximately 101 of these living descendants can be expected to succumb to the deadly influence of this gene. It is not possible, however, to state specifically which ones have it and which have escaped by a study of the pedigree alone.

Hans was more fortunate—he did not receive the gene and there is no trace of Huntington's chorea among his descendants, although he has only 167 living descendants in contrast to the 716 of his brother. Since the gene for this condition is dominant it cannot be carried without causing the affliction, so the descendants of the unafflicted persons will also be unafflicted. On the other hand, those so unfortunate as to have a father or mother who develops this disease have a fifty-fifty chance of having it themselves. You can well imagine the mental anguish these people must suffer when they learn the method of inheritance of an affliction which destroyed one of their parents and realize the heavy odds they face. Their apprehension can be alleviated in some cases. Recent studies have been made which indicate that it is possible to detect those persons who will develop Huntington's chorea by means of an instrument known as the electroencephalograph. This instrument records the pattern of brain waves on a graph and certain deflections from the normal indicate the presence of this gene long before the muscular twitchings begin. Such a test would allow those who are free of the gene to marry and have children secure in the knowledge that the family would not be married by the disease. When the gene is found to be present, certainly reproduction would be out of the question.

Outlaw Genes

Just as in human populations we find some individuals who go wrong and become outlaws, we also find that among the many genes that carry on normal, constructive processes in the building of human bodies there are some genes that go wrong and are destructive in their effects. The gene which causes Huntington's chorea is a good example of such an outlaw gene. Since we have no way to prune them out of the family tree, as we would prune rotten limbs from a fruit tree, they continue through the generations leaving a trail of misery and destruction behind them. There is no tragedy on earth to equal that of the heart-rending grief that comes to a mother and father when they find their joy in new parenthood blackened by the influence of one of these outlaw genes on a newborn baby.

No part of the body is exempt from the harmful effects of outlaw genes. The fingers may be fused as they form to give a clawlike structure rather than a normal hand—eyes may be formed with a pigment over the retina which causes blindness—teeth may be formed which are so soft that they quickly wear down to the gums—the long bones of the arms and legs may be shortened and deformed—blood may be produced which fails to clot normally—the brain may be defective in its organization and a paralysis or mental abnormality will result. These are but a few of the hundreds of known defects which plague the human race as a result of the action of outlaw genes.

When we survey the many hereditary defects which may occur, we may sometimes wonder how any of us manage to get a gene complex which forms a normal body. As a matter of fact, few of us would escape the damage done by these outlaw genes were not most of them recessive in nature. Nearly all of us carry several genes which come in this category of outlaws, but we are protected from their action by dominant genes which produce a normal body. We must realize, however, that there is always the danger that these outlaw genes may find expression in the children of normal parents if both

Outlaw Genes

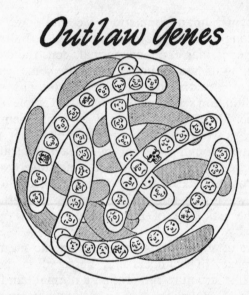

Fig. 25.   Scattered among the many benign and beneficial genes on the chromosomes there are almost certain to be several outlaw genes in every person. Here we represent the genes as human faces; see if you can tell which are intended to be outlaw genes.

parents carry the same outlaw genes. You may have three recessive outlaw genes—let us say, a gene for a defective heart, a gene for deafness, and a gene for stiff fingers. Your marriage partner may also have three recessive outlaw genes—for instance, one gene for bad kidneys, one for crooked vertebrae, and one for blindness. Neither of you shows any of the effects of these genes because each of you carries a dominant gene for each of the recessive outlaws. These dominant genes are like the policemen that stand on the corner and prevent human outlaws from carrying out their evil intents. You may have a dozen children and all will be normal because each of you furnishes a dominant gene to hold the outlaw genes of the other in check. A recessive outlaw gene, like all recessive genes, must come from *both* parents in order to be expressed. If your wife, or husband, should die, and you married a second person who perhaps carried an outlaw gene in common with you, then you could be the parent of a defective child. For instance, your partner might carry the gene for deafness, and should this gene for deafness happen to combine with your gene for deafness when the sperm and egg unite you would produce a deaf child. The developing embryo lacks the protection of a dominant gene for normal hearing and the outlaw genes have their way as human outlaws, too, have their way when the policeman is removed from duty.

A relatively small percentage of the outlaw genes are dominant, such as the one for Huntington's chorea, but these are sometimes better known because they show in all persons who carry one of these genes and in approximately half of their children. The recessive outlaw genes, on the other hand, may be carried for many generations before they are able to express themselves.

Killer Genes

Among the outlaw genes there is one group that deserves special consideration. They are the ones that produce such pronounced defects of the human body that death comes to those who express the defects. These killer genes, or lethal genes, as they are called by the geneticists, are never dominant for the simple reason that they could never be carried by a living person if they were dominant. Hence, they must be carried by both parents and come together in a child in order to carry out their deadly influence. To illustrate, supposing a man carries a recessive gene which causes internal adhesions of the lungs. He marries a woman who carries the same recessive killer gene. Both have perfectly normal lungs since they each have dominant genes also which arrest the killers. The woman becomes pregnant and everything goes along normally without any indication of impending disaster, for the embryo does not use its lungs as long as it is in the mother's body. The day for the birth arrives and as the baby is suddenly cut loose from the cord which has supplied him with life-giving oxygen since his earliest beginnings, he dies of suffocation because his lungs cannot expand properly. The killer genes have had their way.

Undaunted by this tragedy the couple may have other children who may have normal lungs because they do not happen to inherit the combination of two of these killer genes. Unfortunately, however, some of these children will carry the killer gene which may be expressed in future generations. Whenever two people marry who carry this same recessive killer gene, about one-fourth of their children will die from its effects.

Killer genes may strike at various times during embryonic development. It depends upon when the organ, whose abnormality causes death, develops and functions. Defects of the kidneys, lungs, and digestive organs usually are not lethal until birth, for these organs do not begin functioning until then. On the other hand, genes which cause some types of heart defects would be lethal early in embryonic life, for the heart is a necessary part of the embryonic circulation and is one of the first organs of the body to begin functioning.

There is no doubt but that many of the cases of abortion and miscarriage which terminate apparently normal pregnancies are due to the action of killer genes. Whenever the embryo becomes dependent upon a vital organ which killer genes have affected, death results and the embryo is usually expelled from the woman's body. Some of these killer genes may get in their deadly effects so early in the embryonic life that death will occur before the woman is even certain that she is pregnant.

Intermediate Killers

There are a few killer genes which make their presence known when a person carries only one of them. They influence the body structure sufficiently to cause a visible effect, but are not extreme enough to cause death. Whenever one of these genes is transmitted to a child from each parent, however, the

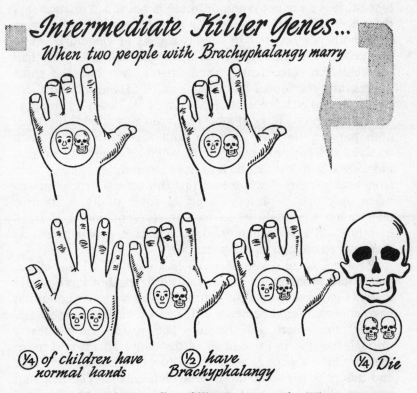

Intermediate Killer Genes...
When two people with Brachyphalangy marry

(¼) *of children have normal hands*   (½) *have Brachyphalangy*   (¼) *Die*

Fig. 26. How intermediate killer genes work. When a person receives one of these genes he has very short fingers, fingers which appear to have only two joints (*brachyphalangy*). Whenever two of these genes come together, however, there are extreme skeletal deformities and the baby cannot live.

effect is so detrimental that death results. Such a gene would be classified as an intermediate gene such as those described in Chapter 8. One of these intermediate killers causes the fingers and toes to be abnormally short, as shown in Fig. 26 when only one of them is present in a person. It appears as if there are only two joints to the fingers because the middle joint is abnormally shortened and is fused to one of the other bones. The condition is known medically as brachyphalangy. Since this gene is not common there is not much chance that there will be an opportunity for a child to receive the gene from both parents, but there was a case in Denmark where two people with this type of short fingers married. They had four children. One had normal fingers, two had the short fingers, and the fourth had no fingers or toes at all and there were other skeletal defects that caused its death in infancy. The child who died, no doubt, received this outlaw gene from both parents, the two children with the short fingers each received it from only one parent, while the one with normal fingers was fortunate enough to have received the normal gene from both parents. Thus, we see that this gene is strong enough when only one is present to get in some of its destructive effects, but it is only when two are present and it is freed of inhibition from the normal gene that it produces effects pronounced enough to cause death.

If a doctor told you that you had multiple telangiectasis, you would probably be scared half to death, but there would really be no great cause for alarm. Persons with this condition have abnormal enlargements of the blood vessels of the nose, tongue, lips, face, and fingers. The vessels show clearly through the skin in these areas of the body. This would mean that you have a gene in your make-up which causes this effect and this gene is one of the intermediate killers. The fact that you are alive shows that you carry only one of them, but if you should marry a person like yourself then this killer gene's nature could be expressed. Any child which you bore who received this gene from each of you would show an extreme enlargement of the blood vessels in the regions mentioned above and some of them would rupture and cause the death of the child within a few months after birth.

Genes That Kill Only Under Certain Conditions

Like Dr. Jekyll and Mr. Hyde, there are some genes that are perfectly harmless under one set of conditions, but in certain other circumstances they become killers. Take the gene for the Rh factor, for instance. There is a very good chance that you have this gene among the thousands of genes that make up your inheritance, for about 85 per cent of the people in the United States have it. In your body it does no harm— it just goes on producing the Rh factor in your red blood cells which makes them neither better nor worse than cells without it. Under certain circumstances, however, this gene can be a killer. Suppose, for instance that a woman does not have this gene, but she becomes sensitized to the Rh factor. The gene for the Rh factor will then become a killer when it is present in a child which this woman bears. The seemingly innocent gene which so many of us carry thus becomes a vicious outlaw that causes a violent disruption in the production of red blood cells of the embryo and usually the child is born dead or dies shortly after birth unless drastic steps are taken.

Then, let us take the gene for albinism. Persons who receive one of these from each parent fail to develop the pigment melanin in their hair, eyes, and skin. In a protected civilization such persons are not greatly handicapped and can live normal lives. There are conditions, however, under which the gene for this characteristic could be a killer. Albinos cannot produce the pigment which acts as a protection from the injurious effects of sunlight. Hence, if albinos were forced to live in an environment where there was extensive exposure to the sunlight, there would be such an extensive burning of the skin that death would result.

Along this same line there are some genes which are killers under normal conditions, but which can be prevented from performing their grim task if conditions are altered. There is one gene that causes an extreme sensitivity of the skin to light, a condition known as xeroderma pigmentosum. A baby that inherits the genes for this condition will be born with normal skin, but exposure even to such light as would come into a room through the windows causes the development of a severe rash on the skin. In time, certain regions of this rash become malignant and death nearly always results. If, at the first sign of the rash, however, the child were taken to a darkened place with only a rather weak artificial light and raised there it could survive. This would be an extreme measure, to be sure, but is one way to thwart the killer gene by altering conditions.

CHAPTER 17

BLOOD MATINGS

The term, blood mating, is used to refer to the mixing of
genes of closely related individuals. Such matings have special
significance from the standpoint of inheritance.

Incestual Relationships

Each year thousands of babies are born in the United
States as a result of unions between such closely related individuals as brother and sister, father and daughter, or son and
mother. Most of us experience a natural repugnance at the
very thought of these unions which violate all of our senses
of decency and morality. Usually it is only among certain
depraved persons who form the bottommost dregs of our
society that such matings occur. Cases can be found, however,
among the better classes of our society; for instance, in the
brother-sister mating described later in this chapter. Among
the numerous ethnic groups of people on the earth, there are
some which condone sexual promiscuity to a greater or lesser
degree, but the line of sanction ends with the mating of very
closely related persons.

201

In most civilized countries an attempt is made to prevent blood matings by prohibiting marriage between closely related persons, the so-called consanguineous marriages. In the United States no man can legally marry his sister, mother, daughter, grandmother, granddaughter, aunt, or niece. State laws in thirty of the states go further and prohibit the marriage of first cousins. As far back as we can trace legal history there have been laws placing some barrier on the degree of relationship which is permissable in marriage.

Whenever a custom or law is found so consistently among the far-flung human social groups there is usually some very good reason behind it. In ancient times we can assume that it was noticed that defective children resulted from such unions more frequently than was the case with non-related matings. Why should this be? Genes are genes—why should those causing defects be any more likely to appear among the children of closely related people than among the children of those unrelated? We shall try to find the answer in this chapter.

Raising the Odds Against the Little Gamblers

Many people have the mistaken impression that blood matings somehow or other create defective genes because of the greater abundance of defectives among the offspring of such matings. This is not true—it merely permits the expression of many outlaw genes which have been in the family all along. We learned in Chapter 16 that most of us are likely to carry several of these outlaw genes, but usually they are not expressed because most of them are recessive and must be received from both parents in order to show. When two non-related persons marry they both probably carry several of these outlaw genes, but because there are so many different kinds of them, there is not a great chance that both will carry the same outlaw genes. It is a pure and simple gamble so far as their future children are concerned. When persons of the same family line marry, however, we raise the odds in the favor of these little gamblers because there is a much greater chance that the parents will carry the same outlaw genes.

As an example, let us assume that you carry an outlaw gene which interferes with the normal calcium absorption of the bones. When this gene is expressed, the bones are so soft and flexible that it is not possible for a person so afflicted to stand, and during his entire life he is a helpless cripple, a tragic condition. You, however, have perfectly normal bones because the gene is recessive and you received a dominant gene from one of your parents which causes a normal calcium deposit. In fact, you don't even know that you carry the recessive gene. This is not a common gene, so let us assume that statistical studies indicate that one person in 20,000 carries it. Now, if you marry a person who is unrelated to you there is only one chance out of 20,000 that you will choose a person who carries this particular gene. Even though your partner did carry it, there is only one chance in four that any one child you bear would receive the outlaw gene from each of you. Thus, the odds against the little gambler with respect to the expression of this gene are 80,000 to 1. On the other hand, if you should decide to marry your first cousin the odds would be quite different. The chance that he or she would carry this same outlaw gene would be 1 in 8, and the chance that any one of your children would be afflicted would be 1 in 32. This illustrates why consanguineous marriages are more likely to produce defectives even though there is nothing about such marriages in themselves that produces genes for defectives.

When the relationship is even closer than first cousins, the chance of defectives increases. Suppose, for instance, that there is a brother-sister mating which produces a child. If the man carries the outlaw gene for defective bones then the chance that his sister also carries it is 1 in 2, and the chance that the child will show the defect is 1 in 8. The same figures hold true for father-daughter or mother-son matings. These calculations assume that the parents do not show the defective gene. In those cases where the parents show the genes, the chances would be even greater. Furthermore, these figures are for only one defective gene. Since we have brought out the point that we all probably carry several defective genes, we can see how the cards are stacked against the little gamblers when there are matings between persons closely related.

Should Cousins Marry?

While we have little difficulty with the desire for marriage among members of the same family group, the question of marriage between cousins comes up frequently. This is especially true in rural areas which are rather sparsely settled, and there is not much opportunity for wide acquaintanceship among young people. Although thirty of our states ban marriages of first cousins, the old saying, "Love will find a way" often holds true. It is always possible to go to nearby states where such a law does not exist, or to fail to mention the relationship when applying for a marriage license.

Sometimes another old saying, "Love is blind," also proves to be true. In spite of all advice to the contrary, cousins frequently persist in marrying. It is not possible, of course, to tell them with certainty that they will have defective children, for there have been many marriages of first cousins which have produced children that are perfectly normal. In fact, there is one case in history which shows that normal children can be produced even in brother-sister marriages. The ancient Ptolemies of Egypt, feeling that there were no others of such fine blood as the royal family, practiced brother-sister marriages for many generations. The famous siren of the Nile, Cleopatra, was a product of such close family inbreeding. Even she was married to her brother when they were both too young to know what it meant, but as she matured she preferred the amorous advances of visiting Romans and never lived with her brother as his wife. The records of this royal family do not indicate that any harmful qualities appeared as a result of this closest form of human inbreeding. It just happened in this case that the family was singularly free of outlaw genes which would have serious effects on the offspring.

A modern example of such inbreeding is cited by Sheldon Reed of the Dight Institute. He tells of a teen-age brother and sister who were from one of the better families of a large city. They had been brought up in such a protected environment that neither realized that there was any relation between sex and childbearing. They had had sexual relations as a result of curiosity and experimentation and the girl had become pregnant. She was sent to a maternity home and a child was born that appeared normal except for a slightly deformed clubfoot. This defect was corrected surgically, and the baby was adopted by a couple who fully understood the circumstances of the birth.

It is a difficult matter to counsel cousins who seem to be deeply in love on the advisability of marriage. They may point to successful marriages of other cousins and cannot understand why their marriage could not be equally successful. To talk in terms of increased probability of defectives means little to them, for through the rose-colored glasses of a young couple in love such tragedies could happen only to others, never to themselves. Sometimes they can better understand what is meant by increased probabilities when we can show them some specific figures. We know that about one-half of one per cent of the marriages in the United States are cousin marriages. If there were no increased chance of abnormalities among cousin marriages then we could expect about one-half of one per cent of all inherited abnormalities to come from cousin marriages. Table IV shows the actual percentages that have been found by statistical tabulation for five rather rare recessive afflictions. It can be seen from this that one-third of all children that have alkaptonuria (a defect of metabolism that causes a darkening of cartilages) have parents who are first cousins. For genes which are more frequent in the population, the percentages are somewhat less pronounced. For instance, it is only eleven per cent for total color blindness, a defect of the eye which prevents the easy distinction of all colors (the gene for this is recessive and not sex-linked as the one for red-green color blindness).

It may impress the cousins considering marriage more if we use a particular case for illustration. Let us use albinism. We know that about one person in 70 carries the recessive gene for this character. This means that the chance of any one man having the gene is 1 in 70 (provided he is not an albino and does not have albinism in his immediate family). If he marries a woman who is not related, her chance of carrying it is also 1 in 70, and the chance that both will carry it is 1 in 4,900 (70 times 70 equals 4,900). On the other hand, if this man should marry his cousin, then the chance that both will carry it is 1 in 560. (If he carries it, then her chance of carrying it is 1 in 8 and 70 times 8 equals 560.) The albino brother and sister shown in Plate XVI are the result of a cousin marriage. They have three brothers and sisters with normal pigmentation. It is obvious that we increase the chance of a defective gene of this frequency being in both parents by about ten times through cousin marriage. For less common genes there would be a greater chance, for more common genes the chance would be less. When genes are common, there is a high probability that any married couple will each carry the genes whether they are related or not. Genes for the most severe abnormalities are not common, however.

TABLE IV

PROPORTION OF INHERITED RECESSIVE ABNORMALITIES WHICH RESULT FROM COUSIN MARRIAGES
(Adapted from Reed)

DISEASE	Per cent of first cousins among the parents	Per cent expected if cousin marriage did not increase chance of the abnormality
ALKAPTONURIA	33.0	0.5
(Disease of metabolism, alcapton excreted in urine, cartilages of body may become darkened.)		
XERODERMA PIGMENTOSA	26.0	0.5
(Extreme sensitivity of skin to light, malignant growths develop on skin and usually cause premature death.)		
CONGENITAL ICTHYOSIS	24.0	0.5
(Leathery skin with deep bleeding fissures in it. Often causes stillbirth or infant death.)		
ALBINISM	17.0	0.5
(Inability to produce the pigment, melanin, in skin, hair, or eyes.)		
TOTAL COLOR BLINDNESS	11.0	0.5
(Difficult perception of all colors —not the red-green, sex-linked color blindness.)		

Most of the rather extreme abnormalities which are inherited are so infrequent that, even when the chance of their showing is multiplied by ten, as in the case of albinism, we still have a frequency so low that cousins are not likely to be perturbed about it. We should remember, however, that there are a great many inherited abnormalities and the chance for each one is increased in a cousin marriage. We brought out in Chapter 16 that every person probably carries several recessive genes for such abnormalities. If we should assume that everyone carries eight such genes then about 16 per cent of the children of cousin marriages will be defective because of these genes. If we reduce the number of harmful, recessive genes in each person to two, which is probably near the minimum, then about 4 per cent of the children will be abnormal due to heredity. This is not a high figure when compared with the average number of abnormal children produced from all marriages which statistical records of hospital births show is about 1 defective child for each 65 births, or about 1½ per cent.

These things should be understood by any cousins seeking advice about marriage. If a thorough study of their common ancestry shows a singular absence of harmful recessive traits, the odds of their children showing such defects would be lessened and they might feel encouraged to take the chance. A large number of such harmful traits, on the other hand, should serve as a warning and, if they felt that they must get married anyway, adoption might be the safest way to bring up children.

If cousins have decided to marry and take the increased chance of bearing defective children, they might be glad to know that there is a bright side to the picture. There is also an increased chance of better-than-average human traits which are due to recessive genes. While there are not as many of these recessive genes as there are recessive genes for defects, still there are some. Abraham Lincoln and Charles Darwin are examples of great men who resulted from cousin marriages. Also, there is at least one circumstance in which similar genes in a married couple are an advantage. This concerns the genes for the Rh factor. When a woman has the genes which make her Rh negative, it is an advantage for her to have a husband who has the same genes for this trait. Some hospital records show that there are 13 per cent fewer cases of Rh-induced erythroblastosis in babies born of cousin marriages. These are bright spots in an otherwise unfavorable outlook.

There is still another aspect of the problem, however, which cousins should consider before making final decision. If they live in a state where cousin marriage is forbidden there can be legal complications. If they go to another state to marry or fail to mention the relationship when applying for a license, it is possible that the marriage may be ruled illegal if the question ever comes to the courts. This could result in a number of serious problems. Jealous relatives might sue for a man's estate on the grounds that his wife was not legally his wife and, therefore, not entitled to a wife's inheritance. It is even possible that the children of such a marriage could be declared illegitimate. A man could take advantage of the situation and leave his wife on the grounds that they were never legally married. Cousins considering marriage should certainly obtain sound legal advice on the laws in the state in which they reside.

We can see that a decision about marrying a cousin is not easy. The final decision, of course, must be made by the couple involved, but they should make it a point to be fully aware of the possible complications which could arise.

Effects of Blood Matings on the General Population

It should be emphasized again that blood matings do not produce defective genes—they merely bring them out. Hence, whenever such matings do occur and defective children are produced there is no addition of outlaw genes to the general population, in fact, they may even be reduced a little. Should we, as a nation, suddenly begin widespread consanguineous marriages, the number of defectives in our population would increase tremendously as children were born as a result of these marriages. These defectives would be a great tragedy to the many individual families that produced them and to the nation which might be called upon to support many of them. We should keep the fact in mind, however, that there would be many of these defects which would be so extreme as to cause death, and others which would prevent normal marriage and reproduction. Hence, there would be a widespread elimination of many of these outlaw genes from the population—a gene purge. In time, this would actually result in a smaller percentage of outlaw genes in our population. Should we then resume our present customs of marriage we could expect fewer defectives as a result of recessive outlaw genes. Certainly no one would advocate this means of purifying our race, but it is a point to consider in connection with blood matings.

Artificial Insemination and Blood Matings

There are many cases where children fail to appear to bless the homes of married couples. Since children are a normal part of a family and a home, such couples often turn to adoption as a means of fulfilling their desires for a complete family life. To many such couples, however, science now offers an alternative to adoption—this is artificial insemination, sometimes called semiadoption. In about 40 per cent of the sterile marriages the fault lies not with the woman, but with the reproductive faculties of her husband. The wife may be fertile and able to bear children, but because of some lack on the part of her husband she does not become pregnant. The question then arises—is it better to adopt a child who will carry none of the genes from the parents, or through artificial insemination to have a child which will receive at least half of its genes from the mother? Moral and legal issues have been raised; however, many couples have chosen the latter course.

All arrangements for artificial insemination are made by a physician, and the donor of the semen never knows to whom it goes. The father's identity is never known by either the woman receiving it, or by her husband. As a rule, the physician selects a man as a donor who is married and has children of his own, a man who shows no trace of serious heredity defects in his family, and a man of the same racial type as the husband of the woman who is to bear the child. Delivery of the child is usually made by another physician who does not know the circumstances of the conception. Hence, he can sign the birth certificate in all honesty as the birth of a legitimate child.

The practice of artificial insemination is already rather widespread and all indications are that it will be used more and more in the future. In the course of time there may be a complicating factor which should be taken into consideration. Suppose a physician in a town of 12,000 people was asked to perform this service for a young married couple. After a rather difficult search he finds a man who fulfills all the qualifications very nicely and the insemination is accomplished. A few weeks later another couple come to him for the same service and since he has already investigated the donor of the semen for the first couple, he decides to use him a second time. Through the years this might be repeated many times. Here then, we have a rather small town in which quite a number of the young children are half-brothers and half-sisters without knowing it.

When these children mature and are ready for marriage it is quite possible that a young man in the group would fall in love with a half-sister and propose marriage. Only the physician would know that they were related by blood. Should he keep quiet and allow the couple to marry with the extra risk of defective children that comes with blood matings, or should he break his solemn promise to the parents that he would never reveal the circumstances of the birth? In order to avoid such a dilemma many physicians have adopted the practice of using one man no more than three times as a donor, and, even then, assuring themselves that the mothers are somewhat separated geographically so there will be little chance that the offspring will ever meet.

CHAPTER 18

NEW GENES FOR OLD

Genes are remarkably stable things—they go on and on reproducing themselves thousands of times over and over again, yet each time a perfect replica results. Each gene carries out its tasks in building the human body just as its predecessors have done for ages past. There are rare occasions, however, when they do change. After having produced thousands of perfect copies through many generations a gene may suddenly become different. One moment it is a gene of a certain nature, then, presto, it is a new gene capable of affecting offspring a different way. Furthermore, this gene will now reproduce itself in its new or changed condition and may go on for hundreds of generations in this changed state. Such a change in a gene is known as a mutation.

How Mutations Occur

To show how a mutation may occur, let us assume that you have blue eyes. Since a recessive gene is responsible for this condition, this means that each cell in your body contains a pair of genes for blue eyes. While you are reading these lines let us assume that a mutation occurs. Before you can finish this sentence, one of those genes for blue eyes changes so that it is now a gene for brown eyes. This happens in just one cell and won't affect the color of your eyes at all. It may happen in a cell of the skin of your foot, but even if it should happen in a cell of the iris of your eye it still would not change the color now, for one microscopic cell would not affect the hundreds of cells which make up the iris. Wherever the cell happens to be, however, it now carries the gene in its new state. Every time that cell divides the new gene divides along

212

with it and all cells descending from this one will carry the gene for brown eyes.

If this mutation to brown eyes occurred in one of your reproductive cells then it could show in a child which you

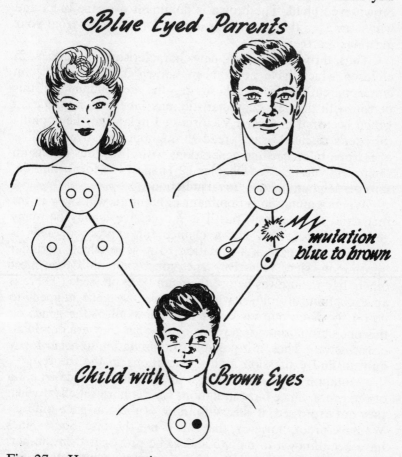

Fig. 27. How a mutation occurs. One gene for blue eyes in one sperm may mutate to a gene for brown eyes. A child formed by this sperm will have brown eyes even though it receives a gene for blue eyes from its mother because brown is dominant over blue

might have in the future if this cell is used in reproduction. Suppose you are married to a person with blue eyes—normally you would expect all blue-eyed children, but if this mutated cell unites with one from your mate then you will have a brown-eyed child. The brown is dominant over the blue, and will show even though there is a gene for blue eyes from your marriage partner.

Thus, through mutation, new characteristics may appear in children which have never been known in the ancestry on either parent's side. Furthermore, the descendants of this person with the new characteristic may inherit it. A mutation which occurred in Queen Victoria of England for hemophilia (bleeder's disease) was spread throughout the royal families of Europe in succeeding generations with disastrous effects on the royal dynasties. See Chapter 12 (page 143) for further details on hemophilia, the "royal affliction."

When a mutation is dominant in nature it will show in the first child to receive it, but if it is recessive it may be many generations before it has a chance for expression. This is especially true if it is a mutation to a gene which is rather uncommon, since recessive genes must wait until they meet others like themselves before they can be expressed. (There is an exception, of course, when the recessive gene happens to lie on the X-chromosome, for men show all of the genes on this one chromosome regardless of whether they are dominant or recessive.) Thus, it is possible for a mutation to occur today only to find expression many generations in the future.

Mutations represent changes in the genes, not destruction of the genes. Since most mutations have a harmful effect when they are expressed, it is easy to think of them as gene injuries. We have proof, however, that this is not the case. Some genes have been known to mutate and to be propagated in the new type for many generations, and then, one gene out of the many that have been reproduced from the original mutant will mutate back to the original type. For instance, take the case of the mutation of the gene for blue eyes to one for brown eyes. This gene might go on until hundreds of descendants have brown eyes because of this gene. Then, sometime in the distant future in one of the offspring there might be a change of the gene back to one for blue eyes. Such reverse mutations show that the gene was not damaged or did not lose anything when it first mutated—it was merely changed. The evidence indicates that genes are actually large molecules of matter, and it seems that mutations represent rearrangements of the electrons within these molecules which give the genes a new influence.

The Frequency of Mutations

The great British geneticist, J. B. S. Haldane, has estimated that a single human gene has a life expectancy of 2,500,000 years without change. This is a very long time and you might wonder how on earth he could obtain an estimate for such a rare occurrence. One method was to observe the number of children who expressed mutations in relation to the total number of births in large hospitals. His study was restricted to dominant genes since we have no way to accurately determine when a recessive mutation has occurred in a parent and been passed on to a child.

As an example, from the records of 128,763 children who were born in two large hospitals in Copenhagen, it was found that fourteen of the children were chondrodystrophic dwarfs. In this type of dwarfism the head and trunk are of normal size, but the arms and legs are extremely short. The condition is known to result from the action of a dominant gene. Three of these children had parents who were also afflicted with this condition, but the others were from normal parents. Each child in the group without dwarfed parents must have arisen as a result of a mutation in the reproductive cells of one of its parents. This would give us an average of one mutation for every 11,500 births, or one mutation for each 23,000 parents, since each child obviously had two parents. If we assume that the average age of the parents was thirty years, then we can estimate that this particular gene mutates once every 690,000 years. This is somewhat more frequent than the estimate for all genes, but genes are known to vary in their rate of mutation and this could be one which mutates more frequently than others. Table V shows the results of studies of the frequencies of several human genes which were determined in a similar manner. This indicates how genes vary in their rate of mutation.

When you look at the statistic of one mutation for a gene about every 2,500,000 years you may feel that such an event is so rare that there is practically no chance of such a change occurring in your reproductive cells. This is true if you are thinking of any particular gene, but you must remember that you have about 20,000 genes in each reproductive cell which you produce. This means that one gene out of this group is likely to mutate about once every 125 years. Now if you are thirty years of age there is about one chance in four that any sperm or egg you produce will receive some sort of mutated gene from you. This doesn't mean that about one-fourth of your children will show some extreme abnormality such as chondrodystrophic dwarfism. Many of these mutations in your reproductive cells will be recessive and will not show at all, and others will have such minor effects that they will not be noticed. Some of the mutations, actually a very small proportion of them, will be of such a nature as to be beneficial to the persons receiving them.

TABLE V

THE RATE OF MUTATION OF SIX GENES IN MAN

(From figures compiled by Haldane)

Characteristic	Mutation appears once in every	Mutation rate in percentage
PELGER'S NUCLEAR ANOMALY (Abnormal white blood cells, tend to reduce resistance to disease.)	12,500 births	.0080
CHONDRODYSTROPHIC DWARFISM (Shortened and deformed legs and arms.)	23,000 births	.0043
HEMOPHILIA (Blood does not clot properly. Causes free bleeding from minor injuries.)	33,333 births	.0030
RETINOBLASTOMA (Tumorous growths on retina of the eye.)	71,429 births	.0014
ANIRIDIA (Absence of the iris of the eyes.)	83,333 births	.0012
EPILOIA (Red lesions appear on face, later tumors develop in brain, kidneys, heart, et cetera.)	166,666 births	.0006
AVERAGE	65,043 births	.0015

Effects of Mutations on Embryonic Cells

On the cover of a recent popular picture magazine there was a color picture of a pretty girl. Well, pretty girls on magazine covers are certainly nothing out of the ordinary, but if you looked at this one closely you noticed a very unusual thing—one of her eyes was blue and one was brown. When this young lady was asked how she thought such a thing occurred she came forth with an eloquent although somewhat unscientific explanation—"I guess my genes just got all loused up."

In rare cases such irregular distribution of inherited characteristics may be found. They may result from a mutation of a gene in the early stages of embryonic development so that some large section of the body descends from the cell containing the mutant gene. Suppose the young lady described above inherited a gene for blue eyes from each parent. In the normal course of events she would have blue eyes. During embryonic development, however, one of these genes for blue might have mutated to become a gene for brown. If the cells of one side of the head were formed from this cell then there would be a brown eye on that side. The eye on the other side, coming from a cell in which no mutation had occurred, would be blue.

The same effect could result if an embryo was formed which received one gene for blue eyes and one for brown eyes. Since the brown is dominant such an embryo is destined to form a person with brown eyes. If there should be a mutation of one of the genes for brown to a gene for blue eyes in one of the cells, however, the cells reproduced from this one would form a blue iris.

Occasionally a person may have brown spots in an otherwise blue iris. This can be explained by a mutation which comes during embryonic development in a later stage than those described above. If a number of cells have already started to form the iris of the eye then a mutation in one of them could make the brown spots.

Mutations and Cancer

It is possible that cancer, that dread affliction of mankind which yields so slowly to the progress of scientific research, may be related to mutations. We know that genes correlate the growth of the cells so that they form a coordinated human body rather than a mass of unrecognizable tissue. The genes apparently produce substances which cause cells to divide when there is need for cells and to cease to divide when this need is satisfied. Thus a proper balance between cell formation and cell destruction is maintained. Now, suppose one of the genes which is a necessary link in this vital correlation mutates to some other state so that the correlation is lost. Let us assume that it is a cell which is in the skin. This cell begins dividing rapidly (since the agent which normally holds it in check is removed) and the cells which are produced are not skin cells, but a mass of wild cells—living parasitically on the tissues of the body of which the first cell was once a normal part. We call this mass of outlaw cells a cancer. Some of the cells may break off from the original site and be carried by the lymph to other parts of the body and start new cancer growths. When this growth interferes with the activity of some vital organ death results.

We know that inheritance plays an important part in a person's predisposition to cancer. Perhaps such inheritance consists of a relatively unstable gene which mutates more easily in persons predisposed to cancer. Such a theory is in line with the known facts relating to other genes. There are a number of cases in both plants and animals where genes are transmitted which have a predisposition to frequent mutation. The variegated pattern on the leaves of some plants is due to such a gene. This theory is further supported by the fact that some of the same agents which are known to induce mutations also have the power to induce cancer.

Cause of Mutations

Now that we know what mutations are, how often they are likely to occur, and their effects on the body, you may want to know what causes them. Why should a gene produce a perfect copy of itself for so many times and then suddenly produce a copy which is different in nature? It is known that various kinds of high-energy radiation (such as X rays) can cause mutations and, since we are all exposed to some high-energy radiations throughout our lifetimes, it is possible that these account for at least a part of the mutations which occur. While you have been reading this page a number of high-energy particles have passed through the ceiling above your head, passed through your body like so many tiny bullets, and continued their journey until they buried themselves in the earth beneath you. Only if you have been shielded by about forty feet of solid rock, or about fourteen inches of lead, have you been protected from these rays. They are known as cosmic rays—they originate somewhere in outer space and bombard our earth constantly. It is entirely probable that when one of these tiny particles passes through your body it may collide with a gene and set up a chain reaction which can cause the gene to mutate. Also, there are rather rare, but ever-present radioactive atoms in our surroundings which also give off high-energy radiations to bombard us on every side. It is possible that these, too, can cause mutations as they collide with genes. It is not necessary, however, for us to go outside of the gene to seek a source of energy for the generation of mutation. We are all now well aware of the tremendous amount of potential energy bound up within the atoms. There could be a shift of this intra-atomic energy within the atoms making up the genes so as to place a strain on one part of the gene molecule. This strain could cause a rearrangement of the molecule and the gene would then be different—a mutation would have occurred. It is only at very rare intervals that sufficient energy to cause such a change would be generated without the stimulation of some outside agent.

Good and Bad Mutations

A mutation of a gene from blue eyes to brown can hardly be considered either advantageous or harmful to the child who expresses the mutation if there are no other effects on the body. So far as we can tell, a person has just as good a chance of survival with either color eyes. It is true that some persons may admire one color or the other more in a person of the opposite sex, but it seems as if brown-eyed girls have just as good a chance of marriage as blue-eyed girls and vice versa. There are many mutations of this nature—they make a person different, but no worse off than he would have been without the mutation. There are a few mutations which may actually be beneficial, but, in the great majority of cases, mutations result in changes to the body which are harmful. Through the process of natural selection man has already become a highly efficient organism. He is not perfect, it is true, and some changes may make him better, but he is so efficient as he is that random changes are much more likely to be harmful than beneficial.

We might compare a man's body to a highly efficient, but not perfect, mechanical instrument—say a watch. Suppose you have a watch that keeps fairly good time, but not perfect time. Although you know nothing about watches you open the case and push a lever which you see in the back. There is a bare possibility that you would just happen to push the right lever in the right direction so that the watch would keep better time. It is much more likely, however, that the change would make the watch keep poorer time, and if the change is too extreme the watch may stop running altogether. Mutations represent random changes in highly efficient organisms and, like a random change in a watch, are very likely to be harmful. When the mutations cause extreme changes they are lethal in their action and life stops just as the watch stops as the result of an extreme change.

In some of the lower forms of life mutations that would

ordinarily be bad turn out to be good so far as man is concerned. For instance, a farmer in New England, Seth Wright, once noticed a peculiar lamb in his small flock. This lamb had unusually short legs which were somewhat deformed so that it had an awkward gait. Ordinarily we would think that such a trait would be harmful, and so it would in a natural environment, but shrewd Mr. Wright figured that it would be to his advantage to have an entire flock like this. He was always having trouble with his sheep jumping his fences, but one like this could not do much jumping. This change had been brought about by a recessive mutation that had occurred in one of his flock several generations before, and two of the genes had come together in this one lamb that showed the character. Wright used this one, which was a ram, to breed with his ewes and in time established a pure flock with the short, deformed legs. These became known as the ancon breed of sheep.

As other examples, the navel orange and the Emperor seedless grape arose as mutations on plants which bore normal seeds. This would be a very harmful mutation so far as the plants are concerned, for they could not reproduce new plants without seeds. To man, however, this new condition is good, for the presence of seed in fruit is one of its more worrisome qualities. Hence, we have established these two mutations and keep them going by cuttings and by budding so that no seed is necessary. The plant and animal breeder are glad to see mutations in their stock, for from them they may be able to get a new variety which will be improved so far as man is concerned at least. Those mutations which happen to be of value can be selected and propagated, while those of no value, or those which are harmful, can be easily eliminated by preventing breeding.

With man, however, it is a different proposition. We cannot select those mutations which are of benefit, and discard the others which do not suit our fancy. We do our best to save every human being that is born and many of those who express harmful mutations are saved who would not be able to survive without the special medical treatment which is provided. Since most mutations are harmful, we have no desire to increase the mutation rate in man even if, in so doing, we might produce a few mutations which would be beneficial to the persons expressing them.

CHAPTER 19

RADIATION AND MUTATIONS

Radiation has come to be a commonly used word in the English language because of the recent discussions of the effects of atomic radiation. The word has a broad meaning. The ordinary light rays that come from the sun or from electric lights in your home represent a form of radiation. Radiation of infrared rays may be used to treat sore muscles or sprains. Ultraviolet radiation may be used for developing an indoor suntan and for certain medical treatments. There are many forms of radiation, but because of the association of the word with the atomic energy, we have come to think of it mainly in connection with the very high-energy, short-wave type of radiation which is liberated when an atom splits.

X Rays and Mutations

Quite a number of years ago it was discovered that the high-energy radiation which we know as X rays could induce mutations when it was applied to the reproductive cells of plants and animals. The great American geneticist, H. J. Muller, in 1927, startled the scientific world when he presented the results of his experiments which showed that the number of mutations which appeared in fruit flies was increased tremendously following a heavy treatment with X rays. Here for the first time man had discovered a tool with which he might alter the delicate mechanism of heredity, thereby influencing future generations. It opened entirely new vistas in the realm of plant and animal breeding. Now the scientists would not have to wait and hope for mutations which might be incorporated into new and improved varieties, but they could actually produce these mutations. Dr. Muller was later awarded the Nobel Prize for this great contribution to the world.

The mutations which X rays induce were found to be no different from those which take place any way—there were just many more of them. Also, it was found that the number of mutations was in direct proportion to the amount of X rays given—the heavier the dosage, the greater the number of mutations. There is a stopping point, however, for it was found that very heavy doses of X rays cause sterility, and there can be no offspring at all to show mutations. With the passage of time this study has been extended to many other forms of life and it has been found that the effects are similar in all that have been studied.

The Nature of X Rays

Before going any further, perhaps it will help in an understanding of the relationship of X rays to mutations if we learn something of the nature of this extremely powerful form of radiation.

These rays are produced within an X-ray tube when a high-voltage, direct electric current causes a shower of electrons to traverse the tube and strike a tungsten target. As the target absorbs these electrons the X rays are given off. The rays cannot be seen with the eye, but they have the power to affect photographic film and to cause a fluorescence in certain materials which they may strike. Because of their high energy, X rays are highly penetrating—they can pass through a human body like so many tiny bullets. An X-ray photograph of the human chest can be made by shooting the rays through the body and onto a photographic film on the other side of the chest. This is possible because, in spite of their high energy, some of the X rays will be stopped in their passage by the human tissue and will not reach the film. A greater number of the rays will be stopped by the denser tissues, such as bone, and a correspondingly smaller number will be stopped by the less dense tissues. This causes the formation of a shadow image of the chest on the photographic film when it is developed.

Measurement of Radiation

We need a standard of measurement for anything we deal with which differs quantitatively. We have pints and gallons for liquids; pounds, bushels, and pecks for solids; inches and feet for distance; foot-candles for light intensity; and so on. Likewise, we need some objective measure of radiation. The unit which is commonly used is the Roentgen unit which is usually abbreviated to the r unit. It is determined by the amount of ionizations which are induced in a gas-filled chamber by the rays. The familiar Geiger counter which is used so commonly to test for radioactivity in work with atomic radiation is an example of such a machine. This counter, which is a part of the standard equipment of uranium prospectors, translates the ionizations into audible sounds which we can count and thereby determine the amount of radiation.

About 0.2 r units of X rays are required to make a photograph of the human chest. In experimental studies on mutation production in mammals we use up to about 800 r units and in insects up to as high as 7,500 r units may be used. About 250 r units administered to the reproductive glands will produce temporary sterility in man.

Cumulative Effect of Radiation

An insidious aspect of high-energy radiation is its cumulative effect. This simply means that the influence of the radiation tends to build up in the tissues, so a series of short exposures can equal a single long exposure. For example, suppose that 600 r units of X rays cause some sort of mutation in 60 per cent of the sperms of an experimental animal. We may give this exposure all at one time, we may give 100 r units per day for six days, or we may give 10 r units per day for 60 days. We may use a high-voltage tube and give it in less than one minute, or we may use very low voltage and spread the exposure out over several hours. Whatever method is used, the mutation rate will remain about the same in each case.

During the early days in the use of X rays, this cumulative effect was not known and many early workers in this field lost their hands, arms, and even their lives, as a result. They soon learned that a continuous heavy exposure would destroy human tissue, but did not realize that a series of shorter exposures would have the same effect. Let us assume that an exposure of two hours to X rays of a certain intensity would cause the destruction of the tissues of the hand. Now suppose an X-ray technician used his hands to hold his patients in place for X-ray photographs. Each photograph requires only a few seconds; let us say his hands average 10 seconds of exposure to the rays per day. If he works six days a week, he will receive 60 seconds exposure per week. After 120 such weeks he will have accumulated a total exposure of two hours, and the tissues of his hands will begin to deteriorate. Today most X-ray technicians take precautions to prevent such a catastrophe.

Differential Effects of X Rays

It has been found that X rays do not affect all types of tissue equally. It seems that mature tissue which does not contain cells which are dividing is least susceptible—muscle and nerve tissue is an example. Conversely, actively dividing cells are most susceptible. The cells of the red bone marrow, which are constantly dividing as they produce new blood cells, are highly susceptible, and a type of anemia will follow over-all exposure to high-energy radiation even when there has been no injury to less susceptible body tissues. The skin contains cells which are constantly dividing as they replace the cells which are sloughed off in the normal course of wear and tear on the body covering. Hence, the skin is highly susceptible to high-energy radiation. This also applies to the "skin" lining the stomach and intestines, and nausea is likely to develop after heavy radiation because of damage to the lining of the stomach. The hair is actively growing from the skin and the hair roots may be injured by radiation to such an extent that

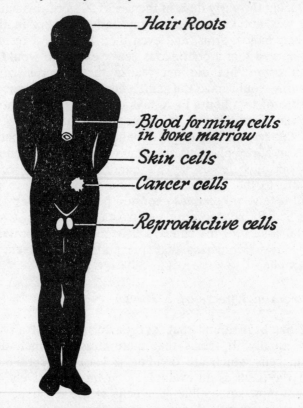

Hair Roots

Blood forming cells in bone marrow

Skin cells

Cancer cells

Reproductive cells

Fig. 28. The parts of the body most susceptible to radiation damage. The cells of the body which are actively dividing are the ones most easily damaged by heavy doses of radiation. This diagram shows where some of these cells are located.

the hair falls out. The reproductive cells are also highly susceptible to this type of radiation because they also are actively dividing cells. This accounts for the sterility which may follow exposure to heavy radiation in the region of the reproductive organs. The cells which are just maturing seem to be most susceptible and the sterility may be temporary if the radiation is not too great. A study made a number of years ago showed that a number of X-ray technicians were sterile as a result of the cumulative exposure to radiation. Today, greater precautions are taken to prevent this—technicians usually retire to lead-lined control rooms during times when the X-ray machine is operating; they may wear lead-impregnated clothing when it is necessary to be near the patient or step behind lead shields.

Cancer cells are actively dividing cells and, in a way, this is fortunate because this makes them highly susceptible to X rays. Because of this, it is possible to destroy cancer cells without injury to normal surrounding tissue by using the proper dose of X rays or rays from radioactive elements such as cobalt-60 or radium which are similar in their effects. The dosage must be carefully regulated, however, or the surrounding tissue may be destroyed if overexposed to radiation.

Before you begin to worry about the use of X rays in routine medical examinations, however, it might be well to point out that the amount of radiation received in the making of an X-ray photograph for diagnostic purposes is so minute in comparison to the amount which can produce detectible increases in the mutation rate or injury to any types of body cells, that you should not hesitate to have necessary X-ray pictures. Extended exposures over a period of time, however, are a different thing and may have marked effects.

Radiation and Chromosome Changes

High-energy radiation has effects on the chromosomes within the cells in addition to the mutations which may be produced. Sometimes pieces may be broken off of chromosomes; sometimes the chromosomes stick together in diversion and give odd numbers in the cell; sometimes groups of genes are changed from one chromosome to another. These changes may have very pronounced effects. An embryo which is formed from reproductive cells that have been so changed may show deformities. In many cases, these will be so extreme as to result in early death and abortion before a normal term of development. At other times the embryo may survive, but will show abnormalities, and, in still other cases, there may be no noticeable effect the first generation, but abnormalities will come out in the second generation.

The sterility which follows extended exposure of the reproductive glands to high-energy radiation results to a great extent from the changes in the chromosomes. When these changes occur in the cells of the reproductive glands they may be of such an extreme nature that the cells cannot produce normal eggs or sperms and sterility results. The sperms and eggs which are already formed will not be destroyed by such changes, but the embryos which they produce may die in a very early stage as a result of these changes. In both cases sterility is the end result.

The sterility which is induced may be temporary provided the radiation received does not greatly exceed the minimum amount required to induce sterility. A man who becomes sterile because of excessive exposure to such radiation may regain his fertility after several years. Some of the cells of the testes which are not active may survive the radiation which renders the more active cells impotent. Only about 250r units are required to produce this temporary sterility. Because of its temporary action, X rays were once used on a limited scale as a means of birth control. To a young couple struggling to get started in life, such a plan may sound attractive—the husband takes the prescribed treatment and the stork does not flap his wings in their direction for several years. Unfortunately, however, when the stork finally does drop his little bundle, it may contain a malformed infant as a result of the chromosomal aberrations which were induced. Another factor makes the picture darker for the future. The gene mutations produced by the X rays will most likely not show any effect on the child which is produced, but they will be carried in the recessive state and appear in future generations.

Other Agents Which Cause Mutations

Radium is a material which constantly gives off radiations of the high-energy type like X rays. It would be expected, therefore, that they would cause mutations and chromosome changes like X rays. Experiments indicate that this is true. Of course, X rays yield a greater dosage of r units within a given time than radium, but by exposing tissue to radium a longer time the same number of r units can be accumulated. Because radium can be placed in close proximity to cancer cells, it is generally used more extensively than X rays to treat cancer. In actual practice it is customary to use the gaseous emanation from radium rather than the radium itself for such treatments. Radium is extremely expensive and could be easily lost if used on cancer patients. The gas from radium, however, gives off the same radiation and the radium itself can be protected. The amount of radiation from the gas, however, diminishes rather rapidly and it is necessary to have accurate knowledge of the age of the emanation in order to estimate its activity.

Ultraviolet rays have been found to induce mutations in some of the small organisms, such as bacteria and molds, but these rays cannot penetrate tissue like X rays or radium rays; consequently they cannot reach the reproductive cells of large animals like a human being.

Atomic fission and fusion produce large quantities of high-energy radiation. It is very important that we know the effects of such radiation because of its significance in a possible atomic war. Studies made by geneticists at the site of atomic bomb explosions show that the radiation released produces mutations and chromosome changes much like those produced by X rays.

Many chemicals have been tested to determine if they

could cause mutations and a few have been found which are effective. These include mustard gas, nitrogen mustard, ethyl urethane, phenol, and even the well-known laboratory preservative, formaldehyde. These studies have been made mostly on experimental animals and in many cases the reproductive glands have been removed from the body and immersed in the chemical and then transplanted back into the animal which is then allowed to reproduce. It is interesting to note that a number of other chemicals which are known to induce cancer in experimental animals also produce mutations when tested in this manner. These include methycholanthrene and dibenzanthracene. This would support the theory that mutations may play a part in the development of cancer.

Of all the agents which have been discovered, radiations of high energy seem to be the only things to which human beings might be exposed in sufficient quantities to cause any significant increase in mutation rate. There is a possible danger in these, however, as will be brought out in the next chapter.

CHAPTER 20

OUR ATOMIC HERITAGE

We have witnessed the dawn of a new age—the age of atomic energy. For many years man has dreamed of what could be done if we could find some way to release the tremendous energy bound up within the atom. We knew the energy was there. Einstein even predicted the exact amount of energy which would result with the annihilation of mass by his famous equation: $e = mc^2$. This simply means that the energy will equal the weight of the mass annihilated times the velocity of light squared. We need no longer dream and speculate—control of atomic energy is an accomplished fact today. Submarines and surface vessels are now traveling the waters of the world powered by atomic engines. Atomic energy generating plants are furnishing electrical power. We will possibly soon be using milk made safe by radiation rather than pasteurization. The home freezer may become obsolete as food preservation by radiation becomes more widespread. There seems to be no end to the many applications of the powerful atomic energy which man now controls for his own uses.

This is not an unmixed blessing, however. To our descendants we have bequeathed a discovery which can revolutionize all concepts of power and bring great blessings for future generations. At the same time we have created one of the greatest problems which has ever faced mankind. We have provided man with agents which can bring about his own destruction. Never before in history has man been faced with such grave responsibility. He must learn to understand and use this great force wisely or join the dinosaurs, the dodo bird, and the passenger pigeon as one of the extinct species of the earth. Every person living today should know something of the dangers which can arise from atomic radiation and do what he can to see that our discoveries become a blessing rather than a curse to our descendants.

The Beginning of the Atomic Age

The atomic age is in its infancy so far as ages go. We can probably set its beginning at December 2, 1942. It was on this fateful date that a group of scientists gathered in a room at the University of Chicago and witnessed the first production of fire and light which man had created from atomic energy. At last man had released the bound energy of the atom. Of course, there were many years of patient work by many scientists which paved the way for this great climax, but this was the culmination—the atom had been split and its energy harnessed.

It was only three years later, on July 16, 1944, that a group of carefully selected scientists watched the first demonstration of the release of atomic energy on a major scale. At the White Sands Proving Ground in New Mexico, in a chill, pre-dawn darkness, miles from the site of the detonation, these men saw a blinding flash—a flash a thousand times brighter than sunlight. This light could be viewed safely only through very dark glasses. The flash was followed by a rising ball of fire and a cloud of dust, then smoke that mushroomed thousands of feet into the air. So intense was the heat generated that the 100-foot steel tower upon which the bomb had rested was vaporized and scattered like dust. The sand around the blast was melted and fused into a mile-wide saucer. But the energy was not spent—the radioactive particles which were generated rose into the upper atmosphere and were spread over a wide area. A rainstorm 1,500 miles away brought some of the particles to earth and fogged photographic film packed in cardboard made from straw which was washed by this rain.

This explosion was kept secret—we were in a war for survival and now we had a weapon of woeful potentialities.

It was not long, however, before the world knew about it. The city of Hiroshima, Japan, was the chosen target for the first atom bomb. There was the same blinding flash and the same mushrooming cloud—and this city was suddenly transformed into a burning inferno which killed 160,000 people. Much of the city has been rebuilt today and most of the inhabitants who survived have recovered from the radiation sickness and other immediate physical effects of the blast. We may well be concerned, however, about the possible future effects which might come about as a result of the radiation released in such an explosion. Even if man survives an atomic war on a major scale, can the human race be doomed by the accumulation of harmful mutations and chromosome changes? Can we set into effect a chain of reactions which will cause the generations yet unborn to have their lives marred, or even destroyed, by our folly? Let us try to evaluate the effects of this radiation in terms of future generations and see if we can answer these vital questions.

When an Atom Splits

What happens when an atom is split? We speak of atomic fission, the great power released from atomic fission, and the dangerous radiation emanating from atomic fission—perhaps, we had better find out just what happens when the atom breaks apart.

Before we can understand what happens when an atom splits, however, we need to know something about its nature before it splits. Without going into the many highly technical physical theories which would be out of place in this book, we can get an elementary concept of the generally accepted plan of organization. An atom consists of a relatively dense nucleus, around which are revolving tiny electrons at a very high rate of speed. The nucleus of the atom of any particular element contains a certain number of particles, known as protons, which have a positive electrical charge. The electrons whirling around the nucleus are negative in charge and in the normal atom positive and negative charges are balanced. For instance, carbon has six protons in its nucleus and six electrons revolving around it. In addition, the nucleus of an atom may contain neutrons which are neither positive or negative; they are neutral. Hence, they add weight to the atom without changing its charge. A normal atom of carbon has six neutrons in its nucleus as well as six protons. These are all held together by tremendous bound energy.

Uranium, which is the element that serves as the basis for most atomic fission has a very heavy atom. It has 92 electrons, 92 protons, and 146 neutrons. This is the stable uranium, atom U^{238} but mixed in with the stable atoms will be some unstable atoms which have only 143 neutrons. This is the well-known U^{235}, which is radioactive and can be split with our modern technique. For an atomic bomb we must first separate these rare U^{235} atoms from the many uranium U^{238} atoms.

When the U^{235} atoms are brought together in the proper mass, some begin splitting; as particles from these atoms strike others, they too, begin splitting and the so-called chain reaction has started. All this fission takes place in time measured in terms of millionths of a second. As each atom splits, the particles composing it fly out at very high speeds. The positive and negative particles (alpha and beta particles) do little damage because they are easily stopped by the skin or clothing of a person if they are not stopped by something else first. A sheet of paper will stop most of them. The free neutrons, however, are dangerous because they are very penetrating. A neutron is stopped only when it has a head-on collision with the nucleus of another atom and this can cause a marked change in the atom which is hit. Also, the bound energy of an atom is released when it is split. A part of the mass of the atom is transformed into energy in accordance with Einstein's famous equation. This is the source of the brilliant light and the searing heat which is given off at the time of an atomic bomb explosion. The heat accounts for much of the damage done by the bomb. Some of the energy is liberated in the form of gamma rays which are in the nature of very high-energy X rays. In a very simplified form, then, this is what happens when the atom is split. The heat rays, the gamma rays, and the neutrons are the products of this fission which can cause the greatest damage.

When Atoms Fuse

Atom fusion as well as atom fission can cause a release of great energy. The super-powerful hydrogen bomb depends upon the fusion of atoms of hydrogen rather than the splitting of the atoms of uranium, although it is generally assumed that a small atom bomb is used as a sort of trigger to generate sufficient heat to cause the hydrogen fusion. How can we get energy from fusion as well as fission? The main point to remember is that the energy is released when mass is annihilated. In the hydrogen bomb, the atoms of hydrogen fuse and form atoms of helium. But the helium weighs very slightly less than the hydrogen which forms it. This small loss of matter is transformed into the powerful energy given off as the fusion takes place.

Radiation Damage from Nuclear Weapons

It is easy to underestimate the damage done by the high-energy radiation generated at the time of the explosion of a nuclear weapon, be it atomic fission or fusion. We cannot see this kind of radiation, we cannot feel it, and its effects may be delayed for hours, days, years, or even centuries. On the other hand, the force of the explosion is spectacular. The brilliant flash of light, the searing heat, and the explosive movement of air do their damage within fractions of a second. People who may be in the central area of the blast may be "burned to a crisp" or literally blown to pieces by these agents. Houses and buildings are reduced to twisted, burning wreckage, trees are denuded of foliage, and the earth laid barren— all before the mushrooming cloud even begins to form.

Those who are outside of this area of total destruction

may feel fortunate at first that they were spared, but they may have received heavy doses of radiation which will have serious effects. Within a short time they may feel as if they have gotten a sunburn all the way through the body. The skin will redden and become ulcerated because of damage done to proliferating cells, and the same may happen to the inner lining of the mouth, stomach, and intestines. Nausea is one of the symptoms of this type internal damage. The blood-forming tissues in the bones may be injured and an anemia will result because of the deficiency of red blood cells which follows within a few days. Small internal hemorrhages may take place; ruptured blood vessels of the skin may show as red splotches. This is associated with the lowered clotting time of the blood due to the destruction of the blood platelets, small cells which initiate blood clotting. Still another effect will be a lowering of the resistance of the body to invading disease germs. The white blood cells are guardians of the body and they destroy disease germs which get into the system. The combination of these effects can lead to death in the days that follow the exposure. Those who survive the miseries of these early effects of radiation can look forward to such conditions as bone cancer, thyroid degeneration, cataract of the eye, loss of hair, and sterility, as possible delayed effects. All of this is not a pretty picture, yet tragic as it is, it is quite possible that the damage to future generations may exceed that done to the present.

It is this damage to future generations which is our primary concern in this book, for these are the effects which are passed on through heredity. Too often this phase of atom bomb damage is given little attention in discussions of atomic explosions. Many of the damages to a person are reversible in nature. The skin will lose its redness in time, the anemia will disappear, the white blood cell count will return to normal, fertility may return, hair will grow back, and we may say the person has recovered from the damage. But there is no recovery from the damage done to the genes through mutation or the chromosomes through breakages. These are irreversible changes which reproduce themselves with every cell division.

A Time Bomb for Our Descendants

If some diabolical genius were to devise a clever time bomb and set it under one of our large cities with the mechanism set to go off within two hundred years so that it would kill many of the inhabitants of the city at that time, we would think him the most loathsome form of humanity in existence. Yet, it is possible that we are preparing a time bomb for our descendants which can go off far in the future and do far more damage than a bomb placed under a large city. There are some who estimate that the future deformities and deaths which will come about because of the irreversible changes of the genes and the chromosomes, due to radiation from man-made weapons, will exceed such damage as may be caused to the people exposed to the explosion of the nuclear weapons themselves. In effect, this would be as serious as a time bomb even though its effects might be spread out for several hundred years.

There is much popular misinformation about the nature of inherited damage resulting from radiation. Some people expected the great majority of the descendants of persons who had been exposed to be monstrosities with legs growing from the tops of their heads, with eyes bulging from their sockets, or other such odd freaks of human anatomy. When children began to be born to the survivors of the explosions in Japan and there was no widespread incidence of such monstrosities, it was then thought that this proved that there was no serious hereditary effects. Even some persons with authority have indicated that effects on heredity were not serious. This is a dangerous assumption which could lead to widespread damage to future generations through needless exposure to radiation in peacetime as well as wartime.

There will be a few abnormalities among the children of parents who have received rather heavy radiation. This is due mainly to damage to the chromosomes, but the number will be small because most of such damage is so severe as to disable the reproductive cell affected and prevent it from functioning at all. Some of those which do function will result in defective embryos which will die soon after conception and never be born as living children. Many of the people who receive lesser dosages, however, may have mutations induced without interfering with the functions of the reproductive cells in which the mutations occur. Most of these mutations will be recessive in nature and may not show until many generations later—when they meet other genes like themselves. Also, most of these mutations, even when they are expressed, produce changes which are so minute in their effects on the physical appearance of a person that they could not be detected by observation.

Then why, you might say, should we worry about them? How are such minute changes to bring about such destruction as we have been discussing? The fact that these effects are minute does not mean that they are unimportant. They may cause such changes as a lowered vitality, greater susceptibility to disease, shortened life span, lowered fertility, depressed energy reserve, and other such hard-to-measure physiological alterations. Any one or a few of these would not greatly harm any individual, but it is the accumulation of them that counts. If the people of a nation are exposed to considerable radiation—it could be spread out over several generations—in the course of time there could be so many such mutations that many of the descendants could not lead a normal life as we know it because of the effects of so many of these mutations.

Of course, there will be some mutations that will be dominant and will show in the first generation; others that will be recessive would have a very striking effect when they are expressed in later generations, but these minute changes are the most dangerous in the long run because they are so much more frequent.

Radioactive Products of Nuclear Weapons

In our discussion we have been speaking only of the radiation which is given off at the instant of a bomb explosion.

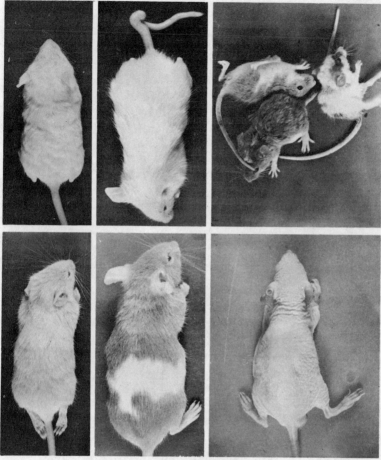

Plate XVII. Some interesting mutations which have occurred in the mouse. From left to right and top to bottom these are: short ear, waved fur, belted body, kinky tail, hairless body, and jittery nervous system.

Courtesy C. Nash Herndon, Department of Medical Genetics, Bowman Gray School of Medicine

Plate XVIII. The results of a mutation of a normal gene to one for chondrodystrophic dwarfism. This unfortunate condition results from the actions of a gene which arises as a mutation in about one reproductive cell out of every 23,000 according to exhaustive studies of this gene in Denmark.

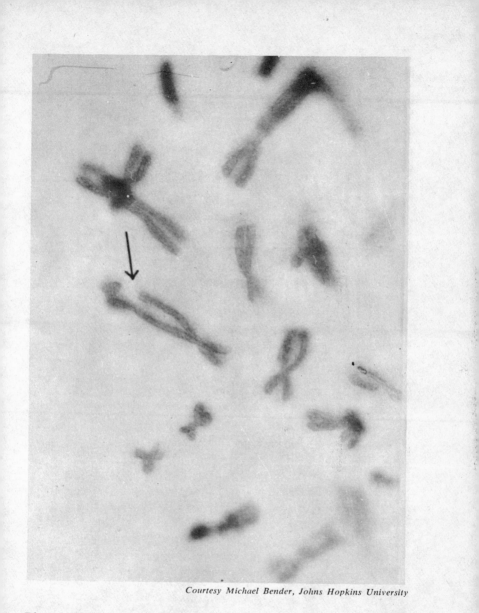

Plate XIX. Damage to human chromosome resulting from radiation. The arrow shows a break in a chromosome of a cell which had been treated with 50 r units of X rays. Over 20 per cent of the cells treated with this dosage showed such breakage.

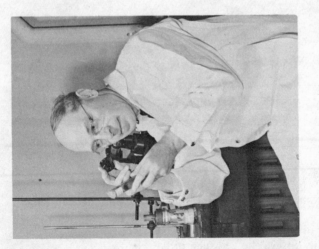

Plate XXb. A mutation passes through three generations. A dominant gene for mono-digital hands and feet.

Plate XXa. H. J. Muller, the man who discovered that the mutation rate could be greatly increased by high energy radiation and who received the Nobel prize for this discovery.

Plate XXI. An atomic bomb explosion at Bikini. The explosion of nuclear weapons such as this one liberates large amounts of radioactive materials which are spread widely. The possible consequences of such elevation of the radioactivity of the earth on future generations is a matter of grave concern to many who are studying the problem.

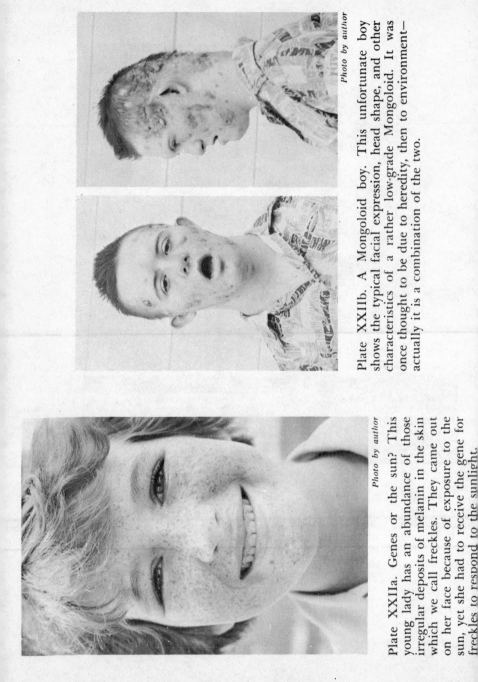

Photo by author

Plate XXIIb. A Mongoloid boy. This unfortunate boy shows the typical facial expression, head shape, and other characteristics of a rather low-grade Mongoloid. It was once thought to be due to heredity, then to environment—actually it is a combination of the two.

Photo by author

Plate XXIIa. Genes or the sun? This young lady has an abundance of those irregular deposits of melanin in the skin which we call freckles. They came out on her face because of exposure to the sun, yet she had to receive the gene for freckles to respond to the sunlight.

Courtesy of Birthright, Inc.

Plate XXIIIa. Feeble minded women. This mental disorder is very common and can bring mental anguish to the parents of such persons. Many, such as the women shown here, must be confined to mental institutions and their care can be quite a burden on the rest of society. A combination of inherited and environmental factors appears to be the cause of this condition.

Courtesy C. Nash Herndon, Department of Medical Genetics, Bowman Gray School of Medicine

Plate XXIIIb. Idiocy in a boy which appears to result from the actions of a sex-linked recessive gene. Some inherited mental disorders are traceable to deflections from normal of a single gene as in this case, but in the majority of cases there seems to be a number of genes involved.

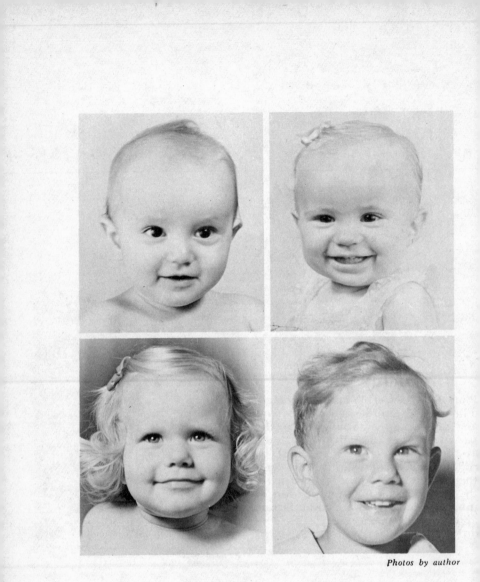

Plate XXIV. A sound mind in a sound body is the birthright of every child. A combination of good heredity and good environment is necessary to produce such bright-eyed children as these.

Unfortunately, this is not the end of the radiation. When the free neutrons are released by atomic fission they may strike the nuclei of other atoms and lodge there. By thus adding to the mass of the new atom they may create an unstable condition which makes the atom radioactive. Carbon, as we have already mentioned, normally has six protons and six neutrons in its nucleus. This is the common carbon (C^{12}) which is stable. If two more neutrons are added to the nucleus, however, we have the unstable, radioactive C^{14}. We call this a radioactive isotope of carbon. In the same way other elements may be made radioactive by neutron bombardment.

Just what do we mean when we say an element is radioactive? It simply means that the nucleus is in an unstable state and may give off neutrons until it reaches stability. A mass of radioactive carbon will give off neutrons which can be just as damaging in their effects as the neutrons from the fission of uranium. A Geiger counter held near such carbon will reveal its radioactivity. The release of these neutrons is comparatively slow, however, and greatly spread out in space. It will take about 5,600 years for one-half of the carbon to lose the extra neutrons and become the stable C^{12}. In another 5,600 years one-half of the remaining C^{14} will become C^{12} and so on.

When an atomic bomb is exploded many of the exposed substances are made radioactive. The dust in the cloud which rises from the site of the explosion is intensely radioactive, as has been shown by remote-controlled airplanes which have flown through it. As this dust settles over the countryside it can create a hazard entirely apart from the damage done at the time of the bomb explosion. Atom bomb tests on the Yucca Flats of Nevada are made only when the conditions of wind and atmosphere are such that the radioactive products will be carried high in the air and become widely scattered before they settle to the earth. The radioactive "fall-out" from the hydrogen bomb appears to be even more dangerous. With its greater explosive force it seems to create a greater amount of radioactive ash which tends to settle more readily than the finer dust particles of the atomic bomb. The Japanese fisher-men who were showered with a "fall-out" from a hydrogen bomb test in the Pacific suffered serious effects, and one of them died even though they were two hundred miles from the site of the explosion.

This is a dangerous phase of radiation which is frequently not understood. Even after a nuclear weapon has exploded and done its initial damage, its threatening radioactive prod-ucts may remain. A person who escapes the explosion could absorb enough radiation to cause his death by unknowingly exposing himself to this radiation. It has been estimated that one hydrogen bomb exploded over a land area could make 7,000 square miles dangerously radioactive. And this is not all—these bombs can be made more dangerous by coating them with materials such as cobalt, which are made radio-active at the time of the explosion. This greatly multiplies the amount of radioactive products produced by the bomb. In fact, it is possible to explode such a bomb out at sea and allow the prevailing winds to carry these radioactive materials over an enemy nation and achieve greater destruction than would be wrought by the initial blast.

Can We Poison the Earth?

There is a growing concern among many of the world's eminent scientists that we may cause significant elevation of the natural radiation of the earth by continued testing of nuclear weapons, even though they are never used for war. In the explosion of a nuclear weapon much of the radioactive material mushrooms high in the air and may be carried over all parts of the earth by a layer of air between the troposphere and the stratosphere. It settles gradually and is so dissipated in this way that it is commonly assumed that it has lost its danger. But it is still radioactive; we do not do away with the radioactivity by spreading it over a great area. Each bomb exploded adds just that much to the natural radioactive ma-terials which are already a part of the earth. Some say that this is such a big planet that we need not worry about this—that the average person has received no more radiation from all the nuclear explosions set off so far than he would get from a chest X ray. But there must be a limit somewhere—is it at the level of thousands, hundreds of thousands, or millions of bombs? The great British physiologist, E. D. Adrian, says that man cannot stand more than a few thousand large atomic explosions, whether they hit or miss. The American geneticist, A. H. Sturtevant, says that the last H-bomb test alone produced more than 70 mutations in the people of the world and these can result in defectives in future generations.

Tests of radioactivity at various parts of the earth far from the site of nuclear weapon tests show a threefold elevation in radiation in some places. The total is still very minute, but if it is built up by continued explosions, whether in war or peace, it can reach a dangerous level in time. It could even get so high that the number of mutations produced in man would exceed the number which could be eliminated by the reproductive mechanism which preserves the species. Eventual extinction of human life would result. This is the reason why we say that man has at his disposal agents which can bring about his own destruction. He must recognize their danger and limit their use or face the horrible and fatal alternatives.

Perhaps, as the full significance of the power and the danger of nuclear weapons becomes evident, we will have a great incentive for the peaceful settlement of man's differences with his fellowman. Perhaps, by the very existence of the most destructive weapon which man has ever created we may see the end of the destruction of war. Our great danger lies in ignorance of the full consequences of atomic warfare by those in position to set off another global struggle.

Peacetime Uses of Atomic Radiation

In spite of all the horrible consequences which could result from the bungling misuse of the radiation of atomic fission, there is a bright side to the picture. There are many valuable scientific applications of this radiation for the extension of man's knowledge and the benefit of humanity. The isotopes of elements made radioactive by neutron bombardment are particularly valuable. There is radioactive iodine, for instance, which may be used in treating cancer of the thyroid gland. High-energy radiation is very destructive to cancer tissue, but the problem comes in applying the radiation to the cancerous area without undue exposure of surrounding tissue. This has always been difficult in the case of internal organs, but radioactive isotopes give us a new weapon. We know that most of the iodine which we take into our bodies is taken up by the thyroid gland. A person suffering from cancer of the thyroid may be given a radioactive iodine "cocktail" which contains a minute amount of this isotope. Within a short time a Geiger counter held over various regions of the body will show that the iodine is in the thyroid gland giving off its radiation. This tends to destroy the cancer cells.

A similar "cocktail" may be prepared for other body afflictions. Some persons have an overactive red bone marrow which produces an abnormally large number of red blood cells, and the blood gets so thick that it cannot circulate properly. Regular bleeding will keep the count down, but this also takes away blood proteins and mineral salts which the body needs. However, since bones absorb the greater proportion of the phosphorus which is taken into the body, administering the radioactive isotope of phosphorus in a manner similar to that used for the iodine makes it possible to concentrate the radiation in the bones and so to destroy some of the excessive red blood cell-producing tissue. This brings the red blood cell count down.

Radioactive isotopes are helping us greatly to understand the utilization of minerals by plants and animals. Radioactive nitrogen can be placed in the soil and its utilization by plants followed accurately by means of the instruments which can detect radioactivity. Experimental animals can be fed on food which includes a radioactive mineral and the course of this mineral in the body can be followed.

Radioactive by-products of atomic fission can be used to produce mutations in domestic animals and cultivated plants. As we have pointed out, most mutations are harmful to the individual who expresses them, but a few will be beneficial. In experimental forms of life we can discard all those which we do not wish to use and breed those which are desirable. Also, there may be some changes which are not beneficial to the plant or animal involved, but which may be beneficial to man. A mutation which caused an apple tree to produce larger fruit might actually be harmful to the tree since the limbs would be more likely to break under the added weight, but it would be desirable so far as man is concerned.

Much that is good can come from our control of atomic fission. There is nothing either good or evil in the energy of the atom—it is man's use of this energy that determines what its effects will be.

CHAPTER 21

NATURE AND NURTURE

Which is more important—heredity or environment? This question is frequently asked, but it is a "loaded" question. It assumes that one or the other must be more important, but, as the song says, this "ain't necessarily so." It is like asking, "Which is more important to make your automobile run—the motor or the gasoline?" Take away either and your car does not run; it takes the combined effect of both. Who can say that one is more important than the other? The motor represents potential power; the gasoline furnishes energy to make this potential power function. Likewise, genes represent potentialities, but without the energy brought in from the environment there can be no realization of function. Genes cannot work in a vacuum and their expression is usually conditioned by the environment in which they operate.

Freckles—Genes or the Sun?

"Is this characteristic due to heredity or environment?" This is one of the most common questions which confronts a genetic counselor when he is called upon for advice by those considering marriage. Such a question can be more than just idle curiosity. A man may bear some disfiguring abnormality and is greatly concerned lest he pass this abnormality on to his children. But this is another "loaded" question. Few characteristics can be said to be due to heredity *or* environment—most are due to heredity *and* environment. For instance, suppose you have a child whose face is covered with those irregular splotches of pigment which we call freckles. You remember that similar splotches graced your own countenance during your childhood and you say that your child inherited his freckles from you. Then, the next time you go to the beach you find a fastidious young lady who says that she cannot sit in the sun because it will cause her skin to freckle. Who is right—you or the young lady? You are both right. A dominant gene gives a person the potentialities of developing freckles—these freckles become prominent, however, only when the skin develops pigment in response to light exposure.

Hot and Cold Rabbits

Since people do not like to serve as subjects for experiments, let us turn to some experiments which have been made with rabbits to show just how heredity and environment can blend in the total expression of a characteristic. There is a breed of rabbits, known as Himalayans, that have a coat pattern which is white over most of the body, but there is black fur on the legs, tail, ears, and nose. Breeding experiments show that this pattern comes out when the rabbits receive two recessive genes, one from each parent. A clear-cut case of heredity, it appears, but let us see what happens when we alter the environment.

Supposing we take some naked, newborn rabbits from a pure Himalayan stock and place them in an environment where the temperature is less than 52° for a short time. When their skins are thoroughly chilled we return them to their mother and they warm up. As their hair grows out it will be black all over their bodies. Somehow this temporary chilling of the skin caused fur to be black which otherwise would have been white. Other experiments show this effect on smaller body areas. We can pluck the hair from the back of a mature

Himalayan rabbit and place an ice pack in this region. After the skin is thoroughly chilled the ice pack is removed, but when the hair grows out in this region it will be black. Also, we can pluck hair from the region of the leg where it is normally black and apply a bandage to this plucked region. When the hair grows out it will be white because the bandage held the body heat and kept the skin warmer than usual.

Thus, it is evident that something other than genes is

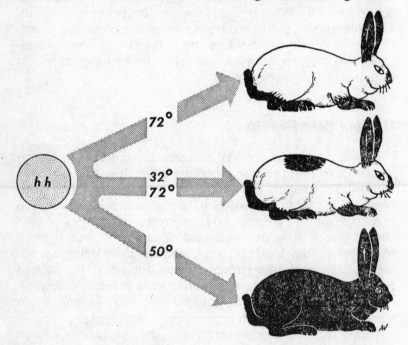

Fig. 29. Environmental alteration of gene expression in the Himalayan rabbit. The normal Himalayan rabbit is shown at the top, raised at a normal temperature. The one in the middle had an ice pack applied to his back and developed a spot of black fur at this point. The one at the bottom was kept in a refrigerator for a time when it was new-born and became black all over. All the rabbits carry the two recessive genes (hh) for the Himalayan coat.

operating in the production of this coat characteristic. It has been found that when the skin temperature drops below 92° the fur which grows out will be black, while the areas which stay in a higher temperature are white. This explains the black legs, ears, tails, and nose—these extremities have a lower temperature than the other areas of the body. One theory to explain this is that Himalayan rabbits have genes which produce black fur, but they also have the recessive gene which produces an inhibitor chemical which prevents the black pigment from forming. Whenever the temperature drops below 92° however, this inhibitor chemical becomes inactive and the pigment is produced even though the drop in temperature is for only a brief period.

Mongolism in Man

To show how opinion may vacillate from one extreme to the other when the full picture of heredity and environment is not kept in mind, let us take the case of Mongolism (Mongolian idiocy) in man. Statistics indicate that about one out of every 1,000 births results in a child afflicted with Mongolism. Such a child has certain abnormalities of the face, tongue, eyelids, and body build which are characteristic of this condition. The name *Mongolism* was chosen because there is often present a fold of the eyelid which gives the victim a superficial resemblance to members of the Mongolian race. (Incidentally, children of the Mongolian race may also have this condition and look similar to those found in the Caucasian race. The Mongolians think these abnormal children look like Caucasians and some have suggested that they might call the condition *Caucasianism*). The trait is accompanied by a very low mentality, and the birth of a child with Mongolism is a major tragedy in any family.

There was a time when it was thought that this condition was brought about because of inheritance alone, it was even postulated that it was introduced into the Caucasian race by some mingling of Mongolian genes in the past. In time, however, it was found that the number of Mongoloids born to older mothers was much higher than was found among children of younger mothers. Women past forty years of age bore between thirty and forty Mongolian idiots per thousand children, as compared with about one per thousand as is found in the average births of all mothers. When this information was revealed, some people swung to the opposite viewpoint, and the concept became prevalent that heredity had nothing to do with the occurrence of Mongolism. It was suggested that, with the increasing age of the woman there were probably some degenerative changes which caused the production of defective eggs, or the defective nourishment of the embryo, and these changes were the cause of Mongolism.

The fallacy of accepting such a purely environmental explanation for Mongolism is illustrated by this case. A young woman went to an army hospital to have her first child delivered while her husband was away on military service. To her great sorrow it turned out to be a Mongoloid child. When her husband returned they visited a physician and asked him about the advisability of their having more children. On the basis of the environmental studies he had come to accept the premise that heredity was not involved. He told them to have no fear—that this birth was just one of those rare events which will crop up in the best of families and since the woman was still young, she need have no worries about future Mongoloid children. During her second pregnancy she was apprehensive, but was relieved when the child arrived as a normal baby. With this encouragement they decided to increase their family. The third baby was taken to the mother twelve hours after its birth and the hospital record states, "The mother made the diagnosis—Mongolism."

There have been too many cases of this nature for us to assume that they were due to chance—there must be some other factors involved. The work of Dr. C. P. Oliver while at the Dight Institute for Human Genetics at the University of Minnesota indicates that when a woman bears a child who is a Mongoloid then there is about one chance in seven that any succeeding child will also be Mongoloid.

A recent study of Mongoloids has revealed that these individuals have 47, instead of 46, chromosomes; one of the standard 23 kinds of chromosomes is present in triplicate. It is now believed that this triploid condition causes Mongolism. This condition may arise if a reproductive cell carries 22 single chromosomes and a twenty-third in duplicate; upon fertilization by a normal gamete, a 47-chromosome complex results.

The increase in the incidence of Mongolism with the increase in the age of the mother indicates that the extra chromosome is probably present in the egg, and that there may be more likelihood of abnormal separation of chromosomes in older women. Egg-forming cells are laid down in the ovary before birth, but they do not undergo the final two divisions until the time of ovulation. As they age, it is possible that they develop a "stickiness" which prevents them from separating properly. This tendency toward increased "stickiness" may be hereditary, as experiments have shown that chromosome aberrations are more frequent in certain strains of animals than in others.

What Twins Tell Us

Statistics show that about one out of every eighty-five pregnancies terminates with the birth of twins. Thus, they are a fairly common occurrence yet a pair of twins always excites interest wherever they are seen. People never cease to marvel at the vivid demonstration of the influence of heredity manifested by a pair of identical twins. "They are as alike as two peas in a pod" is a common expression that is heard. On other occasions, however, they marvel at the differences which may be shown by fraternal twins and wonder why some twins can be so alike and other sets so different. Both types of twins consist of two individuals born at the same time, but the identical twins come from a single fertilized egg and, therefore, have identical genes. Fraternal twins, on the other hand, originate from two separate fertilized eggs and are no more alike from the standpoint of their genes than brothers or sisters born at different times.

Besides being an intriguing curiosity, however, human twins offer us the best possible means of solving the riddle of heredity and environment. In identical twins, all of their genes are identical, so any differences between them must certainly be caused by the differences in their environment. In fraternal twins some of the genes will be different, so the twins will show some differences due to heredity as well as environment. Identical twins are always of the same sex, have the same blood types, hair and eyes of the same color, and the same type of hair growth, while the fraternal twins may differ from one another in all of these characteristics. This shows us that characteristics of this nature result primarily from gene action and are little influenced by the environment. Other characteristics, such as body height and weight, show some degree of variation among identical twins, thus indicating that environment has some effect. When the variations in height and weight between identical twins are compared with these variations between fraternal twins of the same sex, however, we find a greater degree of variation among the fraternal twins. This indicates that heredity also plays a part in these characteristics. In such comparisons we must always use only fraternal twins of the same sex, for sex itself may cause extensive differences both in gene expression and in the environment affecting gene expression.

Extensive studies of large numbers of twins of both types have made it possible for us to determine the relative part played by heredity and environment in several human characteristics. This is often expressed in terms of concordance which is the percentage of agreement between the twins. To show how this is used, suppose we decided to determine if heredity had anything to do with a man becoming a successful surgeon. From a survey we find 50 surgeons who have identical twin brothers. Questioning these men, we find that 40 of the twin brothers are also surgeons—this is a concordance of 80 per cent. This figure does not mean much by itself because it is quite natural that parents would encourage both of their twin sons to go into the same profession and we have no proof that genes are involved. Let us carry our study further, however, and suppose we find 50 other surgeons who have fraternal twin brothers, but only 30 of the brothers are also surgeons. This is a concordance of only 60 per cent. A comparison of the concordance in the two groups indicates that genes must have some small degree of influence on an individual's success as a surgeon.

Identical Twins Reared Apart

Can you imagine how you would feel if you suddenly learned that there was another person on the earth exactly like you with respect to heredity—how you would feel if you had the opportunity to meet this person—to look into his or her face with the strange feeling that you were looking into a mirror? Such an event took place some time ago at the University of Chicago. Dr. H. H. Newman found a case where identical twin girls, named Gladys and Helen, had been born in Ohio. The tragic death of their parents caused them to be separated at eighteen months of age when they were adopted by different foster parents. Gladys was taken to a medium-sized town in Ontario, Canada, where she was reared. She left school after finishing the second grade and remained at home doing housework for her foster father, who was in poor health. At seventeen, she obtained employment in a knitting mill, and two years later moved to Detroit and took a job as a saleswoman. She held this job only a short time and then took a position in a small printing establishment.

Helen had a more fortunate environment. Her foster parents lived in a rural area in southern Michigan. They were prosperous enough to send Helen to a good college after she finished high school. Following graduation she obtained a teaching position in a large city. Here we have an excellent case for a study of the influence of environment, for the two girls had identical genes, yet were raised in considerably different environments.

The twin sisters were brought together when they were thirty-five years old. The physical traits of the two were found to be very similar. Helen was slightly more than one inch taller than her sister, but their weights were almost exactly the same. The facial features, body build, and other physical characteristics were so much alike that one twin could easily be mistaken for the other. The greatest differences showed in personality and intelligence. Helen had a distinct charm and grace, and was an interesting and animated conversationalist; Gladys seemed ill at ease and diffident, and lacked the other attractive personality traits of her sister. On intelligence tests, Helen scored twenty-four points higher than Gladys. No greater argument for the value of education and social contacts could be made than a survey of the contrast between these two girls who started their lives with the same potentialities of development.

Extensive studies of these and other identical twins who have been reared apart give us some very definite information on the place of heredity and environment in the development of the individual. Table VI is a summary of some of the findings of these studies. From this table it is apparent that identical twins reared apart are more alike, on the average, than fraternal twins reared together.

One fact which stands out in the studies is that the so-called "identical" twins are never exactly identical. Even though they are reared together, it is evident that environmental differences can cause slight differences between them. Some of these differences may even be prenatal. At birth one twin is nearly always more robust than the other, perhaps because a more favorable position in the uterus has enabled it to obtain a better food supply or to have more room to exercise. Such a prenatal advantage may be sufficient to have its effect on subsequent physical development. Then after birth, in the struggle for self-expression, one twin may gain the advantage and develop a somewhat different personality as a result.

TABLE VI

EFFECTS OF HEREDITY AND ENVIRONMENT
AS SHOWN BY TWIN STUDIES

Character	Identical Twins	Fraternal Twins	Same-sexed brothers or sisters (not twins)	Identical Twins reared apart
Height (Difference in cm.)	1.7	4.4	4.5	1.8
Weight (Difference in lbs.)	4.1	10.0	10.4	9.9
Head length (Difference in mm.)	2.9	6.2	—	2.2
Total finger ridges	5.9	22.3	—	—
Age of first menstruation in girls (Difference in mo.)	2.8	12.0	12.9	—
I. Q. Binet (Difference in Points)	5.9	9.9	9.8	8.2
Criminal record Concordance (Difference in per cent)	32.0	72.0	—	—

Criminality—Inborn or Induced?

Criminality is commonly thought of as an acquired trait brought about by pathological social conditions, yet twin studies indicate that this trait may be influenced to some degree by heredity. Five different surveys have been made during the past twenty years, each by a different person, on the possible hereditary influence in criminality. Each investigator concluded, from the results of his survey of twins, that there is a greater likelihood of criminal careers for both members of a pair of identical twins, than for both members of a pair of fraternal twins of the same sex. One study found 37 cases in the United States where at least one member of a pair of identical twins had been convicted of a major crime. In 25 of these cases the other twin had also been convicted of a major crime. In other words, there was about a 68 per cent concordance. The same study included 28 cases where at least one member of a pair of fraternal twins of the same sex had been convicted of such a crime. In only five of these cases, however, had the other twin been convicted of a major crime. This is a concordance of only about 18 per cent. These results strongly support the idea that heredity plays a part in criminality.

Studies in Germany support the same conclusion. Of 66 pairs of identical twins of which one member had been convicted of a crime, there were 45 cases in which the other member of the pair had also been convicted. From 84 pairs of fraternal twins of the same sex, there were 32 cases where both twins had been convicted. This gives a concordance of 68 and 38 respectively, figures in close agreement with the results of the study in the United States. In analyzing these results we should keep in mind the fact that similar heredity can play a considerable part in the concordance of fraternal twins, because in such twins about one-half of their genes are identical. If it were possible to study non-related persons of the same age and the same sex who were raised by the same parents, we might find that the concordance would be lower than with fraternal twins. There are very *few such* cases to be found, however.

These studies do not by any means minimize the importance of environment in the production of criminals. They do strongly suggest that there are inherited differences which would lead one person into a life of crime under certain social conditions, while another person under the same circumstances would not be influenced.

From all the many objective studies of heredity and environment we can conclude that the fertilized human egg represents only a potential human being. Within this small sphere are all of the genes which are necessary to produce an intricate human body. Without the proper environment, however, these genes are helpless—they cannot build without building materials. The quality of the building materials and the working conditions under which the genes operate is going to play a large part in the final product. It is impossible to separate nature and nurture.

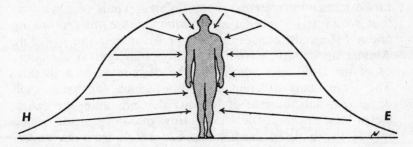

Fig. 30. Human characteristics, tabulated as to the relative influence of heredity and environment, fall into a bell-shaped curve as illustrated. A few, represented by the left side of the curve, come mainly from heredity and are little influenced by environment. A few others, represented by the right-hand side of the curve, are due mainly to environment with little influence of the genes. The great majority, however, lie in the main body of the bell where there is a strong influence of both heredity and environment in the final expression of the characteristic.

CHAPTER 22

HEREDITY AND DISEASE

Can disease be inherited? This question is frequently asked, but like so many other questions on heredity it cannot be answered by a simple yes or no. The word, disease, is a very broad term and covers so many different kinds of conditions that we must be specific as to what disease we are talking about before we can even attempt to answer the question. Almost any departure from normality of any part of the body, or of the body as a whole, can be designated as a disease. There are many different conditions which can cause such departure, and the role of heredity depends upon the cause. Germ diseases are caused by tiny microörganisms which invade the body—deficiency diseases result from an under-supply of some vital food substance—endocrine diseases are caused by an imbalance of the hormones—allergic diseases are caused by hypersensitivity to some environmental sub-stance—organic diseases are caused by abnormal functioning of body organs—mental diseases are caused by some derange-ment in the pathways of nerve impulses or by defects of the organs of the nervous system itself. We shall survey these different kinds of diseases and attempt to evaluate the role of heredity in each of them.

Germ Diseases

Of all the diseases which afflict mankind, those caused by germs would appear to be the least likely to be influenced by heredity. Suppose you are feeling well and you come in contact

258

with a person with a case of the flu. Within a few days you
also have the flu and we say that you caught the disease by
association with an infected person. How can heredity possibly enter into the picture in this case? We must consider
susceptibility. When a group of people are exposed to a contagious disease, some may take the disease while others will
not. This holds true even though none of the group has
previously had the disease or been vaccinated for it. In fact,
some people have such a natural immunity to the germs of
smallpox that a vaccination will not take even though repeated
attempts are made. There is something about the inborn make-
up which accounts for this difference in susceptibility to
diseases caused by germs.

This is brought out very clearly when we compare the
germ diseases of some of the lower animals with those of man.
The germs which cause a disease in one species usually will
not infect other species. Dogs have a disease known as dis-
temper, but people do not contract this disease. Human beings
have bad colds, but dogs do not get this disease from their
masters. Many birds of the United States have malaria, but
people do not take this type of bird malaria. Neither do birds
take the human malaria, which is caused by a different species
of germ. Hoof and mouth disease of cattle, cholera of hogs,
and encephalitis (sleeping sickness) of horses are other
diseases which do not ordinarily affect man.

It is the difference in the genes of the different species
of animals which account for this condition. The germs of the
bird malaria, for instance, are adapted for life in the kind of
blood found in birds. When they are introduced into human
blood, as they frequently are through mosquito bites, conditions are so different that they cannot establish their life
cycle. The genes which construct human blood are too different from those which construct bird blood to permit such
an interchange. Of course, there are some diseases which can
bridge this species barrier and infect several different species
of animals. Rabies, tularemia, and Rocky Mountain spotted
fever are diseases which can infect several species of mammals,

including man. The species differences are not enough to prevent the growth of the germs which cause these diseases.

There are differences among the genes of human beings which cause differences in susceptibility to germ diseases just as there are among the different species. In some people certain germs find things "just to their liking" and they easily become established. In other persons the body structure is not so favorable; consequently the germs find difficulty getting a start and may not even be able to cause an infection at all.

Tuberculosis has been studied in this light rather extensively, for the prevalance of this disease in certain family strains leaves little doubt about its being influenced by heredity. It is caused by a rod-shaped germ, the tubercule bacillus, which is so widely prevalent that hardly any of us can escape contact with it. Most of us get these germs in our systems, but we manage to escape the ravages of the disease if we are blessed with a heredity which gives us a high degree of resistance to it. Of course, the danger of tuberculosis is much greater when a person lives in a family group where there is an active case of the disease, or under conditions which lower his general body condition, but these factors do not refute the influence of heredity. Large scale studies of twins where at least one had this disease showed a 65 per cent concordance for infection among identical twins. In other words, in each 100 cases where one twin had tuberculosis, there were 65 where the other member of the set also had the disease. For fraternal twins the concordance was only 25 per cent. Such a difference leaves no doubt about the influence of heredity.

A further analysis showed that when one identical twin had a particular region of a lobe of the lungs infected, then the other twin was very likely to have the same region of the same lobe infected. Fraternal twins did not show such a strong tendency to have the same body part infected. Thus, it would seem that heredity not only influences the chance for infection, but even influences the particular area of the lungs which may be infected.

The genes for resistance to tuberculosis seem to be most prevalent among the races which have lived in long contact with the disease. Through centuries of selection the people of the white race have acquired a rather high over-all resistance. This is not true with many races which have never come in contact with the disease. There is one classic case of a South Sea Island in the Polynesian group which had never known the disease until a group of English sailors landed there in the seventeenth century. Some of the islanders developed the disease a short time later, and soon it had ravaged the entire island. Thirty years later there were only two men, of the hundreds that had inhabited the island, who were still alive. These two fled to another region to escape the curse which had doomed their population. The Negroes of western Africa, and the American Indians seem to inherit a greater susceptibility to this disease than the European Caucasians who migrated to this continent.

Poliomyelitis is a disease which strikes members of certain families in a region while leaving other families unaffected. We know that it is caused by a virus and that it is contagious, but some people are exposed and do not take the disease, and others develop an infection no worse than a bad cold. Many have the disease in this mild form without knowing it; however, they may spread it to others who can become paralyzed. Studies made by Addair and Snyder in McDowell County in West Virginia during one of the worst epidemics any region has ever known, indicate that the susceptibility to the paralysis form of the disease may be due to a recessive gene which, of course, must be transmitted from 'both parents in order to be expressed.

Measles is one germ disease which strikes so universally among children that it would seem as if heredity can do little to prevent them from taking it. Twin studies show that there is a 95 per cent concordance for identical twins, and 87 per cent concordance for fraternal twins. These figures are so nearly the same that we can assume that almost all of us have genes which make us susceptible to this childhood disease.

Congenital Germ Diseases

When a child is born with a germ disease this does not mean that the disease is inherited. We have already pointed out that germ diseases can be obtained only by an invasion of the body by the germs, so no such disease can be directly inherited. The word *congenital* is used to describe diseases which are present at birth; this means that the child must have been infected either during its embryonic life or at the time of birth.

A mother brought her two-year-old daughter to a clinic in a southwestern city for a routine check-up, and a blood test was made as a part of the medical examination. It showed a strong positive reaction of syphilis. But where could a two-year-old child have caught syphilis? The doctors knew only too well that, in all probability, this was a case of congenital syphilis. They called in the mother, the father, and their three-months-old son for testing. All three were positive and the entire family was sent to a venereal disease center where they received their shots to cure this disease as a family group. Tracing the origin of the disease, it turned out that the man had become infected and had transferred the infection to his wife. She, in turn, gave the infection to their two children congenitally. It is possible for the syphilis germs to penetrate the membranes which separate the mother's blood from the child's blood during pregnancy and a child can be born with its body swarming with these germs. Sometimes this will not be known for several years unless a blood test is made to bring it out, for there may be no clear-cut symptoms to distinguish it.

In other cases, there may be diseases of the genital tract of the mother and a child may be infected during the actual delivery. This is especially likely to happen in the case of gonorrhea. The eyes of a baby are highly susceptible to the germs of this disease and many a person is totally blind because of a congenital gonorrheal infection. Laws now demand that some antiseptic solution must be placed in the eyes of all newborn babies to prevent such tragedies. There is no telling how many thousands of persons have been saved from a lifetime of blindness by this precaution.

This passing of a disease by congenital infection is quite different from passing a disease through heredity, yet, since a child may be born with the disease in either case, the two are sometimes confused. Some diseases may result from abnormalities of organs and other causes. These can be present at birth and may be inherited, but if it is a germ disease we know that it is not inherited in the true sense of the word.

Deficiency Diseases

The human body is so designed that it cannot function properly without a number of essential elements in the food intake. Whenever any one of the necessary vitamins, minerals, or amino acids is not eaten in sufficient quantities various deficiency diseases may develop. Rickets, scurvy, pellagara, and beriberi are some of the diseases which develop when there is a deficiency of one of these vital elements. There would appear to be little chance for any influence of heredity in such diseases.

Take rickets, for instance. Whenever a child fails to get sufficient vitamin D in his diet, or he fails to get enough sunshine to produce the vitamin in his own skin, his bones will not form properly. His bones are likely to grow crooked and be deformed and he will have poorly formed teeth also. In children where vitamin D is in sufficient supply the disease will not develop. Now where could heredity enter into a case like this? Let us turn again to twin studies and see.

For identical twins there was found to be an 88 per cent concordance for rickets, while for fraternal twins the concordance was only 22 per cent. This is a definite indication of the influence of heredity. Studies on rats show us how this happens. In these control cases, certain strains of rats have been selected for high resistance to rickets and other strains have been selected for extreme susceptibility to the disease. As long as the two strains are given large quantities of vitamin D, neither will develop any cases of rickets. Whenever the vitamin is cut down in quantity, however, the rats of the susceptible strain begin to show signs of rickets, while those of the resistant strain continue normally. In time, all of the rats in one group will have rickets while none of those in the other group will have the disease. It seems, therefore, that heredity influences the amount of the vitamin that is required to ward off rickets. One rat may require up to ten times as much the quantity of vitamin D as another because of these hereditary factors. The same is true of human beings. In orphans' homes and similar children's institutions there may be a uniform diet, yet some of the children may develop vitamin deficiency diseases while others do not because of their different hereditary backgrounds. Hence, when we attempt to set standards of the minimum amount of any vitamin that is required for human nutrition we should remember that people are no more completely alike in these requirements than they are alike in the color of their eyes or the shape of their noses.

Fig. 31. The vitamin deficiency disease of rickets influenced by heredity. These two rats were fed on the same diet (low in vitamin D), but the one on the right has developed rickets while the one on the left is healthy. The one that developed rickets is from a strain of rickets susceptible rats and requires a much greater amount of vitamin D to prevent rickets than the other rat that is from a rickets resistance strain.

Diseases Due to Hormone Imbalance

Within the body of every person there are certain glands which secrete vital substances known as hormones. These must be present in exactly the right quantity or some body disturbance results. Too little of one hormone can cause one type of disease, and too much of the same one may cause another type of disease. Some of the diseases which result from an imbalance of these hormones are: diabetes, acromelalgia, myxodema, cretinism, and certain types of arthritis, Heredity plays a very strong part in the development of these diseases.

Studies of diabetes in twins show an 84 per cent concordance for identical twins and a 37 per cent concordance for fraternal twins. Diabetes is a disease which results when there is an insufficient secretion of insulin, a hormone produced by the pancreas. This hormone is necessary for proper sugar metabolism in the body, and when it is deficient, the unused sugar builds up as a waste and is excreted in the urine. If the sugar level gets too high in the blood, a person will go into a diabetic coma and may die. By taking injections of insulin, however, diabetic persons can live a normal life. There is one case of identical twins in which one developed the disease and the other did not. This shows the influence of heredity and environment very well. One twin became the owner and operator of a tavern and in the course of time he developed the habit of drinking large quantities of beer which is high in carbohydrates. (All carbohydrates are converted into simple sugar when they are digested.) He developed diabetes, but the other twin became a salesman and, without such a high intake of carbohydrate, he managed to escape the disease. It seems that heredity conditions each of us to handle a certain amount of carbohydrate, but continued excess beyond this amount may so overwork the hormone-producing parts of the pancreas that they begin to fail and we cannot assimilate the carbohydrate properly.

Obesity, excess body weight, is a condition that is found frequently in our population. It is another one of those characteristics which involves a close interplay of heredity and environment. You have seen a person who, literally, "eats like a horse," yet remains "thin as a rail." Other people count calories, diet, and exercise, yet allow them one small spree where they satisfy their appetites and up go the pounds. When heredity gives us the tendency to obesity we find it extremely hard to keep the body weight under control. And there are many who try just as diligently to gain weight, but without the help of the genes it is a difficult task. Some cases of this nature are caused by variations in the balance of hormones which are related to body metabolism. Where the rate of metabolism is lower than normal the food which is eaten is not burned as rapidly as it should be and the excess food is stored as fat. A lowered output of the thyroid hormone can cause this condition, for this is the hormone which is primarily concerned with the regulation of the rate of metabolism. Sometimes we can overcome the influence of heredity in cases of this nature by taking extra thyroid hormone to raise the metabolism to normal, just as we can give insulin to overcome the deficiency of this hormone in diabetes.

Allergic Diseases

There is a certain woman in Indiana who dreads the approach of mid-August, for each year on about the fifteenth of the month she begins to sneeze, the mucous membranes of her nose become swollen, and her eyes become irritated and bloodshot. For the next six to eight weeks she can look forward to a constant battle to keep the passages of her nose open so she can continue breathing. We say she has hay fever and, in her case, it is due to the inhalation of ragweed pollen which is so prevalent in that section of the country during late summer and early fall. Hay fever, eczema, hives, cyclic vomiting, and some types of asthma form a group of diseases known as allergic diseases. They are caused by contact with some pollen, food, cosmetic, clothing, or other substance to which the afflicted person has become sensitive. Every time such persons contact the offending substance in sufficient quantity the symptoms appear. They represent another class of diseases which, at first sight, appear to have a purely environmental explanation, but which turn out to be influenced by heredity.

Let us get back to the woman from Indiana. She married and had two children. As they matured one of them began to show symptoms of hay fever. Could this be heredity or a coincidence of environment? Had this family moved to the southern coast of California before the children were born they would never have developed hay fever because of ragweed pollen, for there is no ragweed in that region and a person cannot be allergic to a substance with which he has never had contact. Even if they had visited Indiana during ragweed season they would not show any symptoms of hay fever during at least their first visit. In California, however, it is possible that one of the children would have become sensitive to something else. Perhaps he would drink so much orange juice that he would break out with hives every time he drank some. Or, he might develop hay fever, but it might be due to sensitization to the sagebrush pollen which is abundant in California.

Hence, it is evident that a child does not inherit any specific allergy, but may inherit the ability to become easily sensitized and will develop allergies according to things which he contacts repeatedly in his own environment.

TABLE VII

CONCORDANCE FOR DISEASE IN TWINS

Disease	Percentage of Cases Where Both Twins Have Had The Same Disease	
	Identical	Fraternal
Measles	95	87
Tuberculosis	65	25
Scarlet fever	64	47
Diabetes mellitus	84	37
Rickets	88	22
Tumors	61	44
Schizophrenia	68	11

Organic Diseases

There are certain diseases due to pathological conditions of body organs which come under the heading of organic diseases. Various forms of heart trouble, stomach disorders, and kidney trouble are examples of these. The origin of such diseases is somewhat variable: sometimes they are due to simple, outright inheritance; sometimes they result from injuries due to external causes or to damage done by disease germs; in other cases they seem to simply be the result of an embryonic accident which causes a malformation of the organ. Many of the inherited organic diseases are described in Chapter 26.

Stomach ulcers are one of the plagues of modern civilization. We say that the high-tension living associated with our complex life may result in stomach ulcers. Yet we know of some people who live under great tensions and do not develop ulcers—they just are not the ulcer type. It seems that an excess secretion of hydrochloric acid by the stomach causes a corrosion of the stomach wall with the consequent ulceration. Something about the activity of the nervous system is a factor in the excessive secretion of the hydrochloric acid. Heredity conditions the relationship between the nervous system and the activity of the acid-secreting glands, making it easy for ulcers to develop in some persons.

This was brought out rather vividly in a recent study of a group who were taking treatment for ulcers in a large clinic. The families of 255 ulcer patients were studied as well as the families of 400 other patients who had diseases other than stomach ulcers. It was found that ulcers were five times as great among the relatives of the ulcer patients as they were among the relatives of the other patients. Of course, similarities of diet and conditions of stress could play a part in these results, but they strongly suggest a significant influence of heredity.

Cancer is one disease which may afflict almost any organ

of the body with disastrous results. A cancer consists of cells out of control of the rest of the body—cells which deplete, rather than contribute to, the welfare of the body. There seems to be little doubt that heredity plays a part in the predisposition to develop cancer. Studies by Madge Macklin at Ohio State University indicate that not only is the tendency to develop cancer inherited, but the age at which cancer develops, the type of cancer which develops, and even the particular body organ which is affected, are influenced by heredity. Identical twins showed a concordance of 61.3 per cent for the development of cancer, while fraternal twins showed a concordance of 44.4 per cent. When these were analyzed for the particular type of cancer which developed, it was found that 58 per cent of the identical twins had the same type of cancer, as compared to only 24.2 per cent of the fraternal twins. These figures indicate that heredity is certainly not the only factor involved in the development of cancer, but that it can give a person a strong predisposition for the development of the affliction and, to some extent, influence the area of the growth.

There are some conflicting reports on cancer and heredity and more research must be done before we come to a final conclusion. This research is hampered because it is often difficult to get accurate reports on cancer affliction. Some persons may be reluctant to report cases of cancer among their relatives, feeling as if it is a family taint which should be kept secret. Hence, studies which rely upon family pedigrees taken by the word of family members are frequently inaccurate to a rather high degree. An examination of hospital records is more reliable, but even here we sometimes find that deaths are reported for other causes when cancer was the greater contributing agent. For instance, a person might die of a perforated colon, and this cause of death be listed on the hospital record. A more careful study of the case, however, might reveal that it was a cancerous growth on the colon which brought about the perforation.

This illustrates some of the difficulties which we encounter as we attempt to solve the riddle of the influence of heredity on many kinds of disease.

Diseases Which May Be Induced or Inherited

Nature sometimes does things in such a way so as to confound man in his efforts to understand her secrets. This is true in the matter of inheritance of certain diseases. Just as we have made extensive studies which appear to confirm a heredity basis for a certain human affliction, then more data appear which show that the condition can be induced by environmental means. This does not mean that the conclusions from the first studies were wrong, nor from the second study, either—they can both be right. In other words, there are certain human abnormalities which can be proved to be due to inheritance; however, other abnormalities which look identical with them are brought on by environmental agents.

Harelip and cleft palate furnish excellent examples of the above. These are rather common conditions in which there is an incomplete fusion of the bones of the upper jaw which results in a fissure of the lip; the palate within the mouth may be divided as well. One study of twins revealed that, when an identical twin had harelip, the chance that the other twin would have it also was one-third. For fraternal twins, on the other hand, the chance was only one-twentieth. This rather definitely establishes an influence of heredity, but it shows also that heredity is not everything, otherwise, the identical twins would always both have harelip.

Studies of harelip in rats and mice show that harelip can be induced by feeding the mothers on deficient diets or, giving them insufficient oxygen, or injecting certain hormones while the embryos are developing in their bodies. Other rat and mouse studies show that there are races which will have harelip in twenty to thirty per cent of the offspring regardless of diet, oxygen, or hormones. This confused picture becomes clear when we learn that two different causes can give the same end result. There are genes for harelip which can cause this abnormality, yet, it seems an indistinguishable copy of this inherited condition can result without the genes being present because of certain environmental conditions such as dietary deficiencies, low oxygen, and excess hormones, such as cortisone.

This makes it difficult to properly counsel a young married couple who have harelip in the family. It could be a case of the environmental or the hereditary type. A careful study of the ancestry might give the answer. We must be careful in such a study, however, because a clever surgeon can correct the harelip and cleft palate so efficiently that it is not obvious that the conditions ever existed. Such a correction, of course, would not alter the genes if they are there.

CHAPTER 23

HEREDITY AND INTELLIGENCE

Intelligence is the one attribute in which man stands supreme above the entire animal kingdom. Name any other characteristic and you can find other animals which are superior. Strength?—a mature chimpanzee has four or five times the strength of a man in his upper extremities and even a young chimpanzee can tear a man to pieces with his bare hands. Size?—man is a giant when compared to most members of the animal kingdom, but put him beside an elephant or a whale and he looks puny indeed. Senses?—man is outdone on every count. What man can detect the approach of an enemy by scent or follow a trail through the trackless forest as certain animals can? What man has vision equaling that of the buzzard, which can detect a dead rabbit on the ground while flying hundreds of feet above it? What man can detect sounds with the acuity of a dog? Hardiness?—man is a weakling who must have a highly protected existence or perish. We could extend the list, but we would always come to the same conclusion: man is superior to his animal competitors for existence in the world in only one respect—intelligence. There is no other form of animal nervous activity which can approach the intelligence of the human mind.

It is easy to understand, therefore, why we should place so much emphasis on intellect in the human races. If parents were allowed any choice in the determination of characteristics which would appear in their children, there is no doubt that intelligence would come first. Suppose, for instance, you had to choose whether a child you were to bring into this world would have a normal intellect or a normal body; you would certainly not hesitate to choose the normal mind even though it had to be accompanied by a deformed body. Intelligence is the one quality which we can give our children which will make them superior to the lower forms of animal life. A girl considering a proposal of marriage will give great weight to the mental attainments of her prospective spouse. She may overlook certain physical shortcomings, but will not be likely to accept a man who is defective mentally. A man with a defective mind is a social parasite who cannot exist without the help of his more intelligent fellows.

Since intelligence is so vital, we are concerned with its source. Is intelligence something with which we are born and which will manifest itself regardless of training, or can training overcome hereditary deficiencies in intelligence? This is a very important question, for upon the answer rests the solution to many social problems. Also, in some cases it may be a very personal problem. Suppose you are considering a baby for adoption. Is its parental background important so far as its future mental development is concerned or can you give it such good training that it can become highly intelligent regardless of its inheritance?

This vital question is not an easy one to answer. The human mind is one of the most difficult of all human attributes to analyze. Take the brain of a genius and the brain of a moron and place them side by side, examine them, dissect them, and test them with every known chemical test. You will find no differences which will distinguish one from the other. If you did not know which was which, you would be just as likely to assign the brain of the moron to the genius as you would be to classify it correctly. The distinctions between grades of intellect involve fine differences which cannot be determined by examination of brain structure. At the great Wistar Institute of the University of Pennsylvania there is a collection of over 2,000 human brains which have come from persons ranging from moron to genius. These have been studied extensively by scientists from all over the world who have found no physical characteristics to distinguish the brilliant from the dull.

Genes and the I.Q.

Intelligence is a character of degree with no clear-cut lines of demarcation between the lowest and the highest. If heredity is involved, we would expect a number of different genes to contribute to this quantitative character as we found they did in the quantitative physical characters such as stature. Our studies of the influence of heredity show that every person has a basic inborn mental capacity which determines the maximum degree of intelligence which he is capable of developing. This we obtain through our genes. If all persons had exactly the same mental training then we would still have rather great variation in intelligence because of differences in inborn capacity.

All persons do not have the same mental training, however, and the potentialities of different people are developed to different degrees. Hence, there is no way to measure inborn intellect with absolute accuracy. We have the various Intelligence Quotient (I.Q.) tests which attempt to do this, but we recognize the fact that these measures must depend upon achievement to some degree as an indication of intellect. One of the best cases which demonstrates how training influences the I.Q. is that of the identical twins, Gladys and Helen, who had a very different background of mental training (See Chapter 21). Although they had identical heredity and, therefore, identical potentialities, Helen scored twenty-four points higher in I.Q. tests than her sister, evidently because of this difference in training. Other identical twins raised separately who do not have such a difference in training score much closer to each other. The average difference for all such twins studied by Dr. Newman of the University of Chicago was 8.2 points. Identical twins raised together were even closer—they had a difference of only 5.9 points. This is no greater than the difference which might exist between two tests taken by the same person at different times and can be due to the immediate circumstances of the test. Fraternal twins reared together showed an average difference of 9.9 points and ordinary brothers and sisters born at different times showed almost the same difference—specifically, 9.8 points.

These studies fairly well establish the influence of heredity on intelligence as measured by the I.Q. tests. Next, one may want to ask the question, "Do parents with high intelligence always have children with high intelligence, and those with low intelligence have children of low intelligence?" Geneticists would have to answer, no to a question put in this manner. They can say, however, that bright parents tend to have bright children and dull parents, dull children; but this statement must be qualified. Just as parents of rather small stature can occasionally produce tall children, parents with high intelligence can occasionally produce children who will fall into the lower grades of intelligence. The reverse is also true— parents of rather low intelligence can occasionally produce children who are normal or even superior. This is possible because there are a number of genes involved, and by the laws of chance some children may receive a combination which makes them quite different from their parents. The odds are against such an occurrence, however, and the chances are great that if you adopted a child from parents who were mentally dull, that the child would also be mentally dull.

One thing stands out about the inheritance of intelligence which is true of most human quantitative characteristics. Whenever both parents lie at either extreme, there is a tendency to regression toward the average among their children. In other words, very brilliant parents will, in all probability, have children who will be somewhat less brilliant than they, but still more brilliant than the average. Contrariwise, very dull parents will tend to have children somewhat more intelligent than they, but less intelligent than the average. To illustrate, Penrose found that a group of men in highly skilled clerical occupations had a mean I.Q. of 117.1, but the children of these men had a mean I.Q. of 109.1. On the other hand, a group of unskilled laborers had a mean I.Q. of 86.8 and their children had a mean of 92.0. Of course, the degree of regression in both of these groups is probably greater than would be expected if the I.Q. of both parents was considered, for it is possible that the mothers of these children were nearer the mean for the population as a whole than their husbands.

Occupation of the Parents and the I.Q.

A number of studies of inheritance of intelligence have been made on the basis of the occupations of the fathers. These always show high I.Q. ratings for the children of the fathers in the professional occupations where high intellectual capacity is required. Low ratings are found for the children of unskilled day laborers whose occupation involves manual labor almost exclusively. We might well question any quick conclusions from such studies, however, for there is little doubt that the professional men have a better income than the day laborers and can therefore, give their children a much better chance to develop their intellectual capacity. The problem would have to be attacked from another angle before we could say definitely that heredity had any influence in these results. Studies of children reared in foster homes gives us the information we need. Two studies, made by Freeman, Holzinger, and Mitchel, of American children reared in foster homes and institutions showed that most of the children with high I.Q.'s had fathers who were in the occupations where a high I.Q. was necessary. On the other hand, children reared in foster homes rated as good ranked higher than those reared in homes rated average or poor. This brings out the influence of both heredity and environment. Another study, made by Lawrence in England, was based on two groups of children, one from an orphanage where the environment was uniform, the other from an elementary school where the children's home environments were varied. In both groups, the children were rated according to the occupations of the fathers, which ranged from highly skilled and professional work down through unskilled. In both groups most of the children of highly skilled workers and professional men ranked above the 100 I.Q. level, though a few were lower. There were more children in the lower groups from the elementary school than from the institutions, which indicates the probable depressing effect of poor home environments. To sum up, a good environment seems to elevate the I.Q. of children and a bad one to depress it, but there is a definite correlation between the occupation of the fathers and the I.Q.'s of the children.

Sex and the I.Q.

Here we have a real stickler of a question, "Are boys naturally smarter than girls, or is the opposite true?" There was a time, within the memory of some living persons, when it was thought that girls were not capable of developing a higher intellect and most of the institutions of higher learning were reserved for boys. The intellectual attainments of girls who have received modern educational training, however, have dispelled this idea. Achievement in schools and scores on intelligence tests indicate that there is no overall difference in intelligence between the two sexes. This does not mean, however, that there is no difference in the mental processes of the two. All studies show that there are important differences in mental performances on different kinds of problems. Girls, as a rule, achieve a higher score on tests involving use of language, rote memory, esthetic responses, and social responses. Boys do better on tests in such fields as abstract reasoning, mathematics, and mechanical ability. Tests which are supposed to check over-all intelligence are so designed as to provide a balance of questions from the two groups so that one sex will not have an advantage over the other because of the fields of interest included.

We must add mental processes to the long list of other differences which distinguish men from women. Some might say that these differences are due altogether to environment— that the difference in training which a boy and a girl will get simply because of their sex accounts for the differences in their mental processes. One thing is certain in this case, the differences are not due to the gene differences, for the genes which make up the female brain are no different from those which make up the male brain. This does not mean, however, that all the differences must necessarily be due to training. In fact, evidence shows that they are not. Little boys and little girls given no direction, will show spontaneous differences in interests and reactions. Also, in many of the lower animals, there will be characteristic differences in mental performance between the sexes which could not be due to different training. Whatever differences come about naturally between the mental reactions of boys and girls, therefore, must be due to the influence of the sex hormones. We know that these hormones can influence the development of almost all other parts of the body and there is no reason why we should exclude the human brain. These differences can be detected in young boys and girls, but become more pronounced as the sex hormone activity is accelerated during adolescence. This is correlated with the greater differentiation in physical characteristics which comes at this time.

Men and women, as a rule, have different functions to perform in life, and it is well that there are some differences in intellectual interests and attainments. No one today would be so rash as to say that one was more intelligent than the other, but we can say that the evidence at hand indicates some difference in special aptitudes.

Race and the I.Q.

Here again we have a real "hot potato" when we try to make any generalizations about racial differences in intelligence. Racial pride, bigotry, and conflicts developed since early childhood all combine to cloud attempts at an objective study. Conflicting claims and reports are heard on all sides. Without attempting to review the many volumes of studies which have been made, let us dismiss this subject with a few brief statements. First of all, we have no way of measuring basic human intellectual capacity. It is only as that basic intelligence is expressed in response to training that it becomes apparent. We have devised tests which do a fair job of testing intelligence as long as the training of the individuals being tested does not vary too greatly. When we attempt to apply these tests to other races, however, we can expect a great difference in scores because of different backgrounds, different languages, and different training in many respects. We do know that, as in the case of the different sexes, there are differences in ways of thinking and mental performance on different problems among the members of different races. Again, as in the case of the different sexes, no person can say that his race is superior intellectually because his race happens to excel in certain types of intellectual achievements. Other races may excel in certain other intellectual achievements which will balance the over-all picture. Since races living in different geographical locations, and even those living side by side, will have a certain amount of difference in training, a great deal of the differences in intellectual achievement can be ascribed to environment. It is possible that some of the intellectual differences are due to genes which are characteristic of the different races, although there are no adequate tests to either prove or disprove this possibility. Certainly there are genes for physical characteristics which are distinctive for the different races. Mongolians have individual differences among themselves, but they all tend to have certain physical characteristics in common. There is certainly no reason why these common characteristics cannot include the intellectual qualities. There is a good possibility that they do; however, even if this is true, there would still be no reason why one race should consider itself superior to others. Even if one race was slightly superior in one respect it might be decidedly inferior in others and the picture of over-all basic intelligence would balance.

Special Aptitudes

We have already pointed out that over-all intelligence represents a blending of a large number of special aptitudes. It is possible for certain aptitudes to be inherited independently of the others. For example, there was a woman who was rated as a moron on intelligence tests and who could never learn to tell time by the clock, but who could play the piano very nicely by ear. This is an achievement of which few of the 120-plus I.Q. people can boast. This woman was high in one intellectual process, but low in others. Thus, we see that it is possible for a person to inherit high intellectual potentialities in one field independently of other fields. Specific cases in such fields as mechanics, mathematics, drawing, painting, sculpture, and other special categories show this to be true. In general, however, we find that a person who excels in one field also has above-average capabilities in many other fields.

CHAPTER 24

MENTAL DISORDERS

How many people in our population suffer from mental disorders? The number may be higher than you think. On the basis of records kept at the mental institutions in New York State, nearly five per cent of the population of that state are treated for mental disorders at some time during their lives. This is about one person out of every twenty, but even this figure is too low, for there are many persons with mental disorders who are never taken to mental institutions for treatment. These figures place mental disease at the top of the various human afflictions which cause incapacity. Any survey of human heredity which omitted its influence on this widespread disorder would certainly be incomplete.

First, let us make it clear that there are certain types of mental disorder which are entirely environmental in their origin. For instance, when the germs of syphilis penetrate the brain and destroy some of the tissue in this center of intelligence, there will be mental deterioration. A characteristic mental disorder known as paresis, or softening of the brain, results. It is difficult to infer that heredity could play any part in such cases. Brain injuries which result from hard blows on the head may also result in mental disorders which are purely environmental in their origin. The "punch-drunk" boxers, whose brains have been shocked by too many hard blows, show us how this type of mental disorder can arise. Certain dietary deficiencies may be another cause. Such disorders afflict perhaps one-third of all who must be cared for in mental institutions. For the other two-thirds there is good evidence that heredity plays at least some part. We will list some of the disorders and present the probable role of heredity in them according to the information available.

Mental Retardation

By far the greatest number of mental disorders which exist among our general population can be classed as mental retardation. A child will be born that appears quite normal, and it is only with the passing of the years that the parents slowly begin to accept the fact that their child just cannot keep up with other children of its age in activities requiring mental ability. We may say that he "just isn't bright." Such a child can bring just as much anguish to its parents as a child who is born with a clearly defined mental disorder which requires its confinement in an institution.

Mental capacity, of course, shows many degrees of variation from the lowest to the highest. Somewhere, as we go down from the scale of average intellect, we come to the point where we say that a child is mentally retarded, or feeble-minded. Usually, we set an arbitrary line of demarcation at an I.Q. of 70. Those who fall below this point, and yet are above the 50 I.Q. level, are in this group. Within this range there can be several grades of retardation from almost normal to definitely deficient. There are some in this group because of brain injury, but it would be a sad commentary on the efficiency of our obstetricians if as many infants received brain injury at birth as the parents of mentally retarded children would lead us to believe. Most of the cases of this nature result from the action of genes rather than obstetric injuries. Twin studies again give us a valuable insight as to the possible influence of heredity. In one study of 202 pairs of identical twins in which at least one was feeble-minded, it was found that both were feeble-minded in 93.6 per cent of the cases. Among 237 fraternal twins of the same sex, however, it was found that in only about 50 per cent of the cases were both feeble-minded.

Before we allow these results to give undue weight to

heredity, we should refer to studies of brothers and sisters who are not twins to see if the very fact of being a twin increases one's chance of being feeble-minded. In one extensive study it was found that when one child was feeble-minded there was only a 16 per cent chance that any other brother or sister of the same sex would be similarly afflicted. Since this figure is lower than the 50 per cent for fraternal twins we can assume, indeed, that there must be some prenatal environmental factor which has an influence. There may be something in the circumstances of twin pregnancy which has an influence on the production of feeble-mindedness. Hence, we come to the conclusion that this is one of those characteristics which results from a blend of hereditary and environmental factors. The genes which are involved usually act in a cumulative manner— that is, each one which is expressed lowers mental capacity slightly, and the child who is mentally retarded because of heredity expresses a number of such cases.

Phenylketonuria

In contrast to feeble-mindedness which is represented as a part of a continuous gradation of intellect, there are some mental disorders which are quite distinct and which result from variations in one gene only of the group which is involved in the development of intellect. To illustrate, there was a brilliant man who married a woman who also was above average in intellect. There was every reason to believe that any children they produced would be above average in intelligence. Their first child was brilliant as they had expected. The next child, however, was clearly a mental defective, with an I.Q. classification which ranked him as an idiot. When physicians examined his urine they found a certain acid present, phenylpyruvic acid, and diagnosed his condition as phenylketonuria. This acid is produced in the cells of all persons as an intermediate product of protein metabolism. In phenylketonuriacs, however, an abnormally high amount is produced; it interferes with normal mental processes and children with this defect of metabolism are imbeciles or idiots. Apparently the acid acts as a nerve poison.

We know that such a condition arises whenever a child receives a recessive gene from each parent which fails to produce the necessary enzyme for this phase of protein metabolism. Both parents in this case were highly intelligent, but they carried the gene and it came together from both sperm and egg in their second child. The other genes for intellect were probably far above the average; yet this child was defective because of the action of this one pair of genes.

Had this couple been fortunate enough to have borne this child today, instead of several years ago, there is a good possibility that the child would have been able to express the genes for superior intellect which he may have inherited from his parents, for the medical geneticists have now found exactly where the trouble lies. Protein foods are all composed of a combination of different kinds of amino acids. One of those found in most proteins is known as phenylalanine and is the one which leads to the formation of phenylpyruvic acid. Since most proteins (including all meats) contain this acid, it is difficult to prescribe a phenylalanine-free diet. Of course, synthetic amino acid combinations could be taken instead of proteins, but they have a disagreeable taste and would constitute a very dismal lifetime diet. Happily, such a drastic measure is not necessary, as it is possible to extract the phenylalamine from protein foods by treating them with certain chemicals. Because of this, there are today individuals who carry the genes which would make them idiots, but who are developing normally.

Unfortunately, once the idiocy has developed it is not possible to cure it by this method. Therefore, any baby who shows any sign of mental defect should immediately be tested for this acid in the urine so that treatment can be initiated before it is too late.

Schizophrenia

This is the most common mental disease. It affects more

than two per cent of the population. Probably more than half the persons who must be kept in mental hospitals suffer from it. In many cases, however, the trait is not severe enough to require confinement. Persons in this category may occupy gainful occupations, and may merely seem "queer" to their associates. There is no detectable degeneration of the brain in this disorder, but there is some evidence that there is a disturbance of the delicate balance of hormones in the body which lies behind the trouble. Studies on inheritance of schizophrenia are complicated by the fact that it is not clearly defined, and sometimes mental defects resulting from brain injury due to external causes or infections are classed with the type which appears without such injury.

The onset of the disease is often accompanied by some sort of mental stress; consequently, some people believe it to be caused by environment alone. A look at the studies of the affliction among close relatives of persons with this mental defect, however, reveals a clear-cut hereditary influence. When a person has schizophrenia the chance that we will find the same condition in his husband, wife, or stepchildren is about two per cent. This is about the same as is found in the general population. The chance that it will be found in one of his or her parents, however, is nine per cent. The chance that it will be found in a brother or sister is 14 per cent. If he or she has a fraternal twin the chance is 15 per cent, about the same as for a brother or sister born at a different time. For an identical twin, however, the chance jumps to 86 per cent. (These figures are corrected to allow for age variation in the appearance of the disease.) This study leaves little room for doubt as to the influence of heredity.

Many family pedigrees for schizophrenia have been collected, but it is not easy to fix the exact method of inheritance. There is much evidence to support the influence of a single gene with intermediate expression. According to this, when a person receives one gene he develops a schizoid personality. Two of the genes, on the other hand, would make a person a potential full-schizophrenic. Some environmental factor also

seems to be required, because there are some identical twins
(14 per cent) where only one shows the condition. This factor
is probably concerned with metabolic and physiological
changes which could, in turn, be related to stress. It is quite
probable that other genes are involved and these influence
the severity, age of onset, and other variable factors connected
with schizophrenia.

Mongolism

This is a rather common mental disorder which involves
a peculiar interplay of hereditary and environmental factors.
It is discussed rather thoroughly in Chapter 21.

Huntington's Chorea

This disease, which is one form of St. Vitus dance, is
characterized by an uncontrolled twitching of the voluntary
muscles of the body accompanied by mental deterioration.
Unfortunately, from the standpoint of posterity, this condition
does not develop until a person is in his thirties when children
may have already been conceived or born. The life history of
the two brothers in Minnesota (discussed in Chapter 16)
shows how tragic this affliction may be, and how it is spread
by those who do not understand its method of transmission.
It is caused by a dominant gene. Because of the serious nature
of this disease, no person with a parent, brother, or sister who
has developed it should have children.

Amaurotic Idiocy

This is a type of mental defect which exists in two forms.
In the infantile form, the child is normal at birth, but symptoms of the disease begin to appear within several months.
There ensues a gradual decline in mental ability, impairment
of vision leading to blindness, convulsions, progressive muscular weakness, and emaciation. Death usually comes before

the second birthday. There is also a juvenile form of the disease which does not begin to have its effects until a child is around six or seven years of age. At this time there begins a progressive loss of vision and this is followed by mental deterioration. Muscular incoordination then develops, and the muscles gradually waste away. Finally, there is almost complete mental obliteration, and death usually occurs before the afflicted individual reaches twenty-one years of age. Each of these forms of the disease seems to be the result of the action of a recessive gene. There are two distinct genes which have no relation to one another, one for the infantile, and one for the juvenile, form.

Manic-Depressive Psychosis

Almost all persons are likely to have alternate moods of depression and elation, but the two extremes are much more pronounced in some than in others. In its most extreme form this becomes manic-depressive psychosis and persons suffering from extreme depression may even commit suicide to terminate their mental sufferings. This disease, which is more common in women than in men, is probably due to endocrine disturbance rather than to any actual defect of the nervous system. There is no question about the influence of heredity on this mental condition. Pedigrees show the tendency for recurrence of the illness in families and one set of corrected twin studies showed 96 per cent concordance for identical twins and 19 per cent for fraternal twins.

It appears that this condition results from the actions of a single dominant gene. However, only about 50 per cent of the people who have the gene develop the affliction. This is what is known as incomplete penetrance. Even though the gene is dominant, which means that it can show when only one is present, there is still some other factor required for its expression and this factor is found in only about one-half of the people liable to have it.

Senile Dementia

Many persons have normal or brilliant minds during the greater part of their lives, but in old age show a progressive deterioration of mental faculties which may lead to complete loss of normal mentality. This condition is probably due to the degeneration of brain tissue which is a part of the general degeneration of the body organs which occurs in old age. There is a certain degree of such degeneration in most old persons, but it is much more pronounced in some than in others, and the tendency to develop pronounced dementia is influenced by heredity. Kallaman made a study of a large number of twins in New York City and found a concordance of 42.8 per cent among 33 pairs of identical twins over 59 years of age. Of 75 pairs of fraternal twins over 59 which were included in his study, there was only 8 per cent concordance. This indicates the influence of heredity, but it is not possible to trace the condition to any one gene.

Epilepsy

This disease is characterized by sudden convulsive seizures which are known as epileptic fits. In their most extreme form they cause unconsciousness, but in some persons the disease takes a milder form in which the fits are minor in nature. This is a very common nervous affliction which is found in about one person in each two hundred fifty. Still, it is one of those afflictions which has a definite social stigma, and very often is not known outside the immediate family. This is well-illustrated by the fact that one of the Dionne quintuplets, Emilie, had suffered from these seizures since she was three, but it was not until her death in 1954 that it became known to the public. It is remarkable that this condition could be kept secret for seventeen years in a person whose activities were so much in the limelight.

We know that brain injury is an agent which can cause epilepsy. This injury can be in the form of an external damage to the head, germ infection of the brain tissue, or tumor of the brain. The majority of cases, however, arise without any injury and show evidence of having an inherited background. This is brought out by studies of many families which show about four per thousand in the general population, but 62 per thousand for the offspring of a person with epilepsy. When one fraternal twin is affected there is about a three per cent chance that the other will be affected, but the percentages jump to 66 per cent for identical twins.

A great advance in our understanding of the disease has been made possible through the invention and use of the electroencephalograph, a machine which records the electrical brain waves. The pattern of waves in most persons shows a fairly regular rhythm, but all epileptics show great irregularity in the waves; also, some persons who are not epileptics show the same kind of irregularity. Sufficient studies have been made to indicate that the irregular waves are inherited as a dominant trait. Perhaps all persons who show the irregularity are potential epileptics and those who do not show the condition lack some other factor, either another gene or some environmental factor, required for the expression of epilepsy. Epilepsy is frequently found in pedigrees showing various forms of feeble-mindedness, and epileptics are frequently subnormal mentally; however, it is definitely not incompatible with normal mentality. Some highly gifted men, such as the novelist, Dostoievski and the painter, van Gogh, were epileptics.

Spinal Ataxia

The hereditary form of this disease results from a degeneration of the sensory neurons in the spinal cord, and with loss of sensation from the muscles comes defective control of them, so that the afflicted person has difficulty in maintaining his equilibrium. He sways when he stands, and staggers when he walks. As the affliction progresses, the person may lose all power of purposeful action through inability to control his voluntary muscles, and may become a helpless invalid. In most cases this condition results from the action of a rècessive gene, but there are a few pedigrees which show dominant inheritance. The two are different, however, for in the dominant form of the disease the degeneration seems to be in the brain rather than in the spinal cord.

Spastic Paraplegia

This disorder of the nervous system is also characterized by loss of control over the muscles of the body, so that simple tasks are performed with great difficulty and if the afflicted person is able to walk at all, it is with a shuffling gait. Mental retardation may accompany the condition. There is a recessive form of the disease which has its onset at about eleven years of age and a dominant form which begins at about nineteen.

Hypertrophic Neuritis

This is another disease which develops between birth and maturity. It involves an enlargement of the spinal nerves followed by ataxia of the arms and legs and eventual muscular atrophy. Recessive genes seem to be involved in its inheritance.

Shaking Palsy

This disease, paralysis agitans, usually develops between about fifty and sixty years of age. There is a gradual loss of control of the muscles and tremulous motions replace purposeful movements. The hands held in the lap may begin to tremble, then to shake violently, getting completely out of the control of the will of the afflicted person. Some family pedigrees show dominant inheritance and others indicate that a recessive gene may cause the same results. These are two entirely different genes, but it happens that the end result of their action is similar.

CHAPTER 25

FUTURE PROSPECTS

Now that we have completed a survey of some of the principles of heredity as they apply to man, the serious reader may well ask, "What of the future?" Will we be able to use our knowledge to produce a race of "supermen" who will be so far superior to us that they will look back on their primitive ancestors of the twentieth century with the same sense of superiority as we now look back on our cavemen ancestors? Or, will the human race show deterioration because of the operation of social and scientific forces which encourage the development and propagation of harmful genes? Will a young person of the future awake in the morning, insert his contact lenses so he can see to get out of bed, fit the braces to his legs so he can stand, take some medicine to keep his heart beating properly, and go to school where he will study about an age when most people could live without these special devices.

The law of natural selection operates continuously in nature. The great majority of the inferior offspring which are produced die in the terrific struggle for existence before they reach an age when they can reproduce. This is an effective, if rather inhumane, way of weeding out the harmful inherited characteristics which may crop out in the race. There is a constant selection in favor of the good gene combinations in this survival of the fittest. Can we find some substitute for the fierce law of tooth and fang that rules the jungles and keeps the human race at a high level with a method which is in accord with our conception of humanity and morality?

291

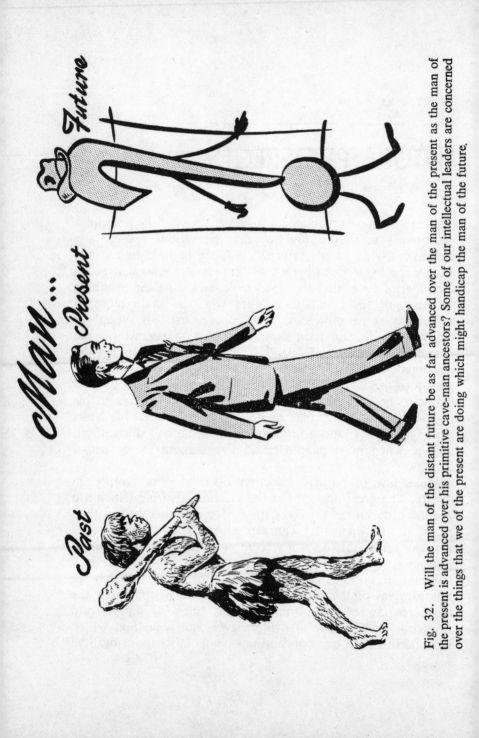

Fig. 32. Will the man of the distant future be as far advanced over the man of the present as the man of the present is advanced over his primitive cave-man ancestors? Some of our intellectual leaders are concerned over the things that we of the present are doing which might handicap the man of the future.

Let us see what the prospects are for the man of the future, and what, if anything, we of today can do to pass on genes, which at least will be as good as those we have received, to those who will populate our planet long after we have departed.

Effect of Medical Progress

Medical science has shown phenomenal progress during the past century. Many diseases and body defects which once took the lives of the afflicted persons now have been brought under control through advances in medicine and surgery. But what is this doing to our genes? We know that susceptibility to many germ diseases is inherited. When we develop a new antibiotic which can cure a disease which has had a rather high death rate, we tend to perpetuate the genes for susceptibility. Preventive medicine also may help perpetuate genes for disease susceptibility. By vaccination, quarantine, sanitation, prophylaxis, and other public health measures we have greatly reduced the dangers of infection from many serious germ diseases. Some of the population may be quite susceptible to smallpox, but by vaccination and quarantine we have practically eliminated this disease within our borders. Thus, many people live who otherwise would die of smallpox were they in a land where these preventive measures are not taken.

Surgery saves many defective genes. A child may be born with a defective heart which permits unoxygenated blood to be mixed with oxygenated blood before it is pumped through the body. Without surgery this child would probably die during the first few years of his life, but by a delicate operation the defect can be corrected and the child can lead a normal life. If there are any genes involved in the production of this defect they would be preserved. Likewise, a woman may inherit a misshapened pelvis which prevents normal delivery in childbirth. Death would terminate her first pregnancy in a primitive society, but modern surgery permits the child to be delivered with little more inconvenience than that which accompanies a normal birth. Thus, both mother and child are saved, along with the genes that may have been involved in this defect.

Medical advance has done great good for mankind—infant mortality has dropped markedly, the life span has been extended, and much of the suffering and disability which results from disease has been greatly reduced. Many of you now reading these lines would not be here were it not for this great progress. No one in his right mind would argue against the utmost use of medical skills to benefit the people of today. We should remember, however, that these benefits are bought at a price. Through their use, we can expect a gradual increase in the number of people in our population who could not exist without the aid of medical science. By its very practice, medical science is increasing the load which it will be called upon to bear in the future.

Effect of Social Welfare

In many primitive societies people who are either mentally or physically incompetent are very likely to die—without the protection of their more fortunate fellows they cannot survive. In the more highly civilized countries, however, we take pride in our humane attitude toward our less fortunate fellow beings and help them to survive. In the United States a sizable portion of our national income goes to the support of such individuals, either through governmental aid or through private charitable contributions. Few in our country actually suffer from lack of food, clothing, shelter, or medical attention, regardless of financial circumstances. Many who receive public assistance have become destitute because of accidents or other unfortunate circumstances, but in some there will be inherited defects which contribute to their inability to take care of themselves. These genes are perpetuated by our kindliness.

A Differential Birth Rate

During the early part of our national history there was room for a rapidly expanding population. Large families were the rule in all classes. Most of the population lived in rural areas where there was plenty of room for children and where children were a definite asset as potential helpers on the farm or in the kitchen. Girls married early, usually at about sixteen, and bore children at a rate of about one every two years for the entire fertile period of their lives. The death rate was quite high, for we had not learned how to control epidemics and other health hazards, but the high birth rate coupled with extensive migration of the people of other lands to our shores caused our population to increase greatly. Then came the industrialization of our nation. Great cities sprang up as factories demanded a concentration of large numbers of people in restricted areas. Agricultural developments made it possible for fewer people to produce more farm products, so the young people left the farms for the greater opportunities in the cities. Transportation was developed to move the supplies from farm to city to take care of the needs of the high urban concentration of population. Our public school system was developed and the period of education was extended.

The cities were not hospitable to large families—no longer were children an asset—they became a definite financial liability. City homes and apartments were not built for large families. The cost of bearing and rearing children soared. Mothers received medical attention during pregnancy and the children were born in hospitals rather than in the home. Medical care was extended to periodical check-ups of the mothers and children after birth—immunization shots and special diets became the custom. Education became compulsory and special lessons in music, dancing, and other subjects were undertaken at an extra cost. A college education soon was considered essential by most parents. Add up the bill and what is the cost? A conservative middle-class family was spending about $20,000 to bring one child into the world and rear him to his twenty-first birthday with the training which they deemed essential. H. J. Muller compares children with other investments in the following manner: "In general, children are not profitable investments; their cost is excessive, the dividends from them are uncertain, they are likely to depreciate in value, are practically non-transferable, and they do not mature soon enough."

As a result of all these changes in our national life the birth rate began to fall. Families of two and three became common instead of the traditional ten and twelve. Then, with the great depression of the thirties, the decline was even more pronounced and, although an increase came with the greater prosperity of the war years and has held through the present, the average birth rate is still far below that of the past century. Such a decline is not a tragedy—it would be most tragic if the rate did not decline. There is limited space in the United States and a limited amount of land which can be cultivated to feed our population. It is better for a country to achieve a voluntary leveling off before it reaches the saturation point as it has done in some countries.

We may well be concerned, however, about the proportion of children born to the different socio-economic groups of our society. The average family size of those in the lower groups is greater than that of those in the higher socio-economic groups. We realize, of course, that a person's socio-economic position in society is no definite indication that he bears good or bad genes. We do know, however, that there are many in the lower groups who are on that level because of mental or physical incompetence and, furthermore, that much of this incompetence is passed on to succeeding generations through heredity.

Also, statistical studies show that the highest reproductive rate was found among those of the lower I.Q. brackets, and the smallest rate of reproduction was found among those of the highest I.Q. level. The high-grade morons (I.Q. 50) were found to average 4.82 children while those with an I.Q. above 120 averaged 3.13 per family. Again, we know that the I.Q.

can be influenced to some extent by environment, but we also know that intellectual capacity is inherited. Finally, several studies show that the birth rate is greatest among the mothers with the least amount of formal education, and lowest among those with the most.

War

Wars are antagonistic to the propagation of the best genes of a nation. When members of the armed services are selected, those who do not come up to certain physical and mental standards are rejected. When there are large numbers of casualties, therefore, some of the best genes of a nation are drained off. To some extent this is compensated for by the fact that wars bring early marriages and a boost in the birth rate. Hitler fully realized the unfavorable genetic effects of war and, in his propaganda, admonished German girls to bear a child by a soldier going to war as a means of preserving the precious germ plasm of the finest youths of the land. As the A-bomb and H-bomb are developed for increased destructiveness, it is probable that civilian casualties of any future wars will counterbalance the loss of military manpower.

Problems of Eugenics

The application of the principles of heredity in an effort to improve mankind is known as eugenics. Man has applied the principles of heredity to produce better hogs, cattle, and sheep—can he now use these principles for an improvement of mankind? The problem is complicated. We can well imagine the consternation which would greet us if we asked a rancher to improve a herd of cattle with the following restrictions. First, all animals must be allowed to reproduce freely according to their own inclinations. Second, whenever any weak or deformed calves appeared they must be given special care to keep them alive and shall be allowed to reproduce if able. Third, each bull must have freedom to choose any cow with

which to mate, but once he has chosen, he must not be allowed
to mate with any other cows. This proposal, of course, is
ridiculous, yet one who would apply the principles of genetics
to improvement of the human race is faced with similar restrictions. The improvement which we have achieved in cattle has
resulted from careful selection of animals with the most
desirable hereditary qualities for breeding and through a rigid
program of elimination of defective calves. The best bulls
have hundreds of offspring, while those of poor quality go to
the slaughterhouse before they have an opportunity to breed.
Such techniques are, of course, out of the question at present
for human beings, although there was a time when a program
of mass artificial insemination to allow outstanding men to
father many offspring was under consideration in Russia.

Neither would people even consider the ruthless destruction of persons of defective stocks such as was practiced in
ancient Sparta. Such a program would violate all of our senti-
ments of mercy, charity, and compassion. But, some may ask,
"Does the preservation of life necessarily require that we also
permit the unfit to reproduce without limitation in the face of
the danger that their offspring might become future burdens
on society?" Or, "Can we substitute an intelligent program of
human selection to replace the more rigorous program of
natural selection which we have to some extent thwarted in
the development of our civilization?"

Reducing Reproduction Among Defectives

Now that we know that many defective traits are transmitted by means of genes, some feel that we should seek
methods to reduce the continued propagation of these genes
when they produce extreme defects. Segregation is one method
of accomplishing this. If we confine the people suffering from
inherited mental defects in institutions and prevent the mingling of the sexes, then we certainly will prevent the transmission of the genes which these defectives carry. This, of
course, has been done and is being done on a rather large scale

today for those who represent the extreme cases of mental deficiency. A greater problem, however, lies with the millions who do not require confinement, but nevertheless are not mentally competent. Experience shows that these incompetents often have very large families. We would not want to segregate these people who are not dangerous to themselves or to society. Our sense of humanity dictates that we give them public assistance so that they may live as unrestrained citizens, but what about the future burden of their children on a benevolent society? Even though such persons bear normal children they can hardly give them the home environment which would produce worth-while citizens.

Sterilization

Some years ago, sterilization was suggested as a humane solution to this problem of the propagation of defective genes. It was proposed that both men and women could have a simple operation and then would be free to live, marry if they wish, and have a normal married life except for the fact that they would have no children. In a man the operation can be accomplished in a few minutes by simply tying off the tube which carries the sperms from the testes to the interior of the body. In a woman the abdomen must be opened and the tubes which carry the eggs tied off. The sex hormones continue to be produced, and sterilized persons retain normal sexual characteristics and impulses. The author knows of men who have had this operation performed voluntarily after they had as many children as they wished and they report no effects on their sex lives whatsoever. Twenty-seven states now have laws which permit eugenic sterilization, although only one, California, has practiced it to any significant extent.

Considerable opposition has developed to this program from several sources. Some say that such laws may be formulated with all good intent, but the power may be abused when unscrupulous persons attain political power. They point to Germany as an example. Eugenic sterilization was practiced there before World War II, but in the hands of a dictator the program backfired. Some German citizens were declared unfit to bear children simply because they had a political philosophy which differed from the Nazi ideology. Class and race prejudice entered into decisions on sterilization. There were even cases reported where extreme ugliness was deemed sufficient cause for sterilization. The laws we now have are hedged with qualifications which are intended to prevent such abuse of power, but the administration of a law is the ultimate test.

Also, it is pointed out that many of the defective traits result from recessive genes, and, even though we sterilize all those who show such traits, there will still be many of these genes existent which are not expressed in the general population. Therefore, we can expect the traits to continue to appear in the future as these recessive genes come together in the children of apparently normal parents. The rate of reduction of the defective genes by total sterilization of all those who show the defects would be very slow. It has been estimated that it would require about 2,000 years of such total sterilization to reduce the genes to one-half of their present total. We could never eliminate them because through mutation new genes for such defects are constantly appearing.

Finally, there are some religious leaders who oppose the program on moral grounds. They contend that, since man does not have the power to give life, neither should he assume the right to take away the power of reproducing life.

Birth Control

Even if widely practiced, sterilization could reduce the birth rate only among those so defective that there would be no question about their undesirability as parents. This would not affect a much larger group who have hereditary taints and who live in conditions which are not conducive for the best development of children, yet who are slightly above the standards we have set for defectives. Some have suggested a freer dissemination of information about methods of birth control so that such people will have an opportunity to voluntarily restrict their family size. Federal law now prohibits the giving of such information on contraception except by a physician to a patient whose life or health would be seriously endangered by pregnancy. We all know, of course, that this law is ignored in many instances, but it still places a stumbling block in the way of instructing those who do not have the intelligence to learn about and use the available contraceptives. Some states have developed birth control clinics which are located at the places where they are needed the most, and social workers visit the poorer families which are already overburdened with children and offer information about contraception.

The great drawback to such a program lies in the fact that our present methods of contraception are somewhat expensive and require a reasonable amount of intelligence for their successful use. These factors restrict their use by those who need them the most. What we need is a reliable, easy, and inexpensive method to prevent conception. Tests with experimental animals and with volunteer human couples show that birth control in pill form is possible. There are hormones which, when taken in pill form by a woman, prevent ovulation and, therefore, fertilization. Other chemicals either kill the sperms or inhibit the action of the enzymes necessary for fertilization. More work has to be done with these contraceptive chemicals before we can be sure that there are no harmful effects from their long-continued use. At the time of this writing there are no such pills available to the general public; they are being tested on volunteers in certain sections of the world with promising results.

There are opponents to any plan which would make contraceptives more easily obtainable. They argue that we would have an unprecedented wave of immorality among our young people—girls would more easily yield to the temptation of extramarital intercourse once they were freed of the restraining influence of the fear of pregnancy. Also, that our married people would have fewer children with this knowledge

of a means of control and there would be more divorces
because statistics show that divorce is much higher among
childless couples. Furthermore, they point out that childless
women tend to be neurotic—denied the satisfaction of one
of their basic instincts, they develop real and imagined ills
which may be more expensive in the long run than the cost
of bearing and rearing children. Contraceptives, they claim,
may harm a woman and their continued use may render her
incapable of bearing children. Finally, there are some who
feel that it is morally wrong to use devices which defeat the
basic purpose of sex—that intercourse under such circumstances is no more than mutual masturbation with self-grati-
fication as its primary aim.

On the other hand, those who favor the free dissemination
of information on birth control contend that children should
be born only to those families who want them. They speak
of "planned parenthood" whereby a couple bears children
when the conditions of finance and health are propitious,
rather than letting conception occur according to the vagaries
of pure chance. They feel that the basic urge to bear children
is so strong that our best citizens will not forego parenthood
simply because they know how to avoid it. The great demand
for adoptions by childless couples testifies to the truth of this.
The proponents of birth control also feel that the moral fiber
of our young people is sufficiently strong that they will not
allow this information to lead them into promiscuity. Those
so inclined do not seem to be deterred at present, and they
often turn to the dangers and evils of abortion if their knowledge of birth control proves inadequate. They contradict the
arguments of harmful effects of contraception by pointing to
the many couples who have used such devices for many years
without apparent harm or loss of fertility.

Nearly all agree that unrestrained reproduction is not
desirable—that the health of the mother, and geographical
limitations make some restriction desirable. Those who oppose
contraception, however, point out that there are other ways
to accomplish this end. For instance, there is continence—

there can be no conception if there is no intercourse. Also, there is a so-called natural method which attempts to take advantage of the fact that the fertile period of a woman's life is limited to a few days only of each month. Some women prevent conception by this "calendar method," but since the time of ovulation may vary it is not always reliable. To paraphrase one of Abraham Lincoln's famous sayings, we might sum up the situation of the calendar method by saying: "It will work with some of the women all of the times and all of the women some of the time, but not all of the women all of the time." A check of basal body temperature each morning makes it possible to pinpoint the time when conception is possible more accurately for individual women, and to increase the chances of success of this method, but both intelligence and willpower (at certain times) are required.

Increasing Family Size

The eugenic methods we have brought out so far are negative in their approach—they seek to prevent excessive propagation of the less desirable genes by reducing the rate of reproduction among the less desirable members of our race. It is just as important that people who seem to have more desirable hereditary qualities have enough children to replace themselves. At present those most capable of rearing children and giving them the maximum opportunities in life are having the smallest families. While, we must emphasize again the fact that socio-economic position is no reliable indication of the desirability of inherited qualities, there is still the probability that the average gene complex for those in the higher groups is more desirable than would be found among those at the bottom of our social scale. Such a positive approach to the eugenic problem is difficult.

In many countries there have been inducements and rewards for parenthood. Adolf Hitler, concerned over the late marriages and small families of his people, devised a system of loans to encourage early marriage and childbearing.

A young couple wishing to marry could obtain a loan to establish their home. The loan was repaid in monthly pay-. ments over a ten-year period. However, one-fourth of the loan was canceled at the birth of each child, and payments on the balance were postponed for twelve months. This encouraged early and frequent childbearing. The number of marriages increased greatly when this program went into effect, and the German officials estimated that the birth rate was increased about one-third because of it. Sweden devised especially large income tax exemptions for parents with children under ten years of age, and special facilities for the care of expectant mothers and the delivery of their babies. France started a system of family allowances in 1932 in a similar effort to prevent the decline of their birth rate. In the United States we offer some encouragement through our income tax laws, and the armed services have special allowances for dependents which prevent hardship when the patter of little feet is heard around the house. Whenever a married couple feels that an increase in family size will not bring too drastic a lowering of the standard of living for the entire family, they usually have more children than they would if financially pressed.

Some feel that too much emphasis on financial rewards is contrary to our American ideals and that other methods can accomplish the same results. As people become better informed about the problems of eugenics they feel that there will be an increase in family size among our better citizens. The educational program of the past seems to have had its effect. It is now becoming somewhat fashionable to have babies. There was a time when a movie star would jeopardize her career if she dared to have a baby. Now she obtains a short leave and returns to the screen after the "blessed event," her charm enhanced rather than dimmed by the experience of motherhood. Such a change in attitude toward childbearing has done more than financial inducements to balance the birth rate among the different classes. Education offers us our greatest hope of positive eugenics.

International Problems of Eugenics

In many countries of the world there is no need for any sort of inducements to have children—nearly all families of all classes are large. Women start bearing children early in life and continue bearing them as long as they are fertile. The death rate among infants and young people has always been very high in these countries, but now that we have introduced techniques to control the death rate there is a problem concerning the birth rate. A country is a restricted area in which its people live, and it can produce only so much food for them. The great majority of the people in such countries live on a semi-starvation diet, getting barely enough food to keep alive. If we teach them better means of agriculture or send them large quantities of food the people live slightly better for a time, but soon the increasing population brings down the per capita amount of food and the population is again living on a semi-starvation diet. There are then more people to consume the extra food, so the gain is canceled.

Medical science has stepped in to save many people in these countries. Public health measures are reducing the deaths from the germ diseases, but this will mean that more may die of starvation. It is estimated that if we could transfer to India all of the world's skill in saving human life, so that the death rate of persons under forty in that country was the same as in the United States, in one hundred years India would produce enough people to populate the earth five times over at the present figure for the world's population. This is assuming that the birth rate remained unchanged. There simply cannot be a high and uncontrolled birth rate together with a low and controlled death rate in a finite boundary. Great Britain did much to improve the lot of the people of India and the population doubled under the British regime.

We share food, technical knowledge, and money with the people of these overpopulated countries, but we seldom arrange to share the thing which makes our way of life possible—a controlled rate of reproduction. But, how can we share such a thing? Certainly we cannot make a reduced birth rate a condition of aid to such nations. In a nation where ancestor worship makes a person wish to have as many children as possible, this would be heresy. In such countries children represent the best possible, and often the only, form of old-age insurance. Education seems to be our best hope. It has been observed time and time again in modern as well as ancient history that the birth rate falls as civilization rises. As people become more cultured, more educated, more civilized, the birth rate declines. Regardless of political and religious beliefs, customs, or other factors, people find some way to keep family size under control.

With advancing culture there is inevitably a rise in the place of woman in society. We come to look upon her as something more than a glorified queen bee whose only justification for existence is to bear and rear children. We realize that she can make a contribution to society as an individual. When this attitude develops there tends to be a drop in birth rate. Fewer babies are born, but more live, and those who live are given greater opportunities to develop into worth-while citizens. A development of such an attitude towards women could be a great contribution to some of the overcrowded and undernourished peoples of the world.

Man of the Future

All of these various trends may seem to throw a pessimistic note on the prospects for future man; but this reckons without one of the most reliable laws of nature. It is sometimes said that the only invariable thing about nature is variation. Nothing on this earth stands still—everything is in flux. The span of life of man on the earth is so brief in terms of planetary time that we can scarcely see these changes—although many men living today have seen great changes which have been wrought in their lifetimes. To see the greater and more significant changes, however, we must take a much longer look.

Suppose we could detach ourselves from this earth and view it from a vantage point in space. Furthermore, let us assume that in becoming so large our sense of time was changed in proportion so that a thousand years was equal to one second. Now let us look at the earth. The various changes of the seasons come and go so rapidly that they could not be detected, but we notice that the ice cap on the poles at times becomes much larger as the world climate becomes colder. Great glaciers cover much of the area which we now know as the temperate zones and the climate in these regions becomes frigid. Then the glaciers recede until the ice is found only at a small spot on the poles. The melting ice causes great floods over regions which were dry land. A tropical climate becomes established in areas formerly covered by ice. We see great continents sink into the sea and others rise up at other places. Huge mountains push up from the land and out of the sea, and volcanoes spew their molten lava over large areas of the earth.

If we could see the earth in this way, and this is a true picture of the earth of the past and, no doubt, is a valid projection of the earth of the future, we would never again think of this terrestrial globe of ours as a static thing. But what about the life on the earth during these great changes? There is only one way for it to survive—that is for it to change along with the changing surroundings. Those who cannot change rapidly enough become extinct. The characteristics which may be very desirable in one set of environmental conditions may be a drawback in others. Thus, life is created as an adaptable thing—all living creatures are endowed with this ability to change. Since we can feel with almost certain conviction that the conditions on our earth will be different in the future from what they are today, we can also feel with equal conviction that man will be different. If this is true, all our worry about the change which present conditions might bring is of little consequence in the long look. True, some very unpleasant developments may come from unwise actions today, but these will be of little consequence to the great stream of human life which is to inhabit the earth of the more distant future.

Yes, man of the future will be different. Just how different we cannot say, because we do not know how the conditions of the future will differ from those of today. It seems most likely that the inborn ingenuity of man, coupled with the plastic adaptability of all protoplasm, will insure his continuation as the dominant inhabitant of the earth, regardless of the errors of any particular generation.

CHAPTER 26

METHODS OF INHERITANCE OF PHYSICAL CHARACTERISTICS

In this chapter we shall list some of the many human physical characteristics which are influenced by heredity, together with their probable method of inheritance. Unfortunately, the information is not always complete and in many cases the conclusions are tentative. Also, we find cases where a number of different genes can have similar effects on the body, and this can be confusing. For example, the second and third toes of some people appear to be grown together. There are two toe nails, but the toes are joined together by a growth of skin between them. This condition of united digits is known as syndactyly. One gene which causes it is known to be recessive and sex-linked as shown by many family pedigrees. In other pedigrees, however, we find that the inheritance is due to a different gene which is recessive but not sex-linked. Hence, when we find a person with syndactyly, we can only determine which of the two genes is operating by a study of his particular ancestry. This is explained by the fact that there are many genes involved in the growth of the toes and variations of two of these can cause an effect which appears identical.

Also, we occasionally have embryonic accidents of growth which may result in physical conditions that may look very much like similar conditions caused by known genes. This can be confusing and again we must turn to family pedigrees to find the answer. Family pedigrees can also have their faults. Surgery is often used early in life to remedy inherited defects. Clubfootedness, for instance, may be inherited, but skilled orthopedic treatment and surgery in early childhood can correct the condition. As a result, an adult may never even know that he had this condition as a child. In tracing ancestry this can give an inaccurate pedigree. Then, too, even though the condition is shown, there are times when it is difficult to get the information about it. Some people are reluctant to admit any sort of defect or deformity in their family tree. They may withhold information about cases of known epilepsy, for instance, since they feel that this is a family taint.

The tabulations of inheritance of physical characteristics are presented, therefore, with a warning that they must be taken with some reservations as to their application. They do represent the results of many studies, however, and should be of value as a guide in the survey of family histories.

Hair

With all the many hues of natural hair color which may be seen on the streets today, it appears that this is a characteristic which must be influenced by a number of different genes. Studies in recent years are complicated by the fact that it is very difficult to tell just what hair color the members of the feminine sex have inherited, since environmental influences of the beauty parlor variety can cause such great deviation. There are a few things we can say, however. We know that the children resulting from marriages between persons of a dark-haired race and persons with very blonde hair are typically dark-haired. This indicates an over-all dominance of the genes for dark hair over the genes for light hair. In a mixed population, such as our own, the children of parents with opposite extremes of hair color are often intermediate in hair shades because the dark-haired parents carry some of the recessive genes for light hair. Marriages between two light blondes in our population, however, will almost invariably yield light blonde-haired children, a fact which again points to the recessive nature of blonde genes as a whole.

Red hair, on the other hand, seems to result from a single pair of recessive genes. The children of two red-haired parents practically always have red hair. Also, red-haired children may be born to parents who are not red-haired and, in such families, approximately one-fourth of the children show this trait, as would be expected when both parents carry a recessive gene which they do not show. When one parent has red hair and the other does not, then either half of the children will have red hair or none of them will have it. Again, this is as would be expected with recessive gene inheritance. Incidentally, hair color may have some relation to the endocrine secretions. A baby born of a dark-haired mother may have dark hair at birth because of the influence of the hormones of the mother even though its genes are for blonde or red hair. Apparently the baby has absorbed something from the mother which results in this dark hair. When this first hair falls out and is replaced by a new growth the lighter color will be produced. This possible hormone influence is supported by the fact that many people have lighter hair as children than as adults. As the changes in endocrines come about during adolescence there is a progressive darkening of the hair.

There seem to be two primary pigments in the hair, each of which is subject to quantitative variation. One of these, black melanin, may result in black, brown, sepia, or light blonde hair with varying shades between. Upon this is superimposed another melanin pigment which may range from sandy-red to yellow. Various genes influence the intensity and the quality of these pigments in such a way as to produce the wide variation in hair color which is characteristic of man.

The recessive gene for albinism interferes with the production of melanin in the hair as well as in the skin and the eyes. This gene, therefore, takes precedence over all of the other genes involved in the production of this pigment in the hair. When it is received from both parents no melanin will be formed regardless of the other genes. Albinos often have some color in their hair as a result of other pigments, however, Negro albinos especially, tend to have sandy-red hair of a very light shade, and white persons often have some reddish or golden-yellow pigmentation.

Gray hair is sometimes thought to result from undue worry or nervous strain and almost invariably appears with the advancing years. There is not complete agreement as to the exact cause of this phenomenon, for one theory holds that it results from the production of a substance known as leuco-keratin, while another maintains that it is due to the formation of air bubbles in the hair shaft. We do know that the age at which the hair begins turning gray is influenced by heredity. It is difficult to establish the exact method of inheritance, however, because of the effects of environmental factors such as diet. In certain family pedigrees, premature grayness is inherited through a dominant gene.

Some people have a white forelock of hair while the rest of the hair has normal pigmentation. This condition is known as a blaze. The white hair comes out of the central part of the forehead and is usually combed back over the head to produce a white streak over the darker hair. We know that a dominant gene produces this condition.

The form of hair is dependent primarily upon its shape in cross section. Straight hair is rounded, while wavy, curly and kinky hair show progressive degrees of flattening. No doubt a number of genes are involved in hair form, but in the white race the evidence indicates that a single pair of genes produces the difference between curly and straight hair. Two genes for straight hair make it straight, two for curly make it curly, and one of each gives an intermediate effect known as wavy. Thus, this is another case where neither gene is dominant—it is intermediate in inheritance.

The kinky hair of the Negro race generally dominates over the hair form of the white race, although there may be some degree of intermediate expression.

Next to color and form, the most striking feature about hair concerns its presence or absence. Baldness is a characteristic which, without doubt, can be induced by environmental agents such as disease, but a majority of the people who are bald became so because of their genes. The condition is inherited as a result of a sex-influenced gene which is dominant in men and recessive in women. The pattern of baldness which develops and the age at which it begins is also influenced by heredity. There is a related condition, hairlessness (hypotrichosis), which is characterized by complete absence of hair on the head from birth or shortly thereafter and a scant growth of hair on other parts of the body. Such a condition is inherited as a recessive trait which is similar to a recessive gene for hairlessness in domestic animals, such as cats.

The opposite condition, excessive amounts of hair on the body (hypertrichosis), may be produced by a dominant gene in man. Also, other genes may produce excessive amounts of hair only on certain body parts. Heavy, bushy eyebrows result from a dominant gene. The gene complex of different races results in variable amounts of body hair. The Ainus of northern Japan are the hairiest people on earth, the white race comes next, followed by the Negroes, while the American Indians, Mongolians, and Eskimos have little hair on the face and body. The intermediate condition of hair growth which is found among the children of interracial marriages suggests that a number of different genes are involved in this characteristic.

The growth of hair on the middle joint of the fingers is an interesting human characteristic which may easily be studied by amateur geneticists. Mid-digital hair may occur on fingers in various combinations. It is most common on the ring finger; next comes the ring finger plus the middle finger; next comes the ring finger, plus the middle finger, plus the little finger; and, least common, is hair on all four fingers. A hypothesis has been proposed to account for the inheritance of these conditions. This hypothesis assumes the presence of hair on all four fingers is dominant to its presence on three; three in turn being dominant to its presence on two; two being dominant to its presence on one; and one dominant to its presence on none. In making such a study a magnifying glass should be used to see the small hairs that might be overlooked with the naked eye.

Near the top part of the back of the head there is a crown or whorl of hair which rotates in a clockwise direction in most people. In a few cases, however, the whorl may be counterclockwise as a result of the presence of a pair of recessive genes. Occasionally, a person will have two whorls rather than one. This seems to be inherited as a recessive character, also. At the center of the forehead the hairline may dip down to form a point which is called a widow's peak. This characteristic is inherited as a dominant character.

Eyes

The color of the iris of the eye is a clearly defined human character which attracts much interest. It was one of the first human traits to be studied from the standpoint of heredity. Davenport, in 1907, studied a number of family pedigrees and suggested that brown eyes are dominant over blue eyes in the white race. There are many variations of eye color, however, which may be influenced by other genes. The blue color of the iris is due to a pigment in the back, or retinal layer, of the iris as seen through a semi-opaque, colorless layer in the front of the iris. This blue layer is present in most persons, but in those with darker eyes, it will be masked by the development of melanin in the front part of the iris. Nearly all babies of the Caucasian race are born with blue eyes, which may darken later as the melanin pigment develops in the front layer of the iris. Gray eyes seem to be a variation of the blue. Green and hazel eyes appear when the melanin partially masks the reflection from the rear of the iris. Brown and "black" (dark brown) represents an almost complete masking. There is also variation in the distribution of the melanin— it may be smoothly distributed, it may be in spots, or it may occur in a ring around the outer edge of the iris.

In most families where both parents have pure blue or

gray eyes, the children all have blue or gray eyes, thus indicating the recessive nature of the genes which influence this
character. The darker colors are generally dominant over the
blue or gray, but there is considerable variation in the expression of the darker colors because a number of genes are
involved. Of course, when the recessive gene for albinism is
expressed there is no formation of melanin. In some albinos
the iris is pink because the blood in the retinal layer becomes
visible. In other albinos there are some reflecting bodies in
the retinal layer and the eyes will appear to be pale blue.

Nearsightedness (myopia) is a very prevalent hereditary
defect of the eyes. It may be brought about by either of two
independent genes. When the eyeball is too long, a normal
lens will bring distant objects to a focus in front of the retina,
thus causing a fuzziness of the image upon the retina. Such
a condition seems to be inherited as a recessive. An excessive
curvature of the cornea is a less common cause of nearsightedness, and seems to be caused by a dominant gene.
There is also a sex-linked form of nearsightedness which has
been discovered in certain pedigrees.

Farsightedness (hyperopia) results when the eyeball is
too short for the curvature of the lens. In a normal eye, when
the muscles within the eye are relaxed, the image from distant
objects is in focus on the retina. When the eyeball is too short,
however, the point of focus is behind the retina. Hence, there
must be a constant strain on the eye muscles to accommodate
for normal vision, and it is sometimes impossible to bring
nearby objects into sharp focus at all. This condition seems
to be a dominant character.

Astigmatism is a defect of vision caused by unequal
curvature of the cornea, which causes objects in one plane
to be in sharper focus than objects in another plane. It, also
seems to result from the action of a dominant gene.

Blindness is, of course, the most serious of eye defects.
It may be induced by many environmental causes and it
may be inherited in many different forms. Keeler lists over
twenty different hereditary causes of blindness. One of the

most common of these is glaucoma, which is responsible for more hereditary blindness than any other cause. In glaucoma the fluid within the chambers of the eye develops a great internal pressure which results in destruction of the optic nerve. This is a case in which preventative surgery may be used to inhibit the development of an inherited defect: An eye operation may provide a channel for a better circulation of the fluids within the eye and, thus, relieve the undue pressure on the optic nerve. The character is dominant, but usually does not make its appearance until middle age, although in some families it has appeared as early as fifteen years of age. Cataract is another eye defect which leads to blindness. The condition is characterized by the development of an opaque condition of the lens or the cornea. We know that there are environmental agents which may lead to the production of cataract, but it is undoubtedly influenced by heredity as well. The tendency to develop cataract is inherited as a dominant, and the age it is likely to develop is also inherited. In some families it is even present at birth. Another inherited cause of blindness is retinitis pigmentosa, which is characterized by the development of a pigment alongside the blood vessels of the retina. The condition is found to result from a dominant gene in some families, and from a recessive gene in others. Optic atrophy, or degeneration of the optic nerve, which also results in blindness, is due to a recessive sex-linked gene. Micropthalmia, an inherited condition characterized by the presence of very small, non-functional eyes, is due to a sex-linked recessive gene.

Red-green color blindness is inherited as a sex-linked recessive character as was described in Chapter 12. Another sex-linked recessive gene results in an impairment of vision known as congenital night blindness. Persons showing this character see very well in good light, but very poorly in dim light. Night blindness may also result from a deficiency of vitamin A in the diet, but feeding vitamin A in large amounts to a person who inherits this gene brings no relief from the condition.

In some persons vision is impaired by an uncontrolled movement of the eyes, known as nystagmus. The eyes may undergo up and down, lateral, or rolling movements. In some families this, character is inherited as a sex-linked recessive, in others as an autosomal dominant.

The eyes of the specialized Mongolians (Chinese, Japanese, etc.) are commonly referred to as "slant-eyes." Actually the position of the eyes is the same as in the other races, but there is a fold of skin from the upper eyelid which extends down over the inner corner of the eye to produce this distinctive appearance. Interracial marriages indicate that this character is inherited as a simple dominant. Another inherited defect of the upper eyelids is called ptosis, or drooping eyelids. Persons receiving a dominant gene for this condition are unable to use the muscles which raise the upper eyelid, which therefore remains drooped down over the eye and leaves only a small slit between the upper and lower lid for vision. There are various degrees of expression of this gene. In some persons the drooping serves only to give a sleepy appearance, but, in others, it is so pronounced that the head must be thrown back in order for the person to see straight ahead.

In the early human embryo the eyelids are fused, but normally they separate at about the seventh month of development. There is an inherited condition called cryptophthalmos in which the lids fail to separate and the baby is born unable to open its eyes. This appears to be due to a recessive gene.

Ears

Many continuous variations in the size and form of the ears as well as their position on the head indicate multiple gene inheritance of ear characteristics. A few of these seem to correspond primarily to variations in a single gene. Free ear lobes seem to dominate over attached ear lobes, but there is variation in the degree of freedom of those which are not attached. The outer, rolled rim varies in size, sometimes, it is almost lacking. In some persons there is a very distinct point which projects inward from this rim. This is called Darwin's point because Charles Darwin suggested that it might be a rudiment of a condition when human ears might have been pointed like those of many other animals. It is, inherited as a dominant trait, but varies in its expression, for some people show it in one ear, but not the other. Nearly all persons have a small enlargement of the cartilage at this point, but it usually does not stand out distinctly.

The outer portions of the ear are the more noticeable, but the important functional parts are embedded in the bone within the skull. Deafness is, of course, the most serious defect of the ears. Since hearing involves the coordination of many parts of the ear, deafness may result from a number of causes. Various types of ear infections and other environmental agents may induce deafness. One inherited form of deafness, however, is present at birth. Since children so afflicted cannot hear the spoken word, they normally do not learn to speak and become deaf-mutes. At least two genes are known which produce such deaf-mutism, and both of them are recessive, so that a person will be a deaf-mute if he receives a pair of either of these two genes. Some special training institutions have been developed to teach such persons to speak and to read lips. The author once held a rather lengthy conversation with a person who had been so trained, only to learn later that the person had heard not a word that was said. Usually, however, the speech of persons born deaf is noticeably different from that of persons with normal hearing.

Another inherited form of deafness makes its appearance after maturity, beginning with a slightly defective hearing and progressing to total or near total deafness in old age. This is known as otosclerosis and is inherited as a dominant. It is usually accompanied by a ringing or buzzing in the ears. It is induced by an abnormal growth of bone around the bones of the middle ear which transmit sound vibrations and make hearing possible. This type of deafness is usually first noticed at about thirty years of age. Still another type of deafness results from atrophy of the auditory nerve which transmits the impulses from the hearing organs of the ears to the brain. This usually begins to manifest itself at about forty years of age and progresses for several years, finally resulting in complete deafness. It seems to be inherited as a dominant.

Nose

We often hear the expression, "as plain as the nose on your face," which emphasizes the fact that the nose is one of the most conspicuous of facial features. As with so many other human characteristics, we find numerous variations of many sorts in the length, width, and shape of the tip of the nose which result from multiple genes. A number of the characteristics of the nose which show simpler inheritance may be mentioned. A high, convex bridge of the nose seems to be dominant over a straight bridge or a concave bridge. The root of the nose, the point at which it joins the forehead, in some persons is quite high, forming a suitable attachment for eyeglasses; while in others it is low. There is variability in this character, but high root seems to dominate low root. A straight tip of the nose seems to be dominant over an upturned tip. The wings which spread out from the point of the nose are also quite variable, and may be wide and spreading, or narrow. The widespread wings seem to show dominance over the more narrow wings. Also, some wings may be higher than the septum of the nose, so that the openings of the nostrils are clearly visible from a side view. In other cases the wings are level with, or lower than, the septum which divides the nostrils. Some geneticists think that the high wings are recessive to the lower types.

Mouth

The lips form the gateway to the mouth and are a very prominent factor in a person's facial expression. Numerous multiple genes determine the general shape and size of the lips. Full lips seem to be dominant over thin lips in some family pedigrees. Harelip is one of the most common abnormalities of the lips. When the upper lip is first formed in early embryonic development it consists of three portions, two lateral and one median. During the second month of embryonic life these processes normally fuse to form the upper lip. On some occasions, however, they fail to fuse, most frequently on the left side, and a baby is born with a distinct cleft extending up toward the nose. The deformity takes its name from the mouth of the hare, but the cleft in this animal's upper lip is median, while that in the human lies to one side of the median line. Harelip is often accompanied by a cleft palate in the roof of the mouth. The evidence indicates that the condition is inherited, although there seem to be some cases where the genes are present yet the harelip still does not exist. Some authorities think that it is due to a recessive gene which, for some reason, is not expressed in all those who receive a pair of these genes. It does show more often in the male than in the female. There may be some other gene or some environmental factor which inhibits it. Surgery performed early in life may correct harelip and cleft palate so that the condition is not evident.

There are many genes which influence the development and conformation of the teeth. Variations in single genes may produce pronounced effects. One dominant gene causes the absence of some of the upper incisors and molars. Another dominant gene causes the absence or reduction of the two lateral incisors in the upper jaw. A sex-linked recessive gene causes the absence of the canines and perhaps some other surrounding teeth. A dominant sex-linked gene causes the absence of enamel on the teeth. This causes them to wear down rapidly so that they often barely protrude from the gums. Still another dominant gene causes a defective dentine, that is soft and opalescent. In this case, the enamel has a bluish color, and the teeth wear down easily. Brown enamel of the teeth results from a recessive sex-linked gene. Tooth decay is without doubt influenced by environmental factors, such as diet, but the susceptibility of the teeth seems to be due to a dominant gene.

As with most other body characteristics the shape and size of the tongue responds to so many different genes that it is not possible to isolate many effects of individual genes. Some people have the distinctive ability to roll their tongue into a U-shape when they extend it from the mouth. This ability seems to be due to the presence of a dominant gene. A much smaller number of people can fold the tip of the tongue over backward against the base of the tongue. This also results from a dominant gene which is not so common as the gene for tongue-rolling. The sense of taste is also associated with the tongue. There are taste buds scattered over this organ. Taste sensitivity may vary greatly, however. It has been discovered that people vary in their ability to taste a certain chemical, phenylthio-carbamide. To some this chemical has a distinctly bitter taste, to others it is quite tasteless. This is an easily measured human characteristic which has been extensively investigated. The ability to taste this substance is dominant, and the inability recessive. About 70 per cent of the American people are tasters.

Chin and Cheeks

The chin is often thought to denote some aspects of a person's character—we speak of the pugnacious, aggressive, protruding chin and the weak, timid, receding chin—but the genes which affect this portion of the human anatomy seem to have no direct relationship to inherited personality traits. The receding chin seems to be inherited as a recessive trait. The chin also varies in its length, from the lower lip to its lowest point, with multiple genes making the variation continuous. Some persons have a distinct depression, or dimple, in the lower part of the chin. This seems to be inherited as a dominant.

From a frontal view, the chin may be square, or rounded, wide or narrow, with variations between. A study of the Hapsburg dynasty of Europe shows that for six centuries there was a rather consistent transmission in the royal family of a narrow, protruding chin, together with an overhanging lower lip. Dominance of this trait certainly seems to be indicated. A double chin, however, clearly reveals the mutual influence of heredity and environment—inheritance of the necessary genes plus excessive intake of fattening foods, and poor posture.

The cheekbones may be high, low, or intermediate. Many races, such as the American Indians, are characterized by high cheekbones. The gene complex involved seems to be dominant. There is quantitative variation in the extent of the fat pads of cheeks, both as to thickness and placement. In some persons the pads are so low as to result in pendulant cheeks which hang downward. Dimples in the cheeks are inherited also, apparently as a dominant, but with some variation in expression. They may occur on one cheek or both, and in rather rare cases there may be two on one cheek.

The color of the cheeks is certainly an environmentally induced characteristic among the female members of our population, but among men, children and women without make-up there is a distinct natural variation. Rosy cheeks naturally accompany a thin skin over this area, for that would allow the blood to show through. Popular opinion to the contrary, this does not mean that such individuals have a blood supply which is richer and more abundant than those with thicker skin and less rosy cheeks. Darwin reported a family in which the tendency to blush and the manner of blushing were inherited.

Hands and Feet

There are genes which produce over-all variations in the length of the fingers and toes relative to the hand or foot, and other genes which influence the relative lengths of the individual fingers and toes. Most genes which influence fingers also influence the toes, but there are a few which affect only one of the two types of digits. There is one dominant gene for a trait, called arachnodactyly, which produces extremely long fingers and toes. Persons with this condition are said to be spider-fingered or spider-toed. Another dominant gene, for brachyphalangy, causes very short fingers, because of an extreme shortening of the middle phalanx of these digits. On the basis of a study of the children of one couple (both of whom had the condition), this gene is believed to be lethal when received from both parents. Another dominant gene causes a shortening of the fingers and toes through the apparent absence of the middle joint. This is known as brachydactyly. X-rays show that this trait involves a fusion of rudimentary middle joints with one of the other joints of the digits. Still another dominant gene, symphalangy, causes a fusion of some of the joints without any shortening. This produces stiff fingers.

Some persons are unable to straighten out their fingers because of an abnormal shortening of the flexor tendons. Possession of such flexed fingers (camptodactyly) is inherited as a dominant. The possession of crooked little fingers is a recessive trait. Hypermobility of thumb joints is another characteristic seemingly inherited as a dominant.

Polydactyly, or the presence of extra fingers and toes, was one of the first inherited traits to be traced in human pedigrees. It appears in a pedigree collected in the first half of the eighteenth century. The extra digit may be appended to the little finger or toe, or it may be attached to the thumb or the big toe. The condition is inherited as a dominant with variable expression. Some persons show it on the hands, but not on the feet, and vice versa. Another dominant gene results in a reduction of the total number of digits. This seems to be due to a fusion of digits and also varies in its expression. The most extreme expression results in "lobster claw," a condition in which there are only two digits to each hand or foot. Other persons carrying this gene may have three or four digits, and in a few cases it may be expressed only in the deformity or the absence of a nail or a single finger. Monodigital hands and feet result from a dominant gene which caused all of the fingers and toes to be fused.

Extremely short nails, brachymegalodactyly, seem to be inherited as a dominant. The complete absence of thumb nails also seem to be inherited as a dominant. In some families there may be an excessive growth of the nail-forming tissue which results in very thick nails, hyperkeratosis subungualis, another trait which is inherited as a dominant. Again, when viewed from the side, nails may show a convex curvature or may be straight. The curved condition seems to be dominant over the straight.

In some families there is a fusion of the skin, and sometimes of the bone also, between some of the toes, usually the second and third toe. This condition, syndactyly, does not extend to the tip of the toes, however. One gene for this condition is one of the very few genes which lie on the Y-chromosome, hence it is passed always from father to son, generation after generation. There is an entirely different gene which may cause the same condition that lies on one of the other chromosomes and, therefore, may show in either sex. This gene is recessive. In "hammertoe," another condition involving the feet, the big toe overlaps the others. This condition appears to be inherited as a dominant.

Swollen tips of the fingers and toes (clubbed fingers and toes) is another inherited condition. X-rays show that there is a broadening of the bones of the terminal phalanges in this condition. Similar conditions arise as a result of pulmonary or heart trouble.

Clubfoot results in serious deformity if corrective measures are not taken early in life. The most common type causes an inward turning of the foot so that the person must walk on the outer side of the foot. This is due to a shortening of the muscles or the tendons attached to the muscles on the inner side of the leg. Other types of clubfoot cause the afflicted person to walk on the front part of the foot, on the heel, or on the inner edge of the foot. Abnormal pressure on the embryonic foot will cause clubfootedness, but the frequency of the condition in some families shows that it may result from some hereditary background. In some family pedigrees it is inherited through a recessive gene, but in others a dominant gene seems to be responsible, although not all who receive the dominant gene show the trait. About one baby out of every thousand is born clubfooted and about half of these show it in both feet. Some authorities estimate that over half of the cases of clubfoot are due to heredity.

Flat-feet may result from environmental conditions, but in some families babies are born with flat feet, so that obviously the defect cannot be due to undue pressure during walking or standing. Since man is the only animal who has a definite arch to the foot, the flat foot represents a condition which is closer to that of other animals, such as bears. It is apparently inherited as a recessive trait.

The hand which we use the most is determined not by the greater development of the hand itself, but by the functional dominance of one side of the brain over the other. Since the nerve pathways cross in the brainstem, a person who is right-handed would be left-brained, in the sense that the left side of his brain would dominate the right. Just how completely heredity influences handedness is not clear, but the evidence indicates that right-handedness may be due to a dominant gene and left-handedness may be due to a recessive gene. The fact that in many pairs of identical twins one is left-handed while the other is not, shows that some other factors may also be involved. In twins there is a tendency for mirror-imaging, so that the right side of one of them will be very much like the left side of his twin. The common occurrence of left-handedness in one member of a pair of identical twins is, therefore, usually ascribed to this influence, but cases of left-handedness in other individuals may, in part at least, result from the presence of a pair of recessive genes.

Skin

Skin color, like so many other human characteristics, is inherited through multiple genes working in conjunction with environmental agents, such as sunlight. The differences in pigmentation which distinguish the white race and the Negro, however, seem to rest upon two pairs of genes, both of which are intermediate in their expression. The typical mulatto condition, with an intermediate shade of skin, results in the children of a union between members of the two races, although, of course, there is some degree of variation in the mulatto coloration due to various other genes which modify it that were present in either of the two parents. Marriages between two mulattoes produce variation from full white to full Negro pigmentation in the rather unusual ratio of 1:4:6:4:1. This topic is discussed in greater detail in Chapter 8. In Negroes a dominant gene has been observed which produces large spots of white on the skin, a piebald condition that prevails regardless of the genes for Negro pigmentation which are present. Also, the recessive gene that produces albinism causes a very fair skin, regardless of the race in which it appears. There is a dominant gene which produces unpigmented spots on the skin, a condition called vitiligo. These spots are smaller than those produced by the piebald gene, and tend to vary during the life of the individual, becoming smaller, then larger, and appearing on different parts of the body. Piebald spots, on the contrary, tend to remain constant. Freckles are the most common form of skin spotting. In freckles, pigment tends to accumulate in isolated little islands which become prominent when darkened by exposure to sunlight. The non-pigmented areas between the freckles burn, but do not tan to any great extent. Freckles seem to be inherited as a dominant in some families.

The iris of the eye, the hair, and the skin all arise from the same embryonic layer, and genes which affect one of these body parts often affects all three. Blue eyes, blond hair, and fair skin typically go together and characterize certain human races, whereas dark hair, eyes, and skin characterize other races. There are some genes, however, which may affect one of these body parts without influencing the others. Among the mixed descendants of mingled races blue eyes may sometimes be seen with dark skin and eyes. This indicates that there are some genes which affect all three of these though other genes may influence each separately.

Butterfly rash, epiloia, is a condition inherited as a dominant which is characterized externally by the appearance of rashes shaped like butterflies on the face. This condition is often accompanied by severe mental deficiency and epilepsy. Most of those with this affliction die before maturity, but in some, the symptoms are sufficiently mild to permit the person to attain adulthood and reproduce the character.

Icthyosis congenita is inherited as a recessive lethal. A baby who receives a gene for this from both parents will be born with a smooth, reddish-brown skin, which is so thick that the child cannot nurse normally because of the firmness of the skin around the lips. Soon the skin develops deep, bleeding fissures which easily become infected, and the baby usually dies within a few weeks after birth.

Icthyosis vulgaris is a much less severe condition, characterized by the development of scales on the skin. The "porcupine" or "alligator" men of the circus usually have inherited this condition. In the northern European races the condition is inherited as a dominant, but in the Latin races a sex-linked recessive form of the condition is more common.

Psoriasis is a rather common skin disease in which red, scaly patches are found on the extensor surfaces of the arms and legs. The condition usually makes its appearance at adolescence. Pedigrees show definitely that it can be inherited, and some pedigrees indicate dominant inheritance, though the majority of them indicate recessive inheritance.

Hyperelasticity of the skin is an interesting character which appears occasionally. The skin may be pulled out from the body like a rubber sheet for eight inches or more without pain. Upon release the skin returns to its normal position. This seems to be due to a deficiency of some of the connective tissue in the subcutaneous regions. It appears to be inherited as a dominant.

The absence of sweat glands in the skin is a serious affliction in warm weather, for a person with this condition will be quickly overcome with heat prostration unless he keeps his clothing wet or spends his time in a bathtub or swimming pool. One form of the disease, anidrotic ectodermal dysplasia, is accompanied by a sparse hair growth on the head and body and a deficiency in the teeth. In some families this is dominant, in others it is sex-linked recessive. The mammary glands are modified sweat glands, and in some persons with this disease the nipples on the mammary glands are absent. In some pedigrees this is inherited as a sex-linked dominant.

Skeleton

There are about two hundred bones in the adult human body, and their size, shape, and arrangement to a large extent determines the body build. Body stature as a whole is due to the combined action of multiple genes and the environment. A single gene, however, may overcome the effects of the other genes which influence bone growth. For instance, a person may inherit a series of genes for large stature, and yet may be a dwarf because of the effect of one gene. Achondroplastic dwarfism seems to result from the influence of a dominant gene. The head and trunk of a person with this type of dwarfism are normal in size, but there is a great reduction in the length of the limbs, and this results in short stature. It is accompanied by a deformity of the long bones because of the inhibition of normal growth. The legs are usually set wide apart at the hips and curve inward as they extend down toward the feet, thus giving a somewhat bowed appearance. A similar condition has been achieved by selection in one breed of dogs. The dachshund has short bowed legs and was bred for this character so that it could get into the burrows of foxes and badgers easily. The gene for this condition is found in entire human groups, such as the Congo pygmies. The shape of the head and trunk of an achondroplastic dwarf is usually somewhat deformed also.

The ateliotic dwarf, on the other hand, is well-proportioned, but small in all parts of the skeleton. This characteristic is due to a deficiency of the growth hormone of the pituitary, which influences the growth of the skeleton. Such persons are commonly called midgets or "Tom Thumb" dwarfs. Extensive studies of family pedigrees indicate that a recessive gene is responsible for this type of dwarfism.

Another type of dwarfism, osteochondrosis, results from an over-all irregularity in bone development which produces deformities of the trunk and limbs. Thus, sometimes the limbs are of normal length, but the trunk is abnormally shortened. In some family pedigrees, this condition is inherited as a sex-linked recessive.

Some persons have such fragile bones that they suffer from repeated fractures no matter how careful they may be. A baby may fracture its leg when it is caught in the sheet as it is being picked up; a schoolgirl may fracture her arm as she bumps against her desk; and a growing boy may have leg bones so fragile that he cannot stand, since his own body weight will cause them to break. Persons with this condition, known as osteopsathryosis, usually suffer so many fractures that their bodies become somewhat deformed because of the imperfect knitting of the bones. This is regularly associated with a blue color of the sclera (white) of the eye and a defect of the ear bones which results in deafness. This shows how a single gene can have multiple effects. It is a dominant gene. Another gene may cause brittle bones without the blue sclera or the deafness, and still another gene may cause this type of deafness without the brittle bones.

A few persons have the ability to fold their shoulders inward until they touch or almost touch under their chin. This is due to the absence of collar bones. It is known as dysostosis cleidocranialiasis and is inherited as a dominant.

Index

nose, 319
nymphomania, 137
nystagmus, 317

obesity, 265
orgasm, 64, 67
outlaw genes, 193, 194, 202
ovary, 53, 66, 126
ovulation, 69

pangenesis, 30
paternity suits, 185
pelger's anomaly, 217
phenylketonuria, 283
placenta, 76, 79
polar body, 92
poliomyelitis, 261
polydactylism, 169, 323
pregnancy, 22
protons, 235
proxy mothers, 49
pseudohermaphrodite, 139
psoriasis, 327

quantitative traits, 160

rabbits, 51, 97, 247
race, 188, 278
radioactivity, 224, 237, 240, 243
recessive genes, 33, 96, 156
retinoblastoma, 217
Rh factor, 180, 199
rickets, 263
r-units, 226

schizophrenia, 284
scrotum, 59
sex characteristics, 122
sex chromosomes, 108
sex determination, 106
sex-influenced genes, 149, 162
sex-limited genes, 150

sex-linked genes, 144, 161
sex ratio, 109
sex transformation, 127
sexual abnormalities, 135
senile dementia, 288
shaking palsy, 290
skin color, 103, 325
spastic paraplegia, 290
sperms, 19, 26, 57, 80, 89
spinal ataxia, 289
sterility, 224, 229
sterilization, 299
superstitions, 35
syphilis, 262

taste, 321
telegony, 41
testes, 57, 128
tic douloureux, 171
tongue rolling, 167, 321
tooth enamel, 149
tuberculosis, 171, 260, 267
twins, 86, 251, 260, 261, 263, 265, 267, 270, 274, 282

ulcers, stomach, 268
ultraviolet rays, 231
uterus (see womb)
uranium, 236

Victoria, Queen, 146, 214

war, 297
war babies, 113
weaker sex, 109
Weismann, August, 31
womb, 24, 67

xeroderma pigmentosum, 200, 207
X-chromosome, 107, 214
X rays, 224

Y-chromosome, 107

Catalog
of
DOVER BOOKS

BOOKS EXPLAINING SCIENCE

(Note: The books listed under this category are general introductions, surveys, reviews, and non-technical expositions of science for the interested layman or scientist who wishes to brush up. Dover also publishes the largest list of inexpensive reprints of books on inter-mediate and higher mathematics, mathematical physics, engineering, chemistry, astronomy, etc., for the professional mathematician or scientist. For our complete Science Catalog, write Dept. catrr., Dover Publications, Inc., 180 Varick Street, New York 14, N. Y.)

CONCERNING THE NATURE OF THINGS, Sir William· Bragg. Royal Institute Christmas Lectures by Nobel Laureate. Excellent plain-language introduction to gases, molecules, crystal struc-ture, etc. explains "building blocks" of universe, basic properties of matter, with simplest, clearest examples, demonstrations. 32pp. of photos; 57 ° figures. 244pp. 5⅜ x 8.
T31 Paperbound **$1.35**

MATTER AND LIGHT, THE NEW PHYSICS, Louis de Broglie. Non-technical explanations by a Nobel Laureate of electro-magnetic theory, relativity, wave mechanics, quantum physics, philosophies of science, etc. Simple, yet accurate introduction to work of Planck, Bohr, Einstein, other modern physicists. Only 2 of 12 chapters require mathematics. 300pp. 5⅜ x 8.
T35 Paperbound **$1.60**

THE COMMON ·SENSE OF THE EXACT SCIENCES, W. K. Clifford. For 70 years, Clifford's work has been acclaimed as one of the clearest, yet most precise introductions to mathematical symbolism, measurement, surface boundaries, position, space, motion, mass and force, etc. Prefaces by Bertrand Russell and Karl Pearson. Introduction by James Newman. 130 figures. 249pp. 5⅜ x 8.
T61 Paperbound **$1.60**

THE NATURE OF LIGHT AND COLOUR IN THE OPEN AIR, M. Minnaert. What causes mirages? haloes? "multiple" suns and moons? Professor Minnaert explains these and hundreds of other fascinating natural optical phenomena in simple terms, tells how to observe them, suggests hundreds of experiments. 200 illus; 42 photos. xvi + 362pp.
T196 Paperbound **$1:95**

SPINNING TOPS AND GYROSCOPIC MOTION, John Perry. Classic elementary text on dynamics of rotation treats gyroscopes, tops, how quasi-rigidity is induced in paper disks, smoke rings, chains, etc, by rapid motion, precession, earth's motion, etc. Contains many easy-to-perform experiments. Appendix on practical uses of gyroscopes. 62 figures. 128pp.
T416 Paperbound **$1.00**

A CONCISE HISTORY OF MATHEMATICS, D. Struik. This lucid, easily followed history of mathematics from the Ancient Near East to modern times requires no mathematical back-ground itself, yet introduces both mathematicians and laymen to basic concepts and discoveries and the men who made them. Contains a collection of 31 portraits of eminent mathematicians. Bibliography. xix + 299pp. 5⅜ x 8.
T255 Paperbound **$1.75**

THE RESTLESS UNIVERSE, Max Born. A remarkably clear, thorough exposition of gases, electrons, ions, waves and particles, electronic structure of the atom, nuclear physics, written for the layman by a Nobel Laureate. "Much ·more thorough and deep than most attempts . . . easy and delightful," CHEMICAL AND ENGINEERING NEWS. Includes 7 animated sequences showing motion of molecules, alpha particles, etc. 11 full-page plates of photo-graphs. Total of nearly 600 illus. 315pp. 6⅛ x 9¼.
T412 Paperbound **$2.00**

WHAT IS SCIENCE?, N. Campbell. The role of experiment, the function of mathematics, the nature of scientific laws, the limitations of science, and many other provocative topics are explored without technicalities by an eminent scientist. "Still an excellent introduction to scientific philosophy," H. Margenau in PHYSICS TODAY. 192pp. 5⅜ x 8.
S43 Paperbound **$1.25**

FADS AND FALLACIES IN THE NAME OF SCIENCE, Martin Gardner. The standard account of the various cults, quack systems and delusions which have recently masqueraded as science: hollow earth theory, Atlantis, dianetics, Reich's orgone theory, flying saucers, Bridey Murphy, psionics, irridiagnosis, many other fascinating fallacies that deluded tens of thousands. "Should be read by everyone, scientist and non-scientist alike," R. T. Birge, Prof. Emeritus, Univ. of California; Former President, American Physical Society. Formerly titled, "In the Name of Science." Revised and enlarged edition. x + 365pp. 5⅜ x 8.
T394 Paperbound **$1.50**

THE STUDY OF THE HISTORY OF MATHEMATICS, THE STUDY OF THE HISTORY OF SCIENCE, G. Sarton. Two books bound as one. Both volumes are standard introductions to their fields by an eminent science historian. They discuss problems of historical research, teaching, pitfalls, other matters of interest to the historically oriented writer, teacher, or student. Both have extensive bibliographies. 10 illustrations. 188pp. 5⅜ x 8. T240 Paperbound **$1.25**

THE PRINCIPLES OF SCIENCE, W. S. Jevons. Unabridged reprinting of a milestone in the development of symbolic logic and other subjects concerning scientific methodology, probability, inferential validity, etc. Also describes Jevons' "logic machine," an early precursor of modern electronic calculators. Preface by E. Nagel. 839pp. 5⅜ x 8. S446 Paperbound **$2.98**

SCIENCE THEORY AND MAN, Erwin Schroedinger. Complete, unabridged reprinting of "Science and the Human Temperament" plus an additional essay "What is an Elementary Particle?" Nobel Laureate Schroedinger discusses many aspects of modern physics from novel points of view which provide unusual insights for both laymen and physicists. 192 pp. 5⅜ x 8.
T428 Paperbound **$1.35**

BRIDGES AND THEIR BUILDERS, D. B. Steinman & S. R. Watson. Information about ancient, medieval, modern bridges; how they were built; who built them; the structural principles employed; the materials they are built of; etc. Written by one of the world's leading authorities on bridge design and construction. New, revised, expanded edition. 23 photos; 26 line drawings, xvii + 401pp. 5⅜ x 8. T431 Paperbound **$1.95**

HISTORY OF MATHEMATICS, D. E. Smith. Most comprehensive non-technical history of math in English. In two volumes. Vol. I: A chronological examination of the growth of mathematics from primitive concepts up to 1900. Vol. II: The development of ideas in specific fields and areas, up through elementary calculus. The lives and works of over a thousand mathematicians are covered; thousands of specific historical problems and their solutions are clearly explained. Total of 510 illustrations, 1355pp. 5⅜ x 8. Set boxed in attractive container. T429, T430 Paperbound, the set **$5.00**

PHILOSOPHY AND THE PHYSICISTS, L. S. Stebbing. A philosopher examines the philosophical implications of modern science by posing a lively critical attack on the popular science expositions of Sir James Jeans and Arthur Eddington. xvi + 295pp. 5⅜ x 8.
T480 Paperbound **$1.65**

ON MATHEMATICS AND MATHEMATICIANS, R. E. Moritz. The first collection of quotations by and about mathematicians in English. 1140 anecdotes, aphorisms, definitions, speculations, etc. give both mathematicians and layman stimulating new insights into what mathematics is, and into the personalities of the great mathematicians from Archimedes to Euler, Gauss, Klein, Weierstrass. Invaluable to teachers, writers. Extensive cross index. 410pp. 5⅜ x 8.
T489 Paperbound **$1.95**

NATURAL SCIENCE, BIOLOGY, GEOLOGY, TRAVEL

A SHORT HISTORY OF ANATOMY AND PHYSIOLOGY FROM THE GREEKS TO HARVEY, C. Singer. A great medical historian's fascinating intermediate account of the slow advance of anatomical and physiological knowledge from pre-scientific times to Vesalius, Harvey. 139 unusually interesting illustrations. 221pp. 5⅜ x 8. T389 Paperbound **$1.75**

THE BEHAVIOUR AND SOCIAL LIFE OF HONEYBEES, Ronald Ribbands. The most comprehensive, lucid and authoritative book on bee habits, communication, duties, cell life, motivations, etc. "A MUST for every scientist, experimenter, and educator, and a happy and valuable selection for all interested in the honeybee," AMERICAN BEE JOURNAL. 690-item bibliography. 127 illus.; 11 photographic plates. 352pp. 5⅜ x 8⅜. S410 Clothbound **$4.50**

TRAVELS OF WILLIAM BARTRAM, edited by Mark Van Doren. One of the 18th century's most delightful books, and one of the few first-hand sources of information about American geography, natural history, and anthropology of American Indian tribes of the time. "The mind of a scientist with the soul of a poet," John Livingston Lowes. 13 original illustrations, maps. Introduction by Mark Van Doren. 448pp. 5⅜ x 8. T326 Paperbound **$2.00**

STUDIES ON THE STRUCTURE AND DEVELOPMENT OF VERTEBRATES, Edwin Goodrich. The definitive study of the skeleton, fins and limbs, head region, divisions of the body cavity, vascular, respiratory, excretory systems, etc., of vertebrates from fish to higher mammals, by the greatest comparative anatomist of recent times. "The standard textbook," JOURNAL OF ANATOMY. 754 illus. 69-page biographical study. 1186-item bibliography. 2 vols. Total of 906pp. 5⅜ x 8. Vol. I: S449 Paperbound **$2.50**
Vol. II: S450 Paperbound **$2.50**

THE BIRTH AND DEVELOPMENT OF THE GEOLOGICAL SCIENCES, F. D. Adams. The most complete and thorough history of the earth sciences in print. Covers over 300 geological thinkers and systems; treats fossils, theories of stone growth, paleontology, earthquakes, vulcanists vs. neptunists, odd theories, etc. 91 illustrations, including medieval, Renaissance wood cuts, etc. 632 footnotes and bibliographic notes. 511pp. 308pp. 5⅜ x 8.   T5 Paperbound **$2.00**

FROM MAGIC TO SCIENCE, Charles Singer. A close study of aspects of medical science from the Roman Empire through the Renaissance. The sections on early herbals, and "The Visions of Hildegarde of Bingen," are probably the best studies of these subjects available. 158 unusual classic and medieval illustrations. xxvii + 365pp. 5⅜ x 8.   T390 Paperbound **$2.00**

SAILING ALONE AROUND THE WORLD, Captain Joshua Slocum. Captain Slocum's personal account of his single-handed voyage around the world in a 34-foot boat he rebuilt himself. A classic of both seamanship and descriptive writing. "A nautical equivalent of Thoreau's account," Van Wyck Brooks. 67 illus. 308pp. 5⅜ x 8.   T326 Paperbound **$1.00**

TREES OF THE EASTERN AND CENTRAL UNITED STATES AND CANADA, W. M. Harlow. Standard middle-level guide designed to help you know the characteristics of Eastern trees and identify them at sight by means of an 8-page synoptic key. More than 600 drawings and photographs of twigs, leaves, fruit, other features. xiii + 288pp. 4⅝ x 6½.
T395 Paperbound **$1.35**

FRUIT KEY AND TWIG KEY ("Fruit Key to Northeastern Trees," "Twig Key to Deciduous Woody Plants of Eastern North America"), **W. M. Harlow.** Identify trees in fall, winter, spring. Easy-to-use, synoptic keys, with photographs of every twig and fruit identified. Covers 120 different fruits, 160 different twigs. Over 350 photos. Bibliographies. Glossaries. Total of 143pp. 5⅝ x 8⅜.   T511 Paperbound **$1.25**

INTRODUCTION TO THE STUDY OF EXPERIMENTAL MEDICINE, Claude Bernard. This classic records Bernard's far-reaching efforts to transform physiology into an exact science. It covers problems of vivisection, the limits of physiological experiment, hypotheses in medical experimentation, hundreds of others. Many of his own famous experiments on the liver, the pancreas, etc., are used as examples. Foreword by I. B. Cohen. xxv + 266pp. 5⅜ x 8.
T400 Paperbound **$1.50**

THE ORIGIN OF LIFE, A. I. Oparin. The first modern statement that life evolved from complex nitro-carbon compounds, carefully presented according to modern biochemical knowledge of primary colloids, organic molecules, etc. Begins with historical introduction to the problem of the origin of life. Bibliography. xxv + 270pp. 5⅜ x 8.   S213 Paperbound **$1.75**

A HISTORY OF ASTRONOMY FROM THALES TO KEPLER, J. L. E. Dreyer. The only work in English which provides a detailed picture of man's cosmological views from Egypt, Babylonia, Greece, and Alexandria to Copernicus, Tycho Brahe and Kepler. "Standard reference on Greek astronomy and the Copernican revolution," SKY AND TELESCOPE. Formerly called "A History of Planetary Systems From Thales to Kepler." Bibliography. 21 diagrams. xvii + 430pp. 5⅜ x 8.
S79 Paperbound **$1.98**

URANIUM PROSPECTING, H. L. Barnes. A professional geologist tells you what you need to know. Hundreds of facts about minerals, tests, detectors, sampling, assays, claiming, developing, government regulations, etc. Glossary of technical terms. Annotated bibliography. x + 117pp. 5⅜ x 8.   T309 Paperbound **$1.00**

DE RE METALLICA, Georgius Agricola. All 12 books of this 400 year old classic on metals and metal production, fully annotated, and containing all 289 of the 16th century woodcuts which made the original an artistic masterpiece. A superb gift for geologists, engineers, libraries, artists, historians. Translated by Herbert Hoover & L. H. Hoover. Bibliography, survey of ancient authors. 289 illustrations of the excavating, assaying, smelting, refining, and countless other metal production operations described in the text. 672pp. 6¾ x 10¾. Deluxe library edition.   S6 Clothbound **$10.00**

DE MAGNETE, William Gilbert. A landmark of science by the man who first used the word "electricity," distinguished between static electricity and magnetism, and founded a new science. P. F. Mottelay translation. 90 figures. lix + 368pp. 5⅜ x 8.   S470 Paperbound **$2.00**

THE AUTOBIOGRAPHY OF CHARLES DARWIN AND SELECTED LETTERS, Francis Darwin, ed. Fascinating documents on Darwin's early life, the voyage of the "Beagle," the discovery of evolution, Darwin's thought on mimicry, plant development, vivisection, evolution, many other subjects Letters to Henslow, Lyell, Hooker, Wallace, Kingsley, etc. Appendix. 365pp. 5⅜ x 8.   T479 Paperbound **$1.65**

A WAY OF LIFE AND OTHER SELECTED WRITINGS OF SIR WILLIAM OSLER. 16 of the great physician, teacher and humanist's most inspiring writings on a practical philosophy of life, science and the humanities, and the history of medicine. 5 photographs. Introduction by G. L. Keynes, M.D., F.R.C.S. xx + 278pp. 5⅜ x 8.   T488 Paperbound **$1.50**

LITERATURE

WORLD DRAMA, B. H. Clark. 46 plays from Ancient Greece, Rome, to India, China, Japan. Plays by Aeschylus, Sophocles, Euripides, Aristophanes, Plautus, Marlowe, Jonson, Farquhar, Goldsmith, Cervantes, Molière, Dumas, Goethe, Schiller, Ibsen, many others. One of the most comprehensive collections of important plays from all literature available in English. Over ⅓ of this material is unavailable in any other current edition. Reading lists. 2 volumes. Total of 1364pp. 5⅜ x 8. Vol. I, T57 Paperbound **$2.00** Vol. II, T59 Paperbound **$2.00**

MASTERS OF THE DRAMA, John Gassner. The most comprehensive history of the drama in print. Covers more than 800 dramatists and over 2000 plays from the Greeks to modern Western, Near Eastern, Oriental drama. Plot summaries, theatre history, etc. "Best of its kind in English," NEW REPUBLIC. 35 pages of bibliography. 77 photos and drawings. Deluxe edition. xxii + 890pp. 5⅜ x 8. T100 Clothbound **$5.95**

THE DRAMA OF LUIGI PIRANDELLO, D. Vittorini. All 38 of Pirandello's plays (to 1935) summarized and analyzed in terms of symbolic techniques, plot structure, etc. The only authorized work. Foreword by Pirandello. Biography. Bibliography. xiii + 350pp. 5⅜ x 8. T435 Paperbound **$1.98**

ARISTOTLE'S THEORY OF POETRY AND THE FINE ARTS, S. H. Butcher, ed. The celebrated "Butcher translation" faced page by page with the Greek text; Butcher's 300-page introduction to Greek poetic, dramatic thought. Modern Aristotelian criticism discussed by John Gassner. lxxvi + 421pp. 5⅜ x 8. T42 Paperbound **$2.00**

EUGENE O'NEILL: THE MAN AND HIS PLAYS, B. H. Clark. The first published source-book on O'Neill's life and work. Analyzes each play from the early THE WEB up to THE ICEMAN COMETH. Supplies much information about environmental and dramatic influences. ix + 182pp. 5⅜ x 8. T379 Paperbound **$1.25**

INTRODUCTION TO ENGLISH LITERATURE, B. Dobrée, ed. Most compendious literary aid in its price range. Extensive, categorized bibliography (with entries up to 1949) of more than 5,000 poets, dramatists, novelists, as well as historians, philosophers, economists, religious writers, travellers, and scientists of literary stature. Information about manuscripts, important biographical data. Critical, historical, background works not simply listed, but evaluated. Each volume also contains a long introduction to the period it covers.

Vol. I: **THE BEGINNINGS OF ENGLISH LITERATURE TO SKELTON, 1509, W. L. Renwick. H. Orton.** 450pp. 5⅛ x 7⅛. T75 Clothbound **$3.50**
Vol. II: **THE ENGLISH RENAISSANCE, 1510-1688, V. de Sola Pinto.** 381pp. 5⅛ x 7⅛. T76 Clothbound **$3.50**
Vol. III: **THE AUGUSTANS AND ROMANTICS, 1689-1830, H. Dyson, J. Butt.** 320pp. 5⅛ x 7⅛. T77 Clothbound **$3.50**
Vol. IV: **THE VICTORIANS AND AFTER, 1830-1914, E. Batho, B. Dobrée.** 360pp. 5⅛ x 7⅛. T78 Clothbound **$3.50**

EPIC AND ROMANCE, W. P. Ker. The standard survey of Medieval epic and romance by a foremost authority on Medieval literature. Covers historical background, plot, literary analysis, significance of Teutonic epics, Icelandic sagas, Beowulf, French chansons de geste, the Niebelungenlied, Arthurian romances, much more. 422pp. 5⅜ x 8. T355 Paperbound **$1.95**

THE HEART OF EMERSON'S JOURNALS, Bliss Perry, ed. Emerson's most intimate thoughts, impressions, records of conversations with Channing, Hawthorne, Thoreau, etc., carefully chosen from the 10 volumes of The Journals. "The essays do not reveal the power of Emerson's mind . . .as do these hasty and informal writings," N. Y. TIMES. Preface by B. Perry. 370pp. 5⅜ x 8. T447 Paperbound **$1.85**

A SOURCE BOOK IN THEATRICAL HISTORY, A. M. Nagler. (Formerly, "Sources of Theatrical History.") Over 300 selected passages by contemporary observers tell about styles of acting, direction, make-up, scene designing, etc., in the theatre's great periods from ancient Greece to the Théâtre Libre. "Indispensable complement to the study of drama," EDUCATIONAL THEATRE JOURNAL. Prof. Nagler, Yale Univ. School of Drama, also supplies notes, references. 85 illustrations. 611pp. 5⅜ x 8. T515 Paperbound **$2.75**

THE ART OF THE STORY-TELLER, M. L. Shedlock. Regarded as the finest, most helpful book on telling stories to children, by a great story-teller. How to catch, hold, recapture attention; how to choose material; many other aspects. Also includes: a 99-page selection of Miss Shedlock's most successful stories; extensive bibliography of other stories. xxi + 320pp. 5⅜ x 8. T245 Clothbound **$3.50**

THE DEVIL'S DICTIONARY, Ambrose Bierce. Over 1000 short, ironic definitions in alphabetical order, by America's greatest satirist in the classical tradition. "Some of the most gorgeous witticisms in the English language," H. L. Mencken. 144pp. 5⅜ x 8. T487 Paperbound **$1.00**

DOVER BOOKS

MUSIC

A DICTIONARY OF HYMNOLOGY, John Julian. More than 30,000 entries on individual hymns, their authorship, textual variations, location of texts, dates and circumstances of composition, denominational and ritual usages, the biographies of more than 9,000 hymn writers, essays on important topics such as children's hymns and Christmas carols, and hundreds of thousands of other important facts about hymns which are virtually impossible to find anywhere else. Convenient alphabetical listing, and a 200-page double-columned index of first lines enable you to track down virtually any hymn ever written. Total of 1786pp. 6¼ x 9¼. 2 volumes.   T133. The Set, Clothbound **$15.00**

STRUCTURAL HEARING, TONAL COHERENCE IN MUSIC, Felix Salzer. Extends the well-known Schenker approach to include modern music, music of the middle ages, and Renaissance music. Explores the phenomenon of tonal organization by discussing more than 500 compositions, and offers unusual new insights into the theory of composition and musical relationships. "The foundation on which all teaching in music theory has been based at this college," Leopold Mannes, President, The Mannes College of Music. Total of 658pp. 6½ x 9¼. 2 volumes.   S418 The set, Clothbound **$8.00**

A GENERAL HISTORY OF MUSIC, Charles Burney. The complete history of music from the Greeks up to 1789 by the 18th century musical historian who personally knew the great Baroque composers. Covers sacred and secular, vocal and instrumental, operatic and symphonic music; treats theory, notation, forms, instruments; discusses composers, performers, important works. Invaluable as a source of information on the period for students, historians, musicians. "Surprisingly few of Burney's statements have been invalidated by modern research . . . still of great value," NEW YORK TIMES. Edited and corrected by Frank Mercer. 35 figures. 1915pp. 5½ x 8½. 2 volumes.   T36 The set, Clothbound **$12.50**

JOHANN SEBASTIAN BACH, Phillip Spitta. Recognized as one of the greatest accomplishments of musical scholarship and far and away the definitive coverage of Bach's works. Hundreds of individual pieces are analyzed. Major works, such as the B Minor Mass and the St. Matthew Passion are examined in minute detail. Spitta also deals with the works of Buxtehude, Pachelbel, and others of the period. Can be read with profit even by those without a knowledge of the technicalities of musical composition. "Unchallenged as the last word on one of the supreme geniuses of music," John Barkham, SATURDAY REVIEW SYNDICATE. Total of 1819pp. 5⅜ x 8. 2 volumes.   T252 The set, Clothbound **$10.00**

HISTORY

THE IDEA OF PROGRESS, J. B. Bury. Prof. Bury traces the evolution of a central concept of Western civilization in Greek, Roman, Medieval, and Renaissance thought to its flowering in the 17th and 18th centuries. Introduction by Charles Beard. xl + 357pp. 5⅜ x 8.
T39 Clothbound **$3.95**
T40 Paperbound **$1.95**

THE ANCIENT GREEK HISTORIANS, J. B. Bury. Greek historians such as Herodotus, Thucydides, Xenophon; Roman historians such as Tacitus, Caesar, Livy; scores of others fully analyzed in terms of sources, concepts, influences, etc., by a great scholar and historian. 291pp. 5⅜ x 8.   T397 Paperbound **$1.50**

HISTORY OF THE LATER ROMAN EMPIRE, J. B. Bury. The standard work on the Byzantine Empire from 395 A.D. to the death of Justinian in 565 A.D., by the leading Byzantine scholar of our time. Covers political, social, cultural, theological, military history. Quotes contemporary documents extensively. "Most unlikely that it will ever be superseded," Glanville Downey, Dumbarton Oaks Research Library. Genealogical tables. 5 maps. Bibliography. 2 vols. Total of 965pp. 5⅜ x 8.   T398, T399 Paperbound, the set **$4.00**

GARDNER'S PHOTOGRAPHIC SKETCH BOOK OF THE CIVIL WAR, Alexander Gardner. One of the rarest and most valuable Civil War photographic collections exactly reproduced for the first time since 1866. Scenes of Manassas, Bull Run, Harper's Ferry, Appomattox, Mechanicsville, Fredericksburg, Gettysburg, etc.; battle ruins, prisons, arsenals, a slave pen, fortifications; Lincoln on the field, officers, men, corpses. By one of the most famous pioneers in documentary photography. Original copies of the "Sketch Book" sold for $425 in 1952. Introduction by E. Bleiler. 100 full-page 7 x 10 photographs (original size). 244pp. 10¾ x 8½
T476 Clothbound **$6.00**

THE WORLD'S GREAT SPEECHES, L. Copeland and L. Lamm, eds. 255 speeches from Pericles to Churchill, Dylan Thomas. Invaluable as a guide to speakers; fascinating as history past and present; a source of much difficult-to-find material. Includes an extensive section of informal and humorous speeches. 3 indices: Topic, Author, Nation. xx + 745pp. 5⅜ x 8.
T468 Paperbound **$2.49**

FOUNDERS OF THE MIDDLE AGES, E. K. Rand. The best non-technical discussion of the transformation of Latin paganism into medieval civilization. Tertullian, Gregory, Jerome, Boethius, Augustine, the Neoplatonists, other crucial figures, philosophies examined. Excellent for the intelligent non-specialist. "Extraordinarily accurate," Richard McKeon, THE NATION. ix + 365pp. 5⅜ x 8.   T369 Paperbound **$1.85**

THE POLITICAL THOUGHT OF PLATO AND ARISTOTLE, Ernest Barker. The standard, comprehensive exposition of Greek political thought. Covers every aspect of the "Republic" and the "Politics" as well as minor writings, other philosophers, theorists of the period, and the later history of Greek political thought. Unabridged edition. 584pp. 5⅜ x 8.
T521 Paperbound **$1.85**

PHILOSOPHY

THE GIFT OF LANGUAGE, M. Schlauch. (Formerly, "The Gift of Tongues.") A sound, middle-level treatment of linguistic families, word histories, grammatical processes, semantics, language taboos, word-coining of Joyce, Cummings, Stein, etc. 232 bibliographical notes. 350pp. 5⅜ x 8.
T243 Paperbound **$1.85**

THE PHILOSOPHY OF HEGEL, W. T. Stace. The first work in English to give a complete and connected view of Hegel's entire system. Especially valuable to those who do not have time to study the highly complicated original texts, yet want an accurate presentation by a most reputable scholar of one of the most influential 19th century thinkers. Includes a 14 x 20 fold-out chart of Hegelian system. 536pp. 5⅜ x 8.
T254 Paperbound **$2.00**

ARISTOTLE, A. E. Taylor. A lucid, non-technical account of Aristotle written by a foremost Platonist. Covers life and works; thought on matter, form, causes, logic, God, physics, metaphysics, etc. Bibliography. New index compiled for this edition. 128pp. 5⅜ x 8.
T280 Paperbound **$1.00**

GUIDE TO PHILOSOPHY, C. E. M. Joad. This basic work describes the major philosophic problems and evaluates the answers propounded by great philosophers from the Greeks to Whitehead, Russell. "The finest introduction," BOSTON TRANSCRIPT. Bibliography, 592pp. 5⅜ x 8.
T297 Paperbound **$2.00**

LANGUAGE AND MYTH, E. Cassirer. Cassirer's brilliant demonstration that beneath both language and myth lies an unconscious "grammar" of experience whose categories and canons are not those of logical thought. Introduction and translation by Susanne Langer. Index. x + 103pp. 5⅜ x 8.
T51 Paperbound **$1.25**

SUBSTANCE AND FUNCTION, EINSTEIN'S THEORY OF RELATIVITY, E. Cassirer. This double volume contains the German philosopher's profound philosophical formulation of the differences between traditional logic and the new logic of science. Number, space, energy, relativity, many other topics are treated in detail. Authorized translation by W. C. and M. C. Swabey. xii + 465pp. 5⅜ x 8.
T50 Paperbound **$2.00**

THE PHILOSOPHICAL WORKS OF DESCARTES. The definitive English edition, in two volumes, of all major philosophical works and letters of René Descartes, father of modern philosophy of knowledge and science. Translated by E. S. Haldane and G. Ross. Introductory notes. Total of 842pp. 5⅜ x 8.
T71 Vol. 1, Paperbound **$2.00**
T72 Vol. 2, Paperbound **$2.00**

ESSAYS IN EXPERIMENTAL LOGIC, J. Dewey. Based upon Dewey's theory that knowledge implies a judgment which in turn implies an inquiry, these papers consider such topics as the thought of Bertrand Russell, pragmatism, the logic of values, antecedents of thought, data and meanings. 452pp. 5⅜ x 8.
T73 Paperbound **$1.95**

THE PHILOSOPHY OF HISTORY, G. W. F. Hegel. This classic of Western thought is Hegel's detailed formulation of the thesis that history is not chance but a rational process, the realization of the Spirit of Freedom. Translated and introduced by J. Sibree. Introduction by C. Hegel. Special introduction for this edition by Prof. Carl Friedrich, Harvard University. xxxix + 447pp. 5⅜ x 8.
T112 Paperbound **$1.85**

THE WILL TO BELIEVE and HUMAN IMMORTALITY, W. James. Two of James's most profound investigations of human belief in God and immortality, bound as one volume. Both are powerful expressions of James's views on chance vs. determinism, pluralism vs. monism, will and intellect, arguments for survival after death, etc. Two prefaces. 429pp. 5⅜ x 8.
T294 Clothbound **$3.75**
T291 Paperbound **$1.65**

INTRODUCTION TO SYMBOLIC LOGIC, S. Langer. A lucid, general introduction to modern logic, covering forms, classes, the use of symbols, the calculus of propositions, the Boole-Schroeder and the Russell-Whitehead systems, etc. "One of the clearest and simplest introductions," MATHEMATICS GAZETTE. Second, enlarged, revised edition. 368pp. 5⅜ x 8.
S164 Paperbound **$1.75**

MIND AND THE WORLD-ORDER, C. I. Lewis. Building upon the work of Peirce, James, and Dewey, Professor Lewis outlines a theory of knowledge in terms of "conceptual pragmatism," and demonstrates why the traditional understanding of the a priori must be abandoned. Appendices. xiv + 446pp. 5⅜ x 8.
T359 Paperbound **$1.95**

THE GUIDE FOR THE PERPLEXED, M. Maimonides One of the great philosophical works of all time, Maimonides' formulation of the meeting-ground between Old Testament and Aristotelian thought is essential to anyone interested in Jewish, Christian, and Moslem thought in the Middle Ages. 2nd revised edition of the Friedländer translation. Extensive introduction. lix + 414pp. 5⅜ x 8.
T351 Paperbound **$1.85**

DOVER BOOKS

THE PHILOSOPHICAL WRITINGS OF PEIRCE, J. Buchler, ed. (Formerly, "The Philosophy of Peirce.") This carefully integrated selection of Peirce's papers is considered the best coverage of the complete thought of one of the greatest philosophers of modern times. Covers Peirce's work on the theory of signs, pragmatism, epistemology, symbolic logic, the scientific method, chance, etc. xvi + 386pp. 5 ⅜ x 8.　　　　　　T216 Clothbound **$5.00**
T217 Paperbound **$1.95**

HISTORY OF ANCIENT PHILOSOPHY, W. Windelband. Considered the clearest survey of Greek and Roman philosophy. Examines Thales, Anaximander, Anaximenes, Heraclitus, the Eleatics, Empedocles, the Pythagoreans, the Sophists, Socrates, Democritus, Stoics, Epicureans, Sceptics, Neo-platonists, etc. 50 pages on Plato; 70 on Aristotle. 2nd German edition tr. by H. E. Cushman. xv + 393pp. 5⅜ x 8.　　　　　　T357 Paperbound **$1.75**

INTRODUCTION TO SYMBOLIC LOGIC AND ITS APPLICATIONS, R. Carnap. A comprehensive, rigorous introduction to modern logic by perhaps its greatest living master. Includes demonstrations of applications in mathematics, physics, biology. "Of the rank of a masterpiece," Z. für Mathematik und ihre Grenzgebiete. Over 300 exercises. xvi + 241pp. 5⅜ x 8.　　　　　　Clothbound **$4.00**
S453 Paperbound **$1.85**

SCEPTICISM AND ANIMAL FAITH, G. Santayana. Santayana's unusually lucid exposition of the difference between the independent existence of objects and the essence our mind attributes to them, and of the necessity of scepticism as a form of belief and animal faith as a necessary condition of knowledge. Discusses belief, memory, intuition, symbols, etc. xii + 314pp. 5⅜ x 8.　　　　　　T235 Clothbound **$3.50**
T236 Paperbound **$1.50**

THE ANALYSIS OF MATTER, B. Russell. With his usual brilliance, Russell analyzes physics, causality, scientific inference, Weyl's theory, tensors, invariants, periodicity, etc. in order to discover the basic concepts of scientific thought about matter. "Most thorough treatment of the subject," THE NATION. Introduction. 8 figures. viii + 408pp. 5⅜ x 8.
T231 Paperbound **$1.95**

THE SENSE OF BEAUTY, G. Santayana. This important philosophical study of why, when, and how beauty appears, and what conditions must be fulfilled, is in itself a revelation of the beauty of language. "It is doubtful if a better treatment of the subject has since appeared," PEABODY JOURNAL. ix + 275pp. 5⅜ x 8.　　　　　　T238 Paperbound **$1.00**

THE CHIEF WORKS OF SPINOZA. In two volumes. Vol. I: The Theologico-Political Treatise and the Political Treatise. Vol. II: On the Improvement of Understanding, The Ethics, and Selected Letters. The permanent and enduring ideas in these works on God, the universe, religion, society, etc., have had tremendous impact on later philosophical works. Introduction. Total of 862pp. 5⅜ x 8.　　　　　　T249 Vol. I, Paperbound **$1.50**
T250 Vol. II, Paperbound **$1.50**

TRAGIC SENSE OF LIFE, M. de Unamuno. The acknowledged masterpiece of one of Spain's most influential thinkers. Between the despair at the inevitable death of man and all his works, and the desire for immortality, Unamuno finds a "saving incertitude." Called "a masterpiece," by the ENCYCLOPAEDIA BRITANNICA. xxx + 332pp. 5⅜ x 8.
T257 Paperbound **$1.95**

EXPERIENCE AND NATURE, John Dewey. The enlarged, revised edition of the Paul Carus lectures (1925). One of Dewey's clearest presentations of the philosophy of empirical naturalism which reestablishes the continuity between "inner" experience and "outer" nature. These lectures are among the most significant ever delivered by an American philosopher. 457pp. 5⅜ x 8.　　　　　　T471 Paperbound **$1.85**

PHILOSOPHY AND CIVILIZATION IN THE MIDDLE AGES, M. de Wulf. A semi-popular survey of medieval intellectual life, religion, philosophy, science, the arts, etc. that covers feudalism vs. Catholicism, rise of the universities, mendicant orders, and similar topics. Bibliography. viii + 320pp. 5⅜ x 8.　　　　　　T284 Paperbound **$1.75**

AN INTRODUCTION TO SCHOLASTIC PHILOSOPHY, M. de Wulf. (Formerly, "Scholasticism Old and New.") Prof. de Wulf covers the central scholastic tradition from St. Anselm, Albertus Magnus, Thomas Aquinas, up to Suarez in the 17th century; and then treats the modern revival of scholasticism, the Louvain position, relations with Kantianism and positivism, etc. xvi + 271pp. 5⅜ x 8.　　　　　　T296 Clothbound **$3.50**
T283 Paperbound **$1.75**

A HISTORY OF MODERN PHILOSOPHY, H. Höffding. An exceptionally clear and detailed coverage of Western philosophy from the Renaissance to the end of the 19th century. Both major and minor figures are examined in terms of theory of knowledge, logic, cosmology, psychology. Covers Pomponazzi, Bodin, Boehme, Telesius, Bruno, Copernicus, Descartes, Spinoza, Hobbes, Locke, Hume, Kant, Fichte, Schopenhauer, Mill, Spencer, Langer, scores of others. A standard reference work. 2 volumes. Total of 1159pp. 5⅜ x 8.　　　　　　T117 Vol. 1, Paperbound **$2.00**
T118 Vol. 2, Paperbound **$2.00**

LANGUAGE, TRUTH AND LOGIC, A. J. Ayer. The first full-length development of Logical Positivism in English. Building on the work of Schlick, Russell, Carnap, and the Vienna school, Ayer presents the tenets of one of the most important systems of modern philosophical thought. 160pp. 5⅜ x 8.　　　　　　T10 Paperbound **$1.25**

ORIENTALIA AND RELIGION

THE MYSTERIES OF MITHRA, F. Cumont. The great Belgian scholar's definitive study of the Persian mystery religion that almost vanquished Christianity in the ideological struggle for the Roman Empire. A masterpiece of scholarly detection that reconstructs secret doctrines, organization, rites. Mithraic art is discussed and analyzed. 70 illus. 239pp. 5⅜ x 8.
T323 Paperbound **$1.85**

CHRISTIAN AND ORIENTAL PHILOSOPHY OF ART. A. K. Coomaraswamy. The late art historian and orientalist discusses artistic symbolism, the role of traditional culture in enriching art, medieval art, folklore, philosophy of art, other similar topics. Bibliography. 148pp. 5⅜ x 8.
T378 Paperbound **$1.25**

TRANSFORMATION OF NATURE IN ART, A. K. Coomaraswamy. A basic work on Asiatic religious art. Includes discussions of religious art in Asia and Medieval Europe (exemplified by Meister Eckhart), the origin and use of images in Indian art, Indian Medieval aesthetic manuals, and other fascinating, little known topics. Glossaries of Sanskrit and Chinese terms. Bibliography. 41pp. of notes. 245pp. 5⅜ x 8.
T368 Paperbound **$1.75**

ORIENTAL RELIGIONS IN ROMAN PAGANISM, F. Cumont. This well-known study treats the ecstatic cults of Syria and Phrygia (Cybele, Attis, Adonis, their orgies and mutilatory rites); the mysteries of Egypt (Serapis, Isis, Osiris); Persian dualism; Mithraic cults; Hermes Trismegistus, Ishtar, Astarte, etc. and their influence on the religious thought of the Roman Empire. Introduction. 55pp. of notes; extensive bibliography. xxiv + 298pp. 5⅜ x 8.
T321 Paperbound **$1.75**

ANTHROPOLOGY, SOCIOLOGY, AND PSYCHOLOGY

PRIMITIVE MAN AS PHILOSOPHER, P. Radin. A standard anthropological work based on Radin's investigations of the Winnebago, Maori, Batak, Zuni, other primitive tribes. Describes primitive thought on the purpose of life, marital relations, death, personality, gods, etc. Extensive selections of original primitive documents. Bibliography. xviii + 420pp. 5⅜ x 8.
T392 Paperbound **$2.00**

PRIMITIVE RELIGION, P. Radin. Radin's thoroughgoing treatment of supernatural beliefs, shamanism, initiations, religious expression, etc. in primitive societies. Arunta, Ashanti, Aztec, Bushman, Crow, Fijian, many other tribes examined. "Excellent," NATURE. New preface by the author. Bibliographic notes. x + 322pp. 5⅜ x 8.   T393 Paperbound **$1.85**

SEX IN PSYCHO-ANALYSIS, S. Ferenczi. (Formerly, "Contributions to Psycho-analysis.") 14 selected papers on impotence, transference, analysis and children, dreams, obscene words, homosexuality, paranoia, etc. by an associate of Freud. Also included: THE DEVELOPMENT OF PSYCHO-ANALYSIS, by Ferenczi and Otto Rank. Two books bound as one. Total of 406pp. 5⅜ x 8.   T324 Paperbound **$1.85**

THE PRINCIPLES OF PSYCHOLOGY, William James. The complete text of the famous "long course," one of the great books of Western thought. An almost incredible amount of information about psychological processes, the stream of consciousness, habit, time perception, memory, emotions, reason, consciousness of self, abnormal phenomena, and similar topics. Based on James's own discoveries integrated with the work of Descartes, Locke, Hume, Royce, Wundt, Berkeley, Lotse, Herbart, scores of others. "A classic of interpretation," PSYCHIATRIC QUARTERLY. 94 illus. 1408pp. 2 volumes. 5⅜ x 8.
T381 Vol. 1, Paperbound **$2.50**
T382 Vol. 2, Paperbound **$2.50**

THE POLISH PEASANT IN EUROPE AND AMERICA, W. I. Thomas, F. Znaniecki. Monumental sociological study of peasant primary groups (family and community) and the disruptions produced by a new industrial system and emigration to America, by two of the foremost sociologists of recent times. One of the most important works in sociological thought. Includes hundreds of pages of primary documentation; point by point analysis of causes of social decay, breakdown of morality, crime, drunkenness, prostitution, etc. 2nd revised edition. 2 volumes. Total of 2250pp. 6 x 9.   T478 2 volume set, Clothbound **$12.50**

FOLKWAYS, W. G. Sumner. The great Yale sociologist's detailed exposition of thousands of social, sexual, and religious customs in hundreds of cultures from ancient Greece to Modern Western societies. Preface by A. G. Keller. Introduction by William Lyon Phelps. 705pp. 5⅜ x 8.   S508 Paperbound **$2.49**

BEYOND PSYCHOLOGY, Otto Rank. The author, an early associate of Freud, uses psychoanalytic techniques of myth-analysis to explore ultimates of human existence. Treats love, immortality, the soul, sexual identity, kingship, sources of state power, many other topics which illuminate the irrational basis of human existence. 291pp. 5⅜ x 8.   T485 Paperbound **$1.75**

ILLUSIONS AND DELUSIONS OF THE SUPERNATURAL AND THE OCCULT, D. H. Rawcliffe. A rational, scientific examination of crystal gazing, automatic writing, table turning, stigmata, the Indian rope trick, dowsing, telepathy, clairvoyance, ghosts, ESP, PK, thousands of other supposedly occult phenomena. Originally titled "The Psychology of the Occult." 14 illustrations. 551pp. 5⅜ x 8.   T503 Paperbound **$2.00**

DOVER BOOKS

YOGA: A SCIENTIFIC EVALUATION, Kovoor T. Behanan. A scientific study of the physiological and psychological effects of Yoga discipline, written under the auspices of the Yale University Institute of Human Relations. Foreword by W. A. Miles, Yale Univ. 17 photographs. 290pp. 5⅜ x 8.   T505 Paperbound **$1.65**

HOAXES, C. D. MacDougall. Delightful, entertaining, yet scholarly exposition of how hoaxes start, why they succeed, documented with stories of hundreds of the most famous hoaxes. "A stupendous collection . . . and shrewd analysis, "NEW YORKER. New, revised edition. 54 photographs. 320pp. 5⅜ x 8.   T465 Paperbound **$1.75**

CREATIVE POWER: THE EDUCATION OF YOUTH IN THE CREATIVE ARTS, Hughes Mearns. Named by the National Education Association as one of the 20 foremost books on education in recent times. Tells how to help children express themselves in drama, poetry, music, art, develop latent creative power. Should be read by every parent, teacher. New, enlarged, revised edition. Introduction. 272pp. 5⅜ x 8.   T490 Paperbound **$1.50**

LANGUAGES

NEW RUSSIAN-ENGLISH, ENGLISH-RUSSIAN DICTIONARY, M. A. O'Brien. Over 70,000 entries in new orthography! Idiomatic usages, colloquialisms. One of the few dictionaries that indicate accent changes in conjugation and declension. "One of the best," Prof. E. J. Simmons, Cornell. First names, geographical terms, bibliography, many other features. 738pp. 4½ x 6¼.
                                                                                          T208 Paperbound **$2.00**

MONEY CONVERTER AND TIPPING GUIDE FOR EUROPEAN TRAVEL, C. Vomacka. Invaluable, handy source of currency regulations, conversion tables, tipping rules, postal rates, much other travel information for every European country plus Israel, Egypt and Turkey. 128pp. 3½ x 5¼.
                                                                                          T260 Paperbound **60¢**

MONEY CONVERTER AND TIPPING GUIDE FOR TRAVEL IN THE AMERICAS (including the United States and Canada), **C. Vomacka.** The information you need for informed and confident travel in the Americas: money conversion tables, tipping guide, postal, telephone rates, etc. 128pp. 3½ x 5¼.   T261 Paperbound **65¢**

DUTCH-ENGLISH, ENGLISH-DUTCH DICTIONARY, F. G. Renier. The most convenient, practical Dutch-English dictionary on the market. New orthography. More than 60,000 entries: idioms, compounds, technical terms, etc. Gender of nouns indicated. xviii + 571pp. 5½ x 6¼.
                                                                                          T224 Clothbound **$2.50**

LEARN DUTCH!, F. G. Renier. The most satisfactory and easily-used grammar of modern Dutch. Used and recommended by the Fulbright Committee in the Netherlands. Over 1200 simple exercises lead to mastery of spoken and written Dutch. Dutch-English, English-Dutch vocabularies. 181pp. 4¼ x 7¼.   T441 Clothbound **$1.75**

PHRASE AND SENTENCE DICTIONARY OF SPOKEN RUSSIAN, English-Russian, Russian-English. Based on phrases and complete sentences, rather than isolated words; recognized as one of the best methods of learning the idiomatic speech of a country. Over 11,500 entries, indexed by single words, with more than 32,000 English and Russian sentences and phrases, in immediately usable form. Probably the largest list ever published. Shows accent changes in conjugation and declension; irregular forms listed in both alphabetical place and under main form of word. 15,000 word introduction covering Russian sounds, writing, grammar, syntax. 15-page appendix of geographical names, money, important signs, given names, foods, special Soviet terms, etc. Travellers, businessmen, students, government employees have found this their best source for Russian expressions. Originally published as U.S. Government Technical Manual TM 30-944. iv + 573pp. 5⅝ x 8⅜.   T496 Paperbound **$2.75**

PHRASE AND SENTENCE DICTIONARY OF SPOKEN SPANISH, Spanish-English, English-Spanish. Compiled from spoken Spanish, emphasizing idiom and colloquial usage in both Castilian and Latin-American. More than 16,000 entries containing over 25,000 idioms—the largest list of idiomatic constructions ever published. Complete sentences given, indexed under single words —language in immediately usable form, for travellers, businessmen, students, etc. 25-page introduction provides rapid survey of sounds, grammar, syntax, with full consideration of irregular verbs. Especially apt in modern treatment of phrases and structure. 17-page glossary gives translations of geographical names, money values, numbers, national holidays, important street signs, useful expressions of high frequency, plus unique 7-page glossary of Spanish and Spanish-American foods and dishes. Originally published as U.S. Government Technical Manual TM 30-900. iv + 513pp. 5⅝ x 8⅜.   T495 Paperbound **$1.75**

SAY IT language phrase books

"SAY IT" in the foreign language of your choice! We have sold over ½ million copies of these popular, useful language books. They will not make you an expert linguist overnight, but they do cover most practical matters of everyday life abroad.

Over 1000 useful phrases, expressions, with additional variants, substitutions.

Modern! Useful! Hundreds of phrases not available in other texts: "Nylon," "air-conditioned," etc.

The ONLY inexpensive phrase book **completely indexed.** Everything is available at a flip of your finger, ready for use.

Prepared by native linguists, travel experts.

Based on years of travel experience abroad.

This handy phrase book may be used by itself, or it may supplement any other text or course; it provides a living element. Used by many colleges and institutions: Hunter College; Barnard College; Army Ordnance School, Aberdeen; and many others.

Available, 1 book per language:

Danish (T818) 75¢
Dutch T(817) 75¢
English (for German-speaking people) (T801) 60¢
English (for Italian-speaking people) (T816) 60¢
English (for Spanish-speaking people) (T802) 60¢
Esperanto (T820) 75¢
French (T803) 60¢
German (T804) 60¢
Modern Greek (T813) 75¢
Hebrew (T805) 60¢

Italian (T806) 60¢
Japanese (T807) 60¢
Norwegian (T814) 75¢
Russian (T810) 75¢
Spanish (T811) 60¢
Turkish (T821) 75¢
Yiddish (T815) 75¢
Swedish (T812) 75¢
Polish (T808) 75¢
Portuguese (T809) 75¢

LISTEN & LEARN language record sets

LISTEN & LEARN is the only language record course designed especially to meet your travel needs, or help you learn essential foreign language quickly by yourself, or in conjunction with any school course, by means of the automatic association method. Each set contains three 33⅓ rpm long- playing records — 1½ hours of recorded speech by eminent native speakers who are professors at Columbia, N.Y.U., Queens College and other leading universities. The sets are priced far below other-sets of similar quality, yet they contain many special features not found in other record sets:

* Over 800 selected phrases and sentences, a basic vocabulary of over 3200 words.
* Both English and foreign language recorded; with a pause for your repetition.
* Designed for persons with limited time; no time wasted on material you cannot use immediately.
* Living, modern expressions that answer modern needs: drugstore items, "air-conditioned," etc.
* 128-196 page manuals contain everything on the records, plus simple pronunciation guides.
* Manual is fully indexed; find the phrase you want instantly.
* High fidelity recording—equal to any records costing up to $6 each.

The phrases on these records cover 41 different categories useful to the traveller or student interested in learning the living, spoken language: greetings, introductions, making yourself understood, passing customs, planes, trains, boats, buses, taxis, nightclubs, restaurants, menu items, sports, concerts, cameras, automobile travel, repairs, drugstores, doctors, dentists, medicines, barber shops, beauty parlors, laundries, many, many more.

"Excellent . . . among the very best on the market," Prof. Mario Pei, Dept. of Romance Languages, Columbia University. "Inexpensive and well-done . . . an ideal present," CHICAGO SUNDAY TRIBUNE. "More genuinely helpful than anything of its kind which I have previously encountered," Sidney Clark, well-known author of "ALL THE BEST" travel books. Each set contains 3   33⅓ rpm pure vinyl records, 128- 196 page   with full record text, and album. One language per set. LISTEN & LEARN record sets are now available in—

FRENCH	the set $4.95		**GERMAN**	the set $4.95
ITALIAN	the set $4.95		**SPANISH**	the set $4.95
RUSSIAN	the set $5.95		**JAPANESE** *	the set $5.95

* Available Sept. 1, 1959

UNCONDITIONAL GUARANTEE: Dover Publications stands behind every Listen and Learn record set. If you are dissatisfied with these sets for any reason whatever, return them within 10 days and your money will be refunded in full.

ART HISTORY

STICKS AND STONES, Lewis Mumford. An examination of forces influencing American architecture: the medieval tradition in early New England, the classical influence in Jefferson's time, the Brown Decades, the imperial facade, the machine age, etc. "A truly remarkable book," SAT. REV. OF LITERATURE. 2nd revised edition. 21 illus. xvii + 228pp. 5⅜ x 8.
T202 Paperbound **$1.60**

THE AUTOBIOGRAPHY OF AN IDEA, Louis Sullivan. The architect whom Frank Lloyd Wright called "the master," records the development of the theories that revolutionized America's skyline. 34 full-page plates of Sullivan's finest work. New introduction by R. M. Line. xiv + 335pp. 5⅜ x 8.
T281 Paperbound **$1.85**

THE MATERIALS AND TECHNIQUES OF MEDIEVAL PAINTING, D. V. Thompson. An invaluable study of carriers and grounds, binding media, pigments, metals used in painting, al fresco and al secco techniques, burnishing, etc. used by the medieval masters. Preface by Bernard Berenson. 239pp. 5⅜ x 8.
T327 Paperbound **$1.85**

PRINCIPLES OF ART HISTORY, H. Wölfflin. This remarkably instructive work demonstrates the tremendous change in artistic conception from the 14th to the 18th centuries, by analyzing 164 works by Botticelli, Dürer, Hobbema, Holbein, Hals, Titian, Rembrandt, Vermeer, etc., and pointing out exactly what is meant by "baroque," "classic," "primitive," "picturesque," and other basic terms of art history and criticism. "A remarkable lesson in the art of seeing," SAT. REV. OF LITERATURE. Translated from the 7th German edition. 150 illus. 254pp. 6⅛ x 9¼.
T276 Paperbound **$2.00**

FOUNDATIONS OF MODERN ART, A. Ozenfant. Stimulating discussion of human creativity from paleolithic cave painting to modern painting, architecture, decorative arts. Fully illustrated with works of Gris, Lipchitz, Leger, Picasso, primitive, modern artifacts, architecture, industrial art, much more. 226 illustrations. 368pp. 6⅛ x 9¼.
T215 Paperbound **$1.95**

HANDICRAFTS, APPLIED ART, ART SOURCES, ETC.

WILD FOWL DECOYS, J. Barber. The standard work on this fascinating branch of folk art, ranging from Indian mud and grass devices to realistic wooden decoys. Discusses styles, types, periods; gives full information on how to make decoys. 140 illustrations (including 14 new plates) show decoys and provide full sets of plans for handicrafters, artists, hunters, and students of folk art. 281pp. 7⅞ x 10¾. Deluxe edition.
T11 Clothbound **$8.50**

METALWORK AND ENAMELLING, H. Maryon. Probably the best book ever written on the subject. Tells everything necessary for the home manufacture of jewelry, rings, ear pendants, bowls, etc. Covers materials, tools, soldering, filigree, setting stones, raising patterns, repoussé work, damascening, niello, cloisonné, polishing, assaying, casting, and dozens of other techniques. The best substitute for apprenticeship to a master metalworker. 363 photos and figures. 374pp. 5½ x 8½.
T183 Clothbound **$7.50**

SHAKER FURNITURE, E. D. and F. Andrews. The most illuminating study of Shaker furniture ever written. Covers chronology, craftsmanship, houses, shops, etc. Includes over 200 photographs of chairs, tables, clocks, beds, benches, etc. "Mr. & Mrs. Andrews know all there is to know about Shaker furniture," Mark Van Doren, NATION. 48 full-page plates. 192pp. Deluxe cloth binding. 7⅞ x 10¾.
T7 Clothbound **$6.00**

PRIMITIVE ART, Franz Boas. A great American anthropologist covers theory, technical virtuosity, styles, symbolism, patterns, etc. of primitive art. The more than 900 illustrations will interest artists, designers, craftworkers. Over 900 illustrations. 376pp. 5⅜ x 8.
T25 Paperbound **$1.95**

ON THE LAWS OF JAPANESE PAINTING, H. Bowie. The best possible substitute for lessons from an oriental master. Treats both spirit and technique; exercises for control of the brush; inks, brushes, colors; use of dots, lines to express whole moods, etc. 220 illus. 132pp. 6⅛ x 9¼.
T30 Paperbound **$1.95**

HANDBOOK OF ORNAMENT, F. S. Meyer. One of the largest collections of copyright-free traditional art: over 3300 line cuts of Greek, Roman, Medieval, Renaissance, Baroque, 18th and 19th century art motifs (tracery, geometric elements, flower and animal motifs, etc.) and decorated objects (chairs, thrones, weapons, vases, jewelry, armor, etc.). Full text. 3300 illustrations. 562pp. 5⅜ x 8.
T302 Paperbound **$2.00**

THREE CLASSICS OF ITALIAN CALLIGRAPHY. Oscar Ogg, ed. Exact reproductions of three famous Renaissance calligraphic works: Arrighi's OPERINA and IL MODO, Tagliente's LO PRESENTE LIBRO, and Palatino's LIBRO NUOVO. More than 200 complete alphabets, thousands of lettered specimens, in Papal Chancery and other beautiful, ornate handwriting. Introduction. 245 plates. 282pp. 6⅛ x 9¼.
T212 Paperbound **$1.95**

THE HISTORY AND TECHNIQUES OF LETTERING, A. Nesbitt. A thorough history of lettering from the ancient Egyptians to the present, and a 65-page course in lettering for artists. Every major development in lettering history is illustrated by a complete alphabet. Fully analyzes such masters as Caslon, Koch, Garamont, Jenson, and many more. 89 alphabets, 165 other specimens. 317pp. 5⅜ x 8.
T427 Paperbound **$2.00**

LETTERING AND ALPHABETS, J. A. Cavanagh. An unabridged reissue of "Lettering," containing the full discussion, analysis, illustration of 89 basic hand lettering tyles based on Caslon, Bodoni, Gothic, many other types. Hundreds of technical hints on construction, strokes, pens, brushes, etc. 89 alphabets, 72 lettered specimens, which may be reproduced permission-free. 121pp. 9¾ x 8. **T53 Paperbound $1.25**

THE HUMAN FIGURÉ IN MOTION, Eadweard Muybridge. The largest collection in print of Muybridge's famous high-speed action photos. 4789 photographs in more than 500 action-strip-sequences (at shutter speeds up to 1/6000th of a second) illustrate men, women, children—mostly undraped—performing such actions as walking, running, getting up, lying down, carrying objects, throwing, etc. "An unparalleled dictionary of action for all artists," AMERICAN ARTIST. 390 full-page plates, with 4789 photographs. Heavy glossy stock, reinforced binding with headbands. 7⅞ x 10¾. **T204 Clothbound $10.00**

ANIMALS IN MOTION, Eadweard Muybridge. The largest collection of animal action photos in print. 34 different animals (horses, mules, oxen, goats, camels, pigs, cats, lions, gnus, deer, monkeys, eagles—and 22 others) in 132 characteristic actions. All 3919 photographs are taken in series at speeds up to 1/1600th of a second, offering artists, biologists, cartoonists a remarkable opportunity to see exactly how an ostrich's head bobs when running, how a lion puts his foot down, how an elephant's knee bends, how a bird flaps his wings, thousands of other hard-to-catch details. "A really marvelous series of plates," NATURE. 380 full-pages of plates. Heavy glossy stock, reinforced binding with headbands. 7⅞ x 10¾. **T203 Clothbound $10.00**

THE BOOK OF SIGNS, R. Koch. 493 symbols—crosses, monograms, astrological, biological symbols, runes, etc.—from ancient manuscripts, cathedrals, coins, catacombs, pottery. May be reproduced permission-free. 493 illustrations by Fritz Kredel. 104pp. 6⅛ x 9¼. **T162 Paperbound $1.00**

A HANDBOOK OF EARLY ADVERTISING ART, C. P. Hornung. The largest collection of copyright-free early advertising art ever compiled. Vol. I: 2,000 illustrations of animals, old automobiles, buildings, allegorical figures, fire engines, Indians, ships, trains, more than 33 other categories! Vol II: Over 4,000 typographical specimens; 600 Roman, Gothic, Barnum, Old English faces; 630 ornamental type faces; hundreds of scrolls, initials, flourishes, etc. "A remarkable collection," PRINTERS' INK.

Vol. I: Pictorial Volume. Over 2000 illustrations. 256pp. 9 x 12. **T122 Clothbound $10.00**
Vol. II: Typographical Volume. Over 4000 specimens. 319pp. 9 x 12. **T123 Clothbound $10.00**
Two volume set, Clothbound, only **$18.50**

DESIGN FOR ARTISTS AND CRAFTSMEN, L. Wolchonok. The most thorough course on the creation of art motifs and designs. Shows you step-by-step, with hundreds of examples and 113 detailed exercises, how to create original designs from geometric patterns, plants, birds, animals, humans, and man-made objects. "A great contribution to the field of design and crafts," N. Y. SOCIETY OF CRAFTSMEN. More than 1300 entirely new illustrations. xv + 207pp. 7⅞ x 10¾. **T274 Clothbound $4.95**

HANDBOOK OF DESIGNS AND DEVICES, C. P. Hornung. A remarkable working collection of 1836 basic designs and variations, all copyright-free. Variations of circle, line, cross, diamond, swastika, star, scroll, shield, many more. Notes on symbolism. "A necessity to every designer who would be original without having to labor heavily," ARTIST and ADVERTISER. 204 plates. 240pp. 5⅜ x 8.

T125 Paperbound $1.90

THE UNIVERSAL PENMAN, George Bickham. Exact reproduction of beautiful 18th century book of handwriting. 22 complete alphabets in finest English roundhand, other scripts, over 2000 elaborate flourishes, 122 calligraphic illustrations, etc. Material is copyright-free. "An essential part of any art library, and a book of permanent value," AMERICAN ARTIST. 212 plates. 224pp. 9 x 13¾. **T20 Clothbound $10.00**

AN ATLAS OF ANATOMY FOR ARTISTS, F. Schider. This standard work contains 189 full-page plates, more than 647 illustrations of all aspects of the human skeleton, musculature, cutaway portions of the body, each part of the anatomy, hand forms, eyelids, breasts, location of muscles under the flesh, etc. 59 plates illustrate how Michelangelo, da Vinci, Goya, 15 others, drew human anatomy. New 3rd edition enlarged by 52 new illustrations by Cloquet, Barcsay. "The standard reference tool," AMERICAN LIBRARY ASSOCIATION. "Excellent," AMERICAN ARTIST. 189 plates, 647 illustrations. xxvi + 192pp. 7⅞ x 10⅝. **T241 Clothbound $6.00**

AN ATLAS OF ANIMAL ANATOMY FOR ARTISTS, W. Ellenberger, H. Baum, H. Dittrich. The largest, richest animal anatomy for artists in English. Form, musculature, tendons, bone structure, expression, detailed cross sections of head, other features, of the horse, lion, dog, cat, deer, seal, kangaroo, cow, bull, goat, monkey, hare, many other animals. "Highly recommended," DESIGN. Second, revised, enlarged edition with new plates from Cuvier, Stubbs, etc. 288 illustrations. 153pp. 11⅜ x 9. **T82 Clothbound $6.00**

ANIMAL DRAWING: ANATOMY AND ACTION FOR ARTISTS, C. R. Knight. 158 studies, with full accompanying text, of such animals as the gorilla, bear, bison, dromedary, camel, vulture, pelican, iguana, shark, etc., by one of the greatest modern masters of animal drawing. Innumerable tips on how to get life expression into your work. "An excellent reference work,' SAN FRANCISCO CHRONICLE. 158 illustrations. 156pp. 10½ x 8½. **T426 Paperbound $2.00**

DOVER BOOKS

THE CRAFTSMAN'S HANDBOOK, Cennino Cennini. The finest English translation of IL LIBRO DELL' ARTE, the 15th century introduction to art technique that is both a mirror of Quatrocento life and a source of many useful but 'nearly forgotten facets of the painter's art. 4 illustrations. xxvii + 142pp. D. V. Thompson, translator. 6⅛ x 9¼. T54 Paperbound **$1.50**

THE BROWN DECADES, Lewis Mumford. A picture of the "buried renaissance" of the post-Civil War period, and the founding of modern architecture (Sullivan, Richardson, Root, Roebling), landscape development (Marsh, Olmstead, Eliot), and the graphic arts (Homer, Eakins, Ryder). 2nd revised, enlarged edition. Bibliography. 12 illustrations. xiv + 266 pp. 5⅜ x 8. T200 Paperbound **$1.65**

STIEGEL GLASS, F. W. Hunter. The story of the most highly esteemed early American glassware, fully illustrated. How a German adventurer, "Baron" Stiegel, founded a glass empire; detailed accounts of individual glasswork. "This pioneer work is reprinted in an edition even more beautiful than the original," ANTIQUES DEALER. New introduction by Helen McKearin. 171 illustrations, 12 in full color. xxii + 338pp. 7⅞ x 10¾. T128 Clothbound **$10.00**

THE HUMAN FIGURE, J. H. Vanderpoel. Not just a picture book, but a complete course by a famous figure artist. Extensive text, illustrated by 430 pencil and charcoal drawings of both male and female anatomy. 2nd enlarged edition. Foreword. 430 illus. 143pp. 6⅛ x 9¼. T432 Paperbound **$1.45**

PINE FURNITURE OF EARLY NEW ENGLAND, R. H. Kettell. Over 400 illustrations, over 50 working drawings of early New England chairs, benches, beds cupboards, mirrors, shelves, tables, other furniture esteemed for simple beauty and character. "Rich store of illustrations . . . emphasizes the individuality and varied design," ANTIQUES. 413 illustrations, 55 working drawings. 475pp. 8 x 10¾. T145 Clothbound **$10.00**

BASIC BOOKBINDING, A. W. Lewis. Enables both beginners and experts to rebind old books or bind paperbacks in hard covers. Treats materials, tools; gives step-by-step instruction in how to collate a book, sew it, back it, make boards, etc. 261 illus. Appendices. 155pp. 5⅜ x 8. T169 Paperbound **$1.35**

DESIGN MOTIFS OF ANCIENT MEXICO, J. Enciso. Nearly 90% of these 766 superb designs from Aztec, Olmec, Totonac, Maya, and Toltec origins are unobtainable elsewhere! Contains plumed serpents, wind gods, animals, demons, dancers, monsters, etc. Excellent applied design source. Originally $17.50. 766 illustrations, thousands of motifs. 192pp. 6⅛ x 9¼. T84 Paperbound **$1.85**

AFRICAN SCULPTURE, Ladislas Segy. 163 full-page plates illustrating masks, fertility figures, ceremonial objects, etc., of 50 West and Central African tribes—95% never before illustrated. 34-page introduction to African sculpture. "Mr. Segy is one of its top authorities," NEW YORKER. 164 full-page photographic plates. Introduction. Bibliography. 244pp. 6⅛ x 9¼. T396 Paperbound **$2.00**

THE PROCESSES OF GRAPHIC REPRODUCTION IN PRINTING, H. Curwen. A thorough and practical survey of wood, linoleum, and rubber engraving; copper engraving; drypoint, mezzotint, etching, aquatint, steel engraving, die sinking, stencilling, lithography (extensively); photographic reproduction utilizing line, continuous tone, photoengravure, collotype; every other process in general use. Note on color reproduction. Section on bookbinding. Over 200 illustrations, 25 in color. 143pp. 5½ x 8½. T512 Clothbound **$4.00**

CALLIGRAPHY, J. G. Schwandner. First reprinting in 200 years of this legendary book of beautiful handwriting. Over 300 ornamental initials, 12 complete calligraphic alphabets, over 150 ornate frames and panels, 75 calligraphic pictures of cherubs, stags, lions, etc., thousands of flourishes, scrolls, etc., by the greatest 18th century masters. All material can be copied or adapted without permission. Historical introduction. 158 full-page plates. 368pp. 9 x 13. T475 Clothbound **$10.00**

* * *

A DIDEROT PICTORIAL ENCYCLOPEDIA OF TRADES AND INDUSTRY, Manufacturing and the Technical Arts in Plates Selected from "L'Encyclopédie ou Dictionnaire Raisonné des Sciences, des Arts, et des Métiers," of Denis Diderot, edited with text by C. Gillispie. Over 2000 illustrations on 485 full-page plates. Magnificent 18th century engravings of men, women, and children working at such trades as milling flour, cheesemaking, charcoal burning, mining, silverplating, shoeing horses, making fine glass, printing, hundreds more, showing details of machinery, different steps in sequence, etc. A remarkable art work, but also the largest collection of working figures in print, copyright-free, for art directors, designers, etc. Two vols. 920pp. 9 x 12. Heavy library cloth. T421 Two volume set **$18.50**

* * *

SILK SCREEN TECHNIQUES, J. Biegeleisen, M. Cohn. A practical step-by-step home course in one of the most versatile, least expensive graphic arts processes. How to build an inexpensive silk screen, prepare stencils, print, achieve special textures, use color, etc. Every step explained, diagrammed. 149 illustrations, 8 in color. 201pp. 6⅛ x 9¼. T433 Paperbound **$1.45**

MATHEMATICS, MAGIC AND MYSTERY, Martin Gardner. Astonishing feats of mind reading, mystifying "magic" tricks, are often based on mathematical principles anyone can learn. This book shows you how to perform scores of tricks with cards, dice, coins, knots, numbers, etc., by using simple principles from set theory, theory of numbers, topology, other areas of mathematics, fascinating in themselves. No special knowledge required. 135 illus. 186pp. 5⅜ x 8.
T335 Paperbound **$1.00**

MATHEMATICAL PUZZLES FOR BEGINNERS AND ENTHUSIASTS, G. Mott-Smith. Test your problem-solving techniques and powers of inference on 188 challenging, amusing puzzles based on algebra, dissection of plane figures, permutations, probabilities, etc. Appendix of primes, square roots, etc. 135 illus. 2nd revised edition. 248pp. 5⅜ x 8.
T198 Paperbound **$1.00**

LEARN CHESS FROM THE MASTERS, F. Reinfeld. Play 10 games against Marshall, Bronstein, Najdorf, other masters, and grade yourself on each move. Detailed annotations reveal principles of play, strategy, etc. as you proceed. An excellent way to get a real insight into the game. Formerly titled, "Chess by Yourself." 91 diagrams. vii + 144pp. 5⅜ x 8.
T362 Paperbound **$1.00**

REINFELD ON THE END GAME IN CHESS, F. Reinfeld. 62 end games of Alekhine, Tarrasch, Morphy, other masters, are carefully analyzed with emphasis on transition from middle game to end play. Tempo moves, queen endings, weak squares, other basic principles clearly illustrated. Excellent for understanding why some moves are weak or incorrect, how to avoid errors. Formerly titled, "Practical End-game Play." 62 diagrams. vi + 177pp. 5⅜ x 8.
T417 Paperbound **$1.25**

101 PUZZLES IN THOUGHT AND LOGIC, C. R. Wylie, Jr. Brand new puzzles you need no special knowledge to solve! Each one is a gem of ingenuity that will really challenge your problem-solving technique. Introduction with simplified explanation of scientic puzzle solving. 128pp. 5⅜ x 8.
T167 Paperbound **$1.00**

THE COMPLETE NONSENSE OF EDWARD LEAR. The only complete edition of this master of gentle madness at a popular price. The Dong with the Luminous Nose, The Jumblies, The Owl and the Pussycat, hundreds of other bits of wonderful nonsense. 214 limericks, 3 sets of Nonsense Botany, 5 Nonsense Alphabets, 546 fantastic drawings, much more. 320pp. 5⅜ x 8.
T167 Paperbound **$1.00**

28 SCIENCE FICTION STORIES OF H. G. WELLS. Two complete novels, "Men Like Gods" and "Star Begotten," plus 26 short stories by the master science-fiction writer of all time. Stories of space, time, future adventure that are among the all-time classics of science fiction. 928pp. 5⅜ x 8.
T265 Clothbound **$3.95**

SEVEN SCIENCE FICTION NOVELS, H. G. Wells. Unabridged texts of "The Time Machine," "The Island of Dr. Moreau," "First Men in the Moon," "The Invisible Man," "The War of the Worlds," "The Food of the Gods," "In the Days of the Comet." "One will have to go far to match this for entertainment, excitement, and sheer pleasure," N. Y. TIMES. 1015pp. 5⅜ x 8.
T264 Clothbound **$3.95**

MATHEMAGIC, MAGIC PUZZLES, AND GAMES WITH NUMBERS, R. V. Heath. More than 60 new puzzles and stunts based on number properties: multiplying large numbers mentally, finding the date of any day in the year, etc. Edited by J. S. Meyer. 76 illus. 129pp. 5⅜ x 8.
T110 Paperbound **$1.00**

FIVE ADVENTURE NOVELS OF H. RIDER HAGGARD. The master story-teller's five best tales of mystery and adventure set against authentic African backgrounds: "She," "King Solomon's Mines," "Allan Quatermain," "Allan's Wife," "Maiwa's Revenge." 821pp. 5⅜ x 8.
T108 Clothbound **$3.95**

WIN AT CHECKERS, M. Hopper. (Formerly "Checkers.") The former World's Unrestricted Checker Champion gives you valuable lessons in openings, traps, end games, ways to draw when you are behind, etc. More than 100 questions and answers anticipate your problems. Appendix. 75 problems diagrammed, solved. 79 figures. xi + 107pp. 5⅜ x 8.
T363 Paperbound **$1.00**

CRYPTOGRAPHY, L. D. Smith. Excellent introductory work on ciphers and their solution, history of secret writing, techniques, etc. Appendices on Japanese methods, the Baconian cipher, frequency tables. Bibliography. Over 150 problems, solutions. 160pp. 5⅜ x 8.
T247 Paperbound **$1.00**

CRYPTANALYSIS, H. F. Gaines. (Formerly "Elementary Cryptanalysis.") The best book available on cryptograms and how to solve them. Contains all major techniques: substitution, transposition, mixed alphabets, multafid, Kasiski and Vignere methods, etc. Word frequency appendix. 167 problems, solutions. 173 figures. 236pp. 5⅜ x 8.
T97 Paperbound **$1.95**

FLATLAND, E. A. Abbot. The science-fiction classic of life in a 2-dimensional world that is considered a first-rate introduction to relativity and hyperspace, as well as a scathing satire on society, politics and religion. 7th edition. 16 illus. 128pp. 5⅜ x 8.
T1 Paperbound **$1.00**

DOVER BOOKS

HOW TO FORCE CHECKMATE, F. Reinfeld. (Formerly "Challenge to Chessplayers.") No board needed to sharpen your checkmate skill on 300 checkmate situations. Learn to plan up to 3 moves ahead and play a superior end game. 300 situations diagrammed; notes and full solutions. 111pp. 5⅜ x 8.   T439 Paperbound **$1.25**

MORPHY'S GAMES OF CHESS, P. W. Sergeant, ed. Play forcefully by following the techniques used by one of the greatest chess champions. 300 of Morphy's games carefully annotated to reveal principles. Bibliography. New introduction by F. Reinfeld. 235 diagrams. x + 352pp. 5⅜ x 8.   T386 Paperbound **$1.75**

MATHEMATICAL RECREATIONS, M. Kraitchik. Hundreds of unusual mathematical puzzlers and odd bypaths of math, elementary and advanced. Greek, Medieval, Arabic, Hindu problems; figurate numbers, Fermat numbers, primes; magic, Euler, Latin squares; fairy chess, latruncles, reversi, jinx, ruma, tetrachrome other positional and permutational games. Rigorous solutions. Revised second edition. 181 illus. 330pp. 5⅜ x 8.   T163 Paperbound **$1.75**

MATHEMATICAL EXCURSIONS, H. A. Merrill. Revealing stimulating insights into elementary math, not usually taught in school. 90 problems demonstrate Russian peasant multiplication, memory systems for pi, magic squares, dyadic systems, division by inspection, many more. Solutions to difficult problems. 50 illus. 5⅜ x 8.   T350 Paperbound **$1.00**

MAGIC TRICKS & CARD TRICKS, W. Jonson. Best introduction to tricks with coins, bills, eggs, ribbons, slates, cards, easily performed without elaborate equipment. Professional routines, tips on presentation, misdirection, etc. Two books bound as one: 52 tricks with cards, 37 tricks with common objects. 106 figures. 224pp. 5⅜ x 8.   T909 Paperbound **$1.00**

MATHEMATICAL PUZZLES OF SAM LOYD, selected and edited by **M. Gardner.** 177 most ingenious mathematical puzzles of America's greatest puzzle originator, based on arithmetic, algebra, game theory, dissection, route tracing, operations research, probability, etc. 120 drawings, diagrams. Solutions. 187pp. 5⅜ x 8.   T498 Paperbound **$1.00**

THE ART OF CHESS, J. Mason. The most famous general study of chess ever written. More than 90 openings, middle game, end game, how to attack, sacrifice, defend. exchange, form general strategy. Supplement on "How Do You Play Chess?" by F. Reinfeld. 448 diagrams. 356pp. 5⅜ x 8.   T463 Paperbound **$1.85**

HYPERMODERN CHESS as Developed in the Games of its Greatest Exponent, ARON NIMZOVICH, F. Reinfeld, ed. Learn how the game's greatest innovator defeated Alekhine, Lasker, and many others; and use these methods in your own game. 180 diagrams. 228pp. 5⅜ x 8.
                                                        T448 Paperbound **$1.35**

A TREASURY OF CHESS LORE, F. Reinfeld, ed. Hundreds of fascinating stories by and about the masters, accounts of tournaments and famous games, aphorisms, word portraits, little known incidents, photographs, etc., that will delight the chess enthusiast, captivate the beginner. 49 photographs (14 full-page plates), 12 diagrams. 315pp. 5⅜ x 8.
                                                        T458 Paperbound **$1.75**

A NONSENSE ANTHOLOGY, collected by **Carolyn Wells.** 245 of the best nonsense verses ever written: nonsense puns, absurd arguments, mock epics, nonsense ballads, "sick" verses, dog-Latin verses, French nonsense verses, limericks. Lear, Carroll, Belloc, Burgess, nearly 100 other writers. Introduction by Carolyn Wells. 3 indices: Title, Author, First Lines. xxxiii + 279pp. 5⅜ x 8.   T499 Paperbound **$1.25**

SYMBOLIC LOGIC and THE GAME OF LOGIC, Lewis Carroll. Two delightful puzzle books by the author of "Alice," bound as one. Both works concern the symbolic representation of traditional logic and together contain more than 500 ingenious, amusing and instructive syllogistic puzzlers. Total of 326pp. 5⅜ x 8.   T492 Paperbound **$1.50**

PILLOW PROBLEMS and A TANGLED TALE, Lewis Carroll. Two of Carroll's rare puzzle works bound as one. "Pillow Problems" contain 72 original math puzzles. The puzzles in "A Tangled Tale" are given in delightful story form. Total of 291pp. 5⅜ x 8.   T493 Paperbound **$1.50**

PECK'S BAD BOY AND HIS PA, G. W. Peck. Both volumes of one of the most widely read of all American humor books. A classic of American folk humor, also invaluable as a portrait of an age. 100 original illustrations. Introduction by E. Bleiler. 347pp. 5⅜ x 8.
                                                        T497 Paperbound **$1.35**

Dover publishes books on art, music, philosophy, literature, languages, history, social sciences, psychology, handcrafts, orientalia, puzzles and entertainments, chess, pets and gardens, books explaining science, intermediate and higher mathematics mathematical physics, engineering, biological sciences, earth sciences, classics of science, etc. Write to:

Dept. catrr.
Dover Publications, Inc.
180 Varick Street, N. Y. 14, N. Y.

15370